This book is in the

ADDISON-WESLEY SERIES IN MATHEMATICS

Consulting Editor: LYNN H. LOOMIS

DAVID M. BURTON, University of New Hampshire

INTRODUCTION TO
MODERN ABSTRACT ALGEBRA

ADDISON-WESLEY PUBLISHING COMPANY

READING, MASSACHUSETTS · PALO ALTO · LONDON · DON MILLS, ONTARIO

PREFACE

This book has been written with the intention of providing an introduction to modern abstract algebra for mathematics majors. The reader is not presumed at the outset to possess any previous knowledge of the concepts of modern algebra. Accordingly, our beginning is somewhat elementary, with the exposition in the earlier sections proceeding at a leisurely pace; much of this early material may be covered rapidly on a first reading. An attempt has been made to keep the book as self-contained as possible. To smooth the path for the unexperienced reader, the first chapter is devoted to a review of the basic facts concerning sets, functions and number theory; it also serves as a suitable vehicle for introducing some of the notation and terminology used subsequently.

A cursory examination of the table of contents will reveal few surprises; the topics chosen for discussion in courses at this level are fairly standard. However, our aim has been to give a presentation which is logically developed, precise, and in keeping with the spirit of the times. Thus, set notation is employed throughout, and the distinction is maintained between algebraic systems as ordered pairs or triples and their underlying sets of elements. Guided by the principle that a steady diet of definitions and examples soon becomes unpalatable, our efforts are directed towards establishing the most important and fruitful results of the subject in a formal, rigorous fashion. The chapter on groups, for example, culminates in a proof of the classic Sylow Theorems, while ring and ideal theory are developed to the point of obtaining the Stone Representation Theorem for Boolean rings. En route, it is hoped that the reader will gain an appreciation of precise mathematical thought and the current standards of rigor.

At the end of each section, there will be found a collection of problems of varying degrees of difficulty; these constitute an integral part of the book. They introduce a variety of topics not treated in the main text, as well as impart much additional detail about material covered earlier. Some, especially in the latter sections, provide substantial extensions of the theory. We have, on the whole, resisted the temptation to use the exercises to develop results that will be needed subsequently; as a result, the reader need not work all the problems in order to read the rest of the book. Problems whose solutions do not appear particularly straightforward are accompanied by hints. Besides the general index, a glossary of special symbols is also included.

The text is not intended to be encyclopedic in nature; many important topics vie for inclusion and some choice is obviously imperative. To this end, we merely followed our own taste, condensing or omitting altogether certain of the concepts found in the usual first course in modern algebra. Despite these omissions, we believe the coverage will meet the needs of most students; those who are stimulated to pursue the matter further will have a firm foundation upon which to build.

It is a pleasure to record our indebtedness to Lynn Loomis and Frederick Hoffman, both of whom read the original manuscript and offered valuable criticism for its correction and improvement. Of our colleagues at the University of New Hampshire, the advice of Edward Batho and Robb Jacoby proved particularly helpful; in this regard, special thanks are due to William Witthoft who contributed a number of incisive suggestions after reading portions of the galley proofs. We also take this occasion to express our sincere appreciation to Mary Ann MacIlvaine for her excellent typing of the manuscript. To my wife must go the largest debt of gratitude, not only for her generous assistance with the text at the various stages of its development, but for her constant encouragement and understanding.

Finally, we would like to acknowledge the fine cooperation of the staff of Addison-Wesley and the usual high quality of their work.

Durham, New Hampshire   D.M.B.
March 1967

CONTENTS

CHAPTER 1

PRELIMINARY NOTIONS

1-1 THE ALGEBRA OF SETS

This chapter briefly summarizes some of the basic notions concerning sets, functions, and number theory; it also serves as a vehicle for establishing conventions in notation and terminology used throughout the text. Inasmuch as this material is intended to serve primarily for background purposes, the reader who is already acquainted with the ideas in this chapter may prefer to embark directly on the next.

Within the confines of one section, it is obviously impossible to give complete coverage to set theory or, for that matter, to achieve a logically coherent exposition of such a formalistic discipline. The subsequent presentation should thus be regarded simply as a summary of the fundamental aspects of the subject, and not as a systematic development.

Rather than attempt to list the undefined terms of set theory and the various axioms relating them, we shall take an informal or naive approach to the subject. To this end, the term *set* will be intuitively understood to mean a collection of objects having some common characteristic. The objects that make up a given set are called its *elements* or *members*. Sets will generally be designated by capital letters and their elements by small letters. In particular, we shall employ the following notations: Z is the set of integers, Q the set of rational numbers, and $R^{\#}$ the set of real numbers. The symbols Z_+, Q_+, and $R^{\#}_+$ will stand for the positive elements of these sets.

If x is an element of the set A, it is customary to use the notation $x \in A$ and to read the symbol $\in$ as "belongs to." On the other hand, when x fails to be an element of the set A, we shall denote this by writing $x \notin A$.

There are two common methods of specifying a particular set. First, we may list all of its elements within braces, as with the set $\{-1, 0, 1, 2\}$, or merely list some of its elements and use three dots to indicate the fact that certain obvious elements have been omitted, as with the set $\{1, 2, 3, 4, \ldots\}$. When such a listing is not practical, we may indicate instead a characteristic property whereby we can determine whether or not a given object is an element of the set. More specifically, if $P(x)$ is a statement concerning x, then the set of all elements x for which the statement $P(x)$ is true is denoted by $\{x \mid P(x)\}$. For example, we might have $\{x \mid x$ is an odd integer greater than 21$\}$. Clearly,

1

certain sets may be described both ways:

$$\{0, 1\} = \{x \mid x \in Z \text{ and } x^2 = x\}.$$

It is customary, however, to depart slightly from this notation and write $\{x \in A \mid P(x)\}$ instead of $\{x \mid x \in A \text{ and } P(x)\}$.

Definition 1–1. Two sets A and B are said to be *equal*, written $A = B$, if and only if every element of A is an element of B and every element of B is an element of A. That is, $A = B$ provided A and B have the same elements.

Thus a set is completely determined by its elements. For instance,

$$\{1, 2, 3\} = \{3, 1, 2, 2\},$$

since each set contains only the integers 1, 2 and 3. Indeed, the order in which the elements are listed in a set is immaterial, and repetition conveys no additional information about the set.

An *empty set* or *null set*, represented by the symbol $\emptyset$, is any set which has no elements. For instance,

$$\emptyset = \{x \in R^{\#} \mid x^2 < 0\} \qquad \text{or} \qquad \emptyset = \{x \mid x \neq x\}.$$

Any two empty sets are equal, for in a trivial sense they both contain the same elements (namely, none). In effect, then, there is just one empty set, so that we are free to speak of *the empty set* $\emptyset$.

The set whose only member is the element x is called *singleton* x and it is denoted by $\{x\}$:

$$\{x\} = \{y \mid y = x\}.$$

In particular, $\{0\} \neq \emptyset$ since $0 \in \{0\}$.

Definition 1–2. The set A is a *subset* of, or is *contained* in, the set B, indicated by writing $A \subseteq B$, if every element of A is also an element of B.

Our notation is designed to include the possibility that $A = B$. Whenever $A \subseteq B$ but $A \neq B$, we will write $A \subset B$ and say that A is a *proper subset* of B.

It will be convenient to regard all sets under consideration as being subsets of some master set U, called the *universe* (*universal set, ground set*). While the universe may be different in different contexts, it will usually be fixed throughout any given discussion.

There are several immediate consequences of the definition of set inclusion.

Theorem 1–1. If A, B, and C are subsets of some universe U, then

a) $A \subseteq A$, $\emptyset \subseteq A$, $A \subseteq U$,
b) $A \subseteq \emptyset$ if and only if $A = \emptyset$,
c) $\{x\} \subseteq A$ if and only if $x \in A$; that is, each element of A determines a subset of A,

d) if $A \subseteq B$ and $B \subseteq C$, then $A \subseteq C$,

e) $A \subseteq B$ and $B \subseteq A$ if and only if $A = B$.

Observe that the result $\emptyset \subseteq A$ follows from the logical principle that a false hypothesis implies any conclusion whatsoever. Thus, the statement "if $x \in \emptyset$, then $x \in A$" is true since $x \in \emptyset$ is always false.

The last assertion of Theorem 1–1 indicates that a proof of the equality of two specified sets A and B is generally presented in two parts. One part demonstrates that if $x \in A$, then $x \in B$; the other part demonstrates that if $x \in B$, then $x \in A$. An illustration of such a proof will be given shortly.

We now consider several important ways in which sets may be combined with one another. If A and B are subsets of some universe U, the operations of union, intersection, and difference are defined as follows.

Definition 1–3. The *union* of A and B, denoted by $A \cup B$, is the subset of U defined by

$$A \cup B = \{x \mid x \in A \text{ or } x \in B\}.$$

The *intersection* of A and B, denoted by $A \cap B$, is the subset of U defined by

$$A \cap B = \{x \mid x \in A \text{ and } x \in B\}.$$

The *difference* of A and B (sometimes called the *relative complement* of B in A), denoted by $A - B$, is the subset of U defined by

$$A - B = \{x \mid x \in A \text{ but } x \notin B\}.$$

In the definition of union, the word "or" is used in the "and/or" sense. Thus the statement "$x \in A$ or $x \in B$" allows the possibility that x is in both A and B. It might also be noted parenthetically that, utilizing this new notion, we could define A to be a proper subset of B provided $A \subseteq B$ with $B - A \neq \emptyset$.

The particular difference $U - B$ is called the (absolute) *complement* of B and designated simply by $-B$. If A and B are two nonempty sets whose intersection is empty, that is, $A \cap B = \emptyset$, then they are said to be *disjoint*. We shall illustrate these concepts with an example.

Example 1–1. Let the universe be $U = \{0, 1, 2, 3, 4, 5, 6\}$, the set $A = \{1, 2, 4\}$, and the set $B = \{2, 3, 5\}$. Then

$$A \cup B = \{1, 2, 3, 4, 5\}, \qquad A \cap B = \{2\}, \qquad A - B = \{1, 4\},$$

and

$$B - A = \{3, 5\}.$$

Also,

$$-A = \{0, 3, 5, 6\}, \qquad -B = \{0, 1, 4, 6\}.$$

Observe that $A - B$ and $B - A$ are disjoint.

In the following theorem, some simple consequences of the definitions of union, intersection, and complementation are listed.

Theorem 1–2. If A, B, and C are subsets of some universe U, then

a) $A \cup A = A$,
   $A \cap A = A$,
b) $A \cup B = B \cup A$,
   $A \cap B = B \cap A$,
c) $A \cup (B \cup C) = (A \cup B) \cup C$,
   $A \cap (B \cap C) = (A \cap B) \cap C$,
d) $A \cup (B \cap C) = (A \cup B) \cap (A \cup C)$,
   $A \cap (B \cup C) = (A \cap B) \cup (A \cap C)$,
e) $A \cup \emptyset = A$, $A \cap \emptyset = \emptyset$,
f) $A \cup U = U$, $A \cap U = A$.

We shall verify the first equality of (d), since its proof illustrates a technique mentioned previously. Suppose that $x \in A \cup (B \cap C)$. Then, either $x \in A$ or $x \in B \cap C$. Now, if $x \in A$, then clearly both $x \in A \cup B$ and $x \in A \cup C$, so that $x \in (A \cup B) \cap (A \cup C)$. On the other hand, if $x \in B \cap C$, then $x \in B$ and therefore $x \in A \cup B$; also $x \in C$ and therefore $x \in A \cup C$. The two conditions together imply that

$$x \in (A \cup B) \cap (A \cup C).$$

This establishes the inclusion,

$$A \cup (B \cap C) \subseteq (A \cup B) \cap (A \cup C).$$

Conversely, suppose $x \in (A \cup B) \cap (A \cup C)$. Then both $x \in A \cup B$ and $x \in A \cup C$. Since $x \in A \cup B$, either $x \in A$ or $x \in B$; at the same time, since $x \in A \cup C$, either $x \in A$ or $x \in C$. Together, these conditions mean that $x \in A$ or $x \in B \cap C$; that is, $x \in A \cup (B \cap C)$. This proves the opposite inclusion,

$$(A \cup B) \cap (A \cup C) \subseteq A \cup (B \cap C).$$

By part (e) of Theorem 1–1, the two inclusions are sufficient to establish the equality,

$$A \cup (B \cap C) = (A \cup B) \cap (A \cup C).$$

If A, B, and C are sets such that $C \subseteq A$ and $C \subseteq B$, then it is clear that $C \subseteq A \cap B$. Thus it is possible to think of $A \cap B$ as the *largest* set which is a subset of both A and B. Analogously, $A \cup B$ may be interpreted as the *smallest* set which contains both A and B.

The next theorem relates the operation of complementation to other operations of set theory.

Theorem 1–3. Let A and B be subsets of the universe U. Then

a) $-(A \cup B) = (-A) \cap (-B)$,
b) $-(A \cap B) = (-A) \cup (-B)$,
c) if $A \subseteq B$, then $(-B) \subseteq (-A)$,
d) $-(-A) = A$, $-\emptyset = U$, $-U = \emptyset$,
e) $A \cup (-A) = U$, $A \cap (-A) = \emptyset$.

To give the reader a little more familiarity with set-theoretic argument, we shall establish the first of the above assertions. For the proof, let x be an arbitrary element of $-(A \cup B)$. Then $x \notin A \cup B$. Hence x is in neither A nor B. This implies that $x \in -A$ and $x \in -B$, from which it follows that $x \in (-A) \cap (-B)$. Thus $-(A \cup B) \subseteq (-A) \cap (-B)$.

Conversely, if $x \in (-A) \cap (-B)$, then x belongs to both $-A$ and $-B$. In other words, $x \notin A$ and $x \notin B$. This guarantees $x \notin A \cup B$, that is

$$x \in -(A \cup B).$$

We consequently have the inclusion $(-A) \cap (-B) \subseteq -(A \cup B)$ and the desired equality holds.

The first two parts of the above theorem are commonly known as *DeMorgan's rules*.

There will be occasions when we wish to consider sets whose elements themselves are sets; in order to avoid the awkward repetition "set of sets," we shall frequently refer to these as *families* of sets. One family which will prove to be of considerable importance is the so-called power set of a given set.

Definition 1–4. If A is an arbitrary set, then the set whose elements are all the subsets of A is known as the *power set* of A and denoted by $P(A)$:

$$P(A) = \{B \mid B \subseteq A\}.$$

A few remarks are in order before considering a specific example. First, since $\emptyset \subseteq A$ and $A \subseteq A$, we always have $\{\emptyset, A\} \subseteq P(A)$ no matter what the nature of the set A. (If $A = \emptyset$, then of course $P(A) = \{\emptyset\}$.) The next thing to observe is that if $x \in A$, then $\{x\} \subseteq A$, hence $\{x\} \in P(A)$. From this, we infer that the power set of A has, at the very least, as many elements as the set A. Indeed, it can be shown that whenever A is a finite set with n elements, then $P(A)$ is itself a finite set having 2^n elements. For this reason, the power set of A is often represented by the symbol 2^A.

Example 1–2. Suppose the set $A = \{a, b, c\}$. The power set of A, which has as its elements all the subsets of $\{a, b, c\}$, is then

$$P(A) = \{\emptyset, \{a\}, \{b\}, \{c\}, \{a, b\}, \{a, c\}, \{b, c\}, A\}.$$

It is both desirable and possible to extend our definitions of union and intersection from two sets to any number of sets. Assume to this end that α is a nonempty family of subsets of the universe U. The union and intersection of this arbitrary family are defined by,

$$\cup\alpha = \{x \mid x \in A \text{ for some set } A \in \alpha\},$$

$$\cap\alpha = \{x \mid x \in A \text{ for every set } A \in \alpha\}.$$

At times we will resort to an indexing set to define these notions. To be more precise, let I be a set, finite or infinite, and with each $i \in I$ associate a set A_i. The resulting family of sets,

$$\alpha = \{A_i \mid i \in I\},$$

is then said to be *indexed* by the elements of I, and the set I is called an *index set* for α. When this notation is employed, it is customary to denote the union and intersection of the family α by

$$\cup\{A_i \mid i \in I\} \qquad \text{and} \qquad \cap\{A_i \mid i \in I\}.$$

If the nature of the index set I is clearly understood or if the emphasizing of it is inessential for some reason, we simply write,

$$\cup A_i \qquad \text{and} \qquad \cap A_i.$$

Example 1–3. If $A_n = \{x \in R^{\#} \mid -1/n \le x \le 1/n\}$ for $n \in Z_{+}$, then

$$\cup\{A_n \mid n \in Z_{+}\} = \{x \mid x \in A_n \text{ for some } n \in Z_{+}\} = A_1,$$

$$\cap\{A_n \mid n \in Z_{+}\} = \{x \mid x \in A_n \text{ for every } n \in Z_{+}\} = \{0\}.$$

In passing, we should note that by a *chain* of sets is meant a nonempty family $\mathcal{C}$ of subsets of some universe U such that if $A, B \in \mathcal{C}$ then either $A \subseteq B$ or $B \subseteq A$. For instance, the family in Example 1–3 constitutes a chain of sets.

From our definition of set equality, $\{a, b\} = \{b, a\}$, since both sets contain the same two elements a and b. That is, no preference is given to one element over the other. When we wish to distinguish one of these elements as being the first, say a, we write (a, b) and call this an ordered pair.

It is possible to give a purely set-theoretic definition of the notion of an ordered pair as follows:

Definition 1–5. The *ordered pair* of elements a and b, with its first component a and second component b, denoted by (a, b), is the set

$$(a, b) = \{\{a, b\}, \{a\}\}.$$

Note that according to this definition, a and b are not elements of (a, b) but rather components. The actual elements of the set (a, b) are $\{a, b\}$, the unordered pair involved, and $\{a\}$, that member of the unordered pair which has been selected to be first. This agrees with our intuition that an ordered pair should be an entity representing two elements in a given order.

For $a \neq b$, the sets $\{\{a, b\}, \{a\}\}$ and $\{\{b, a\}, \{b\}\}$ are unequal, having different elements, so that $(a, b) \neq (b, a)$. Hence, if a and b are distinct, there are two distinct ordered pairs whose components are a and b, namely, the pairs (a, b) and (b, a). Ordered pairs thus provide a way of handling two things as one while losing track of neither.

In the next theorem, a useful criterion for the equality of ordered pairs is obtained; the proof is subtle, but simple, relying mainly on Definitions 1–1 and 1–5.

Theorem 1–4. Two ordered pairs (a, b) and (c, d) are equal if and only if $a = c$ and $b = d$.

Proof. If $a = c$ and $b = d$, then it is clear from Definition 1–1 that

$$\{a\} = \{c\} \qquad \text{and} \qquad \{a, b\} = \{c, d\}.$$

This in turn implies $\{\{a, b\}, \{a\}\} = \{\{c, d\}, \{c\}\}$, whence $(a, b) = (c, d)$.

As for the converse, suppose that $\{\{a, b\}, \{a\}\} = \{\{c, d\}, \{c\}\}$. We distinguish two possible cases:

1) $a = b$. In this case, the ordered pair (a, b) reduces to a singleton, since

$$(a, b) = (a, a) = \{\{a, a\}, \{a\}\} = \{\{a\}\}.$$

According to our hypothesis, we then have

$$\{\{a\}\} = \{\{c, d\}, \{c\}\},$$

which means $\{a\} = \{c, d\} = \{c\}$. From this, it follows that the four elements a, b, c, d are all equal.

2) $a \neq b$. Here, both $\{a\} \neq \{a, b\}$ and $\{c\} \neq \{a, b\}$. If the latter equality were to hold, we would have $c = a$ and $c = b$, hence the contradiction $a = b$. Now, by virtue of the hypothesis, each member of the set (c, d) belongs to (a, b); in particular,

$$\{c\} \in \{\{a, b\}, \{a\}\}.$$

This means that $\{c\} = \{a\}$ and accordingly $a = c$.

Again by supposition, $\{a, b\} \in \{\{c, d\}, \{c\}\}$ with $\{a, b\} \neq \{c\}$. It may thus be inferred that $\{a, b\} = \{c, d\}$ and therefore $b \in \{c, d\}$. As b cannot equal c (this would imply that $a = b$), we must conclude that $b = d$. In either case the desired result is established.

Having faced the problem of defining ordered pairs, it is natural to consider ordered triples, ordered quadruples and, for that matter, ordered n-tuples. What simplifies the situation is that these notions can be formulated in terms of ordered pairs. For instance, the *ordered triple* of a, b, and c is just an ordered pair whose first component is itself an ordered pair:

$$(a, b, c) = ((a, b), c).$$

Assuming that ordered $(n - 1)$-tuples have been defined, we shall take the *ordered n-tuple* of $a_1, a_2, \ldots, a_n$ to mean the ordered pair $((a_1, a_2, \ldots, a_{n-1}), a_n)$, abbreviated by $(a_1, a_2, \ldots, a_n)$. It should come as no surprise that two ordered n-tuples equal whenever their corresponding components are equal; in other words,

$$(a_1, a_2, \ldots, a_n) = (b_1, b_2, \ldots, b_n)$$

if and only if $a_k = b_k$ for $k = 1, 2, \ldots, n$.

Definition 1–6. The *Cartesian product* of two nonempty sets A and B, designated by $A \times B$, is the set

$$A \times B = \{(a, b) \mid a \in A \text{ and } b \in B\}.$$

Whenever we employ the Cartesian product notation, it will be with the understanding that the sets involved are nonempty, even though this may not be explicitly stated at the time. Observe that if the set A contains n elements and B contains m elements, then $A \times B$ has nm elements, which accounts for the use of the word "product" in Cartesian product.

Example 1–4. Let $A = \{-1, 0, 1\}$ and $B = \{0, 2\}$. Then,

$$A \times B = \{(-1, 0), (-1, 2), (0, 0), (0, 2), (1, 0), (1, 2)\},$$

while

$$B \times A = \{(0, -1), (0, 0), (0, 1), (2, -1), (2, 0), (2, 1)\}.$$

Clearly the sets $A \times B$ and $B \times A$ are not identical. In fact, $A \times B = B \times A$ if and only if $A = B$.

By a (binary) *relation* in a nonempty set A is meant a subset R of the Cartesian product $A \times A$. If the element $(a, b) \in R$, we say that a is related to b with respect to the relation R and write aRb. For instance, the relation $<$ in $R^{\#}$ consists of all points in the plane lying above the line $y = x$; one usually writes $3 < 4$ rather than the awkward $(3, 4) \in <$.

Frankly, the concept of a relation as defined is far too general for our purposes. We shall instead limit our attention to a specialized relation known as an equivalence relation.

Definition 1–7. A relation R in a set A is said to be an *equivalence relation* in A provided it satisfied the three properties,

1) reflexive property: aRa, for each $a \in A$,

2) symmetric property: if aRb for some $a, b \in A$, then bRa,

3) transitive property: if aRb and bRc for some $a, b, c \in A$, then aRc.

Equivalence relations are customarily denoted by the symbol $\sim$ (pronounced "wiggle"). With this change in notation, the conditions of Definition 1–7 may be restated in a more familiar form:

1) $a \sim a$, for each $a \in A$,

2) $a \sim b$ implies $b \sim a$,

3) both $a \sim b$ and $b \sim c$ imply $a \sim c$.

In the following examples, we leave to the reader the task of verifying that each relation described actually is an equivalence relation.

Example 1–5. Let A be an arbitrary nonempty set and define for $a, b \in A$, $a \sim b$ if and only if $a = b$ ($a = b$ is tacitly interpreted to mean that a and b are identical elements of A). This yields an equivalence relation in A.

Example 1–6. Consider the set L of all lines in a fixed plane and let $a, b \in L$. Then $\sim$ is an equivalence relation in L provided $a \sim b$ means that a is parallel to b; let us agree that any line is parallel to itself.

Example 1–7. Take Z to be the set of integers. Given $a, b \in Z$, we define an equivalence relation $\sim$ in Z by requiring that $a \sim b$ if and only if $a - b \in Z_e$, the set of even integers.

Example 1–8. As a final illustration, suppose $A = Z_+ \times Z_+$ and define $(a, b) \sim (c, d)$ to mean $ad = bc$. A simple calculation reveals this is an equivalence relation in A.

One is frequently led to conclude that the reflexive property is redundant in Definition 1–7. The argument goes like this: If $a \sim b$, then the symmetric property implies $b \sim a$; since $a \sim b$ and $b \sim a$, using the transitive property, it follows that $a \sim a$. Thus, there appears to be no necessity for the reflexive condition at all. The flaw in this reasoning lies in the fact that for some element $a \in A$, there may not exist any $b \in A$ such that $a \sim b$. Accordingly, we would not have $a \sim a$ for every member of A, as the reflexive property requires.

Perhaps the principal reason for considering equivalence relations in a set A is that they separate A into certain convenient subsets. To be more precise, suppose $\sim$ is a given equivalence relation in A. For each $a \in A$, we let $[a]$ denote the subset of A consisting of all elements which are equivalent to a:

$$[a] = \{x \in A \mid x \sim a\}.$$

This set $[a]$ is referred to as the *equivalence class determined by* a.

Some of the basic properties of equivalence classes are listed in the next theorem.

Theorem 1–5. Let $\sim$ be an equivalence relation in the set A. Then,

1) for each $a \in A$, $[a] \neq \emptyset$,

2) if $b \in [a]$, then $[a] = [b]$; that is, any element of the equivalence class $[a]$ determines the class,

3) for any $a, b \in A$, with $[a] \neq [b]$, $[a] \cap [b] = \emptyset$,

4) $\cup\{[a] \mid a \in A\} = A$.

Proof. Clearly, $a \in [a]$, since $a \sim a$. To prove (2), let $b \in [a]$, so that $b \sim a$. Now, suppose $x \in [a]$, which implies $x \sim a$. Using the symmetric and transitive properties of $\sim$, it follows that $x \sim b$, hence $x \in [b]$. This establishes the inclusion $[a] \subseteq [b]$. A similar argument yields the opposite inclusion and thus the equality $[a] = [b]$.

We derive (3) by assuming, to the contrary, that there is some element $c \in [a] \cap [b]$. Then by statement (2), which has just been verified, $[a] = [c] = [b]$, an obvious contradiction. Finally, since each class $[a] \subseteq A$, the inclusion $\cup\{[a] \mid a \in A\} \subseteq A$ is apparent. To obtain the reverse inclusion one need only demonstrate that each element a in A belongs to some equivalence class; but this is evident: if $a \in A$, then $a \in [a]$.

We next connect the idea of an equivalence relation in A with the concept of a partition of A.

Definition 1–8. A *partition* of a set A is a family $\{A_i\}$ of nonempty subsets of A with the properties

1) if $A_i \neq A_j$, then $A_i \cap A_j = \emptyset$ (pairwise disjoint),

2) $\cup A_i = A$.

Briefly, a partition of A is a family $\{A_i\}$ of nonempty subsets of A such that every element of A belongs to one and only one member of $\{A_i\}$. The integers, for instance, have a partition consisting of the sets of odd and even integers: $Z = Z_e \cup Z_o$, $Z_e \cap Z_o = \emptyset$. Another partition of Z might be the sets Z_+ (positive integers), Z_- (negative integers), and $\{0\}$.

Theorem 1–5 may be viewed as asserting that if $\sim$ is an equivalence relation in A, then the family of all equivalence classes (with respect to the relation $\sim$) forms a partition of A. We now reverse the situation and show that a given partition of A induces a natural equivalence relation in A.

Theorem 1–6. If $\{A_i\}$ is a partition of the set A, then there is an equivalence relation in A whose equivalence classes are precisely the sets A_i.

Proof. For elements $a, b \in A$, we take $a \sim b$ if and only if a and b belong to the same subset A_i. The reader may check that the relation $\sim$, so defined, is actually an equivalence relation in A. Now suppose the element $a \in A_i$. Then $b \in A_i$ if and only if $b \sim a$, that is, if and only if $b \in [a]$. This demonstrates the equality $A_i = [a]$.

In summary, the above discussion shows that there is no essential distinction between partitions of a set and equivalence relations in the set; if we start with one, we get the other.

Example 1–9. Let $A = R^\# \times R^\#$ and define the relation $\sim$ by

$$(a, b) \sim (c, d) \text{ if and only if } a - c = b - d.$$

Then $\sim$ is an equivalence relation in A. The equivalence class determined by the element (a, b) is simply

$$[(a, b)] = \{(c, d) \mid a - c = b - d\}.$$

This set may be represented geometrically as a straight line with slope 1 passing through the point (a, b). Therefore, the relation $\sim$ partitions A into a family of parallel lines.

PROBLEMS

In the following exercises A, B, and C are subsets of some universe U.

1. Prove that $A \cap B \subseteq A \cup B$.

2. Suppose $A \subseteq B$. Show that
   a) $A \cap C \subseteq B \cap C$,   b) $A \cup C \subseteq B \cup C$.

3. Prove that $A - B = A \cap (-B)$, and use this result to verify each of the following identities:
   a) $A - \emptyset = A, \emptyset - A = \emptyset, A - A = \emptyset$,
   b) $A - B = A - (A \cap B) = (A \cup B) - B$,
   c) $(A - B) \cap (B - A) = \emptyset$.

4. Simplify the following expressions to one of the symbols A, B, $A \cup B$, $A \cap B$, $A - B$:
   a) $A \cap (A \cup B)$,
   b) $A - (A - B)$,
   c) $-((A \cap B) \cup (-A))$.

5. Prove that $A \cap (B \cup C) = (A \cap B) \cup (A \cap C)$.

6. Establish the following results on differences:
   a) $(A - B) - C = A - (B \cup C)$,
   b) $A - (B - C) = (A - B) \cup (A \cap C)$,
   c) $A \cup (B - C) = (A \cup B) - (C - A)$,
   d) $A \cap (B - C) = (A \cap B) - (A \cap C)$.

7. The notion of set inclusion may be expressed either in terms of union or intersection. To see this, prove that
   a) $A \subseteq B$ if and only if $A \cup B = B$,
   b) $A \subseteq B$ if and only if $A \cap B = A$.

8. a) If $A \subseteq B$ and $A \subseteq -B$, prove that $A = \emptyset$.
   b) If $A \subseteq B$ and $-A \subseteq B$, prove that $B = U$.

9. Establish the two *absorption laws:*

$$A \cup (A \cap B) = A, \qquad A \cap (A \cup B) = A.$$

10. Assume that A, B, and C are sets for which

$$A \cup B = A \cup C \quad \text{and} \quad A \cap B = A \cap C.$$

   Prove that $B = C$. [*Hint:* $B = B \cap (B \cup A)$.]

11. Let $\mathcal{Q} = \{A_1, A_2, \ldots\}$ be a family of subsets indexed by the positive integers Z_+. Define a new family $\mathcal{B} = \{B_1, B_2, \ldots\}$ as follows:

   $$B_1 = A_1; \qquad B_n = A_n - \cup\{A_k \mid k = 1, 2, \ldots, n - 1\} \text{ for } n > 1.$$

   Show that
   a) the members of B are disjoint sets,   b) $\cup\mathcal{Q} = \cup\mathcal{B}$.

12. For any three sets A, B and C, establish that
   a) $A \times (B \cup C) = (A \times B) \cup (A \times C)$,
   b) $A \times (B \cap C) = (A \times B) \cap (A \times C)$,
   c) $A \times (B - C) = (A \times B) - (A \times C)$,
   d) $A \times B = \cup\{A \times \{b\} \mid b \in B\}$.

13. Classify each of the following relations R in the set Z of integers as to whether they do or do not have the properties of being reflexive, symmetric, and transitive:
   a) aRb if and only if $a < b$,
   b) aRb if and only if $a - b$ is an odd integer,
   c) aRb if and only if $ab \geq 0$,
   d) aRb if and only if $a^2 = b^2$,
   e) aRb if and only if $|a - b| < 1$.

14. Let S be a finite set, but otherwise arbitrary. Determine if the relations defined below are equivalence relations in $P(S)$:
   a) $A \sim B$ means $A \subseteq B$,
   b) $A \sim B$ means A and B have the same number of elements.

15. How many distinct equivalence relations are there in a set of 4 elements?

16. Prove that the following relations $\sim$ are equivalence relations in the Cartesian product $R^{\#} \times R^{\#}$:
   a) $(a, b) \sim (c, d)$ if and only if $b - d = m(a - c)$, m a fixed real number,
   b) $(a, b) \sim (c, d)$ if and only if $a + d = b + c$,
   c) $(a, b) \sim (c, d)$ if and only if $a - c \in Z$, $b = d$.

1-2 FUNCTIONS AND ELEMENTARY NUMBER THEORY

Let us turn next to the concept of a function, one of the most important ideas in mathematics. We shall avoid the traditional view of a function as a "rule of correspondence" and give instead a definition in terms of ordered pairs. What this latter approach lacks in naturalness is more than compensated for by its clarity and precision.

Definition 1-9. A *function* (or *mapping*) f is a set of ordered pairs such that no two distinct pairs have the same first component. Thus $(x, y_1) \in f$ and $(x, y_2) \in f$ implies $y_1 = y_2$.

The collection of all first components of a function f is called the *domain* of the function and is denoted by D_f, while the collection of all second components is called the *range* of the function and is denoted by R_f. In terms of set notation,

$$D_f = \{x \mid (x, y) \in f \text{ for some } y\},$$
$$R_f = \{y \mid (x, y) \in f \text{ for some } x\}.$$

If f is a function and $(x, y) \in f$, then y is said to be the *functional value* or *image* of f at x and is denoted by $f(x)$. That is, the symbol $f(x)$ represents the unique second component of that ordered pair of f in which x is the first component. We shall occasionally observe the convention of simply writing fx for $f(x)$.

Example 1-10. If the function f is the finite set of ordered pairs,

$$f = \{(-1, 0), (0, 0), (1, 2), (2, 1)\},$$

then

$$D_f = \{-1, 0, 1, 2\}, \qquad R_f = \{0, 1, 2\},$$

and we write $f(-1) = 0, f(0) = 0, f(1) = 2$ and $f(2) = 1$.

It is often convenient to describe a function by giving a formula for its ordered pairs. For instance, we might have

$$f = \{(x, x^2 + 2) \mid x \in R^{\#}\}.$$

Using the functional value notation, one would then write $f(x) = x^2 + 2$ for each $x \in R^{\#}$. Needless to say, there are functions whose ordered pairs would be difficult—if not impossible—to express in terms of a formula. The discerning reader is advised to keep in mind the distinction between a function and its values or, as the case may be, its formula; although the notation sometimes leads to confusion, these concepts are obviously quite different.

Definition 1-10. Consider a function $f \subseteq X \times Y$. If $D_f = X$, then we say that f is a function from X *into* Y, or that f *maps* X *into* Y; this situation is expressed symbolically by writing $f: X \to Y$.

The function f is said to be *onto* Y, or an "onto" function, whenever f is a function from X into Y and $R_f = Y$. Thus f is onto Y if and only if for each $y \in Y$ there exists some $x \in D_f$ with $(x, y) \in f$, so that $y = f(x)$.

Since functions are sets, we have a ready-made definition of equality of functions: two functions f and g are equal if and only if they have the same members. Accordingly, $f = g$ if and only if $D_f = D_g$ and $f(x) = g(x)$ for each element x in their common domain.

Suppose f and g are two specific functions whose ranges are subsets of a system in which addition, subtraction, multiplication and division are permissible (one may think of functions from $R^\#$ into $R^\#$). The following formulas define functions $f + g$, $f - g$, $f \cdot g$ and f/g by specifying the value of these functions at each point of their respective domains:

$$\left. \begin{array}{l} (f + g)(x) = f(x) + g(x), \\ (f - g)(x) = f(x) - g(x), \\ (f \cdot g)(x) = f(x)g(x), \end{array} \right\} \quad \text{where} \quad x \in D_f \cap D_g$$

$$(f/g)(x) = f(x)/g(x), \quad \text{where} \quad x \in (D_f \cap D_g) - \{x \in D_g \mid g(x) = 0\}.$$

We term $f + g$, $f - g$, $f \cdot g$ and f/g, the pointwise sum, difference, product and quotient of f and g.

Example 1–11. Suppose

$$f = \{(x, \sqrt{4 - x^2}) \mid -2 \le x \le 2\} \quad \text{and} \quad g = \left\{ \left(x, \frac{2}{x}\right) \,\middle|\, R^\# - \{0\} \right\},$$

so that

$$f(x) = \sqrt{4 - x^2}, \qquad g(x) = \frac{2}{x}.$$

Then for $x \in D_f \cap D_g = D_f - \{0\}$,

$$(f + g)(x) = \sqrt{4 - x^2} + \frac{2}{x},$$

$$(f - g)(x) = \sqrt{4 - x^2} - \frac{2}{x},$$

$$(f \cdot g)(x) = (\sqrt{4 - x^2})\,\frac{2}{x},$$

$$(f/g)(x) = \frac{\sqrt{4 - x^2}}{2/x} = \frac{x}{2}\sqrt{4 - x^2}.$$

The function operations just considered plainly depend on the algebraic properties on the range; the domain merely furnishes the points for these pointwise operations. The most important operation involving functions, functional composition, is independent of such algebraic structure and relies only on the underlying sets.

Definition 1–11. The *composition* of two functions f and g, denoted by $f \circ g$, is the function

$$f \circ g = \{(x, y) \mid \text{for some } z, (x, z) \in g \text{ and } (z, y) \in f\}.$$

Written in terms of functional values, this gives

$$(f \circ g)(x) = f(g(x)), \quad \text{where} \quad D_{f \circ g} = \{x \in D_g \mid g(x) \in D_f\}.$$

This last notation serves to explain the order of symbols in $f \circ g$; the letter g is written directly beside x, since the functional value $g(x)$ is obtained first. It is apparent from the definition that, so long as $R_g \cap D_f \neq \emptyset$, $f \circ g$ is meaningful. Also, $D_{f \circ g} \subseteq D_g$ and $R_{f \circ g} \subseteq R_f$.

Example 1–12. Let

$$f = \{(x, \sqrt{x}) \mid x \in R^{\#}, x \geq 0\},$$

and

$$g = \{(x, 2x + 3) \mid x \in R^{\#}\},$$

so that $f(x) = \sqrt{x}$, $g(x) = 2x + 3$. Then,

$$(f \circ g)(x) = f(g(x)) = f(2x + 3) = \sqrt{2x + 3},$$

where

$$D_{f \circ g} = \{x \in D_g \mid g(x) \in D_f\} = \{x \in R^{\#} \mid 2x + 3 \in D_f\}$$
$$= \{x \mid 2x + 3 \geq 0\}.$$

On the other hand,

$$(g \circ f)(x) = g(f(x)) = g(\sqrt{x}) = 2\sqrt{x} + 3,$$

where

$$D_{g \circ f} = \{x \in D_f \mid f(x) \in D_g\} = \{x \geq 0 \mid \sqrt{x} \in R^{\#}\}$$
$$= \{x \mid x \geq 0\}.$$

One observes that $f \circ g$ is different from $g \circ f$; indeed, rarely does $f \circ g = g \circ f$.

The next theorem concerns some of the basic properties of the operation of functional composition. Its proof is an exercise in the use of the definitions of this section.

Theorem 1–7. If f, g and h are functions for which the following operations are defined, then

1) $(f \circ g) \circ h = f \circ (g \circ h)$,
2) $(f + g) \circ h = (f \circ h) + (g \circ h)$,
3) $(f \cdot g) \circ h = (f \circ h) \cdot (g \circ h)$.

Proof. We establish here only property (3). The other parts of the theorem are obtained in a similar fashion and so are left as an exercise. Observe first that

$$\begin{aligned} D_{(f \cdot g) \circ h} &= \{x \in D_h \mid h(x) \in D_{f \cdot g}\} \\ &= \{x \in D_h \mid h(x) \in D_f \cap D_g\} \\ &= \{x \in D_h \mid h(x) \in D_f\} \cap \{x \in D_h \mid h(x) \in D_g\} \\ &= D_{f \circ h} \cap D_{g \circ h} = D_{(f \circ h) \cdot (g \circ h)}. \end{aligned}$$

Now, for $x \in D_{(f \cdot g) \circ h}$, we have

$$\begin{aligned} [(f \cdot g) \circ h](x) = (f \cdot g)(h(x)) &= f(h(x)) \cdot g(h(x)) \\ &= (f \circ h)(x) \cdot (g \circ h)(x) \\ &= [(f \circ h) \cdot (g \circ h)](x), \end{aligned}$$

which, according to the definition of equality of functions, shows that

$$(f \cdot g) \circ h = (f \circ h) \cdot (g \circ h).$$

Once again, consider an arbitrary function $f : X \to Y$. While no element of X can be mapped under f onto more than one element of Y, it is clearly possible that several (perhaps, even all) elements may map onto the same element of Y. When we wish to avoid this situation, the notion of a one-to-one function is useful. The formal definition follows.

Definition 1–12. A function f is termed *one-to-one* if and only if $x_1, x_2 \in D_f$, with $x_1 \neq x_2$, implies $f(x_1) \neq f(x_2)$. That is, distinct elements in the domain have distinct functional values.

When establishing one-to-oneness, it will often prove to be more convenient to use the contrapositive of Definition 1–12:

$$f(x_1) = f(x_2) \text{ implies } x_1 = x_2.$$

In terms of ordered pairs, a function f is one-to-one if and only if no two distinct ordered pairs of f have the same second component. Thus the collection of ordered pairs obtained by interchanging the components of the pairs of f is also a function. This observation indicates the importance of such functions.

More specifically, the inverse of a one-to-one function f, symbolized by f^{-1}, is the set of ordered pairs,

$$f^{-1} = \{(y, x) \mid (x, y) \in f\}.$$

The function f^{-1} has the properties

$$(f^{-1} \circ f)(x) = x \text{ for } x \in D_f,$$

$$(f \circ f^{-1})(y) = y \text{ for } y \in D_{f^{-1}} = R_f.$$

To state this result a little more concisely, let us introduce some special terminology.

Definition 1–13. Given a nonempty set X, the function $i_X \colon X \to X$ defined by $i_X(x) = x$ for each $x \in X$ is called the *identity function* on X; that is to say, i_X merely maps each element of X onto itself.

Expressed in terms of the identity function, what was just seen is that for any function $f \colon X \to Y$ which is both one-to-one and onto Y,

$$f^{-1} \circ f = i_X \qquad \text{and} \qquad f \circ f^{-1} = i_Y.$$

It might also be mentioned at this point that the identity function i_X is itself a one-to-one mapping onto the set X such that $i_X^{-1} = i_X$.

Example 1–13. The function $f = \{(x, 3x - 2) \mid x \in R^{\#}\}$ is one-to-one, for $3x_1 - 2 = 3x_2 - 2$ implies $x_1 = x_2$. Consequently, the inverse of f exists and is the set of ordered pairs $f^{-1} = \{(3x - 2, x) \mid x \in R^{\#}\}$. It is preferable, however, to have f^{-1} defined in terms of its domain and the image at each point of the domain. Observing that

$$\{(3x - 2, x) \mid x \in R^{\#}\} = \{(x, \tfrac{1}{3}(x + 2)) \mid x \in R^{\#}\},$$

we choose to write

$$f^{-1} = \{(x, \tfrac{1}{3}(x + 2) \mid x \in R^{\#}\}.$$

In terms of functional values, $f^{-1}(x) = \tfrac{1}{3}(x + 2)$ for each $x \in R^{\#}$.

An important situation arises when we consider the behavior of a function on a subset of its domain. For example, it is frequently advantageous to limit the domain so that the function becomes one-to-one. Suppose, in general, that $f \colon X \to Y$ is an arbitrary function and the subset $A \subseteq X$. The composition $f \circ i_A \colon A \to Y$ is known as the *restriction* of f to the set A and is, by established custom, denoted by $f \mid A$; dually, the function f is referred to as an *extension* of $f \mid A$ to all of X. For the reader who prefers the ordered pair approach,

$$f \mid A = \{(x, y) \mid (x, y) \in f \text{ and } x \in A\}.$$

In any event, if the element $x \in A$, then $(f \mid A)(x) = f(x)$ so that both f and $f \mid A$ coincide on the set A. It is well worth noting that while there is only one restriction of the given function f to the subset A, f is not necessarily uniquely determined by $f \mid A$. The particular restriction $i_X \mid A = i_A$, when viewed as a function from A into X, is termed the *inclusion* or *injection* map from A to X.

The next definition embodies a frequently employed notational device. Observe that despite the use of the symbol f^{-1}, the function f is not required to be one-to-one.

Definition 1–14. Consider a function $f: X \to Y$. If $A \subseteq X$, then the *direct image* of A, denoted by $f(A)$, is the subset of Y defined by

$$f(A) = \{f(x) \mid x \in A\}.$$

On the other hand, if $B \subseteq Y$, then the *inverse image* of B, denoted by $f^{-1}(B)$, is the subset of X defined by

$$f^{-1}(B) = \{x \mid f(x) \in B\}.$$

It shall be our convention to omit unnecessary parentheses whenever possible. In regard to singletons, for instance, we shall write direct and inverse images as $f(x)$ and $f^{-1}(x)$, rather than $f(\{x\})$ and $f^{-1}(\{x\})$. The student who worries about notation may feel somewhat uneasy about this double use of the symbol f^{-1}. The abuse of notation should not cause any confusion, however, for in any given context it should be perfectly clear how f^{-1} is to be interpreted.

Certain properties of the function f may be conveniently characterized in terms of inverse images. To be more explicit, f is a one-to-one function if and only if the inverse image of each element of R_f is a singleton. Whereas f maps onto Y if and only if the inverse image of each nonempty subset of Y is nonempty.

We shall now present two short theorems which will establish the relationship between direct and inverse images; these results are rather trivial but will be essential for later study. In the two theorems, suppose f to be an arbitrary function from the set X into the set Y.

Theorem 1–8. For each subset $B \subseteq Y$,

$$f(f^{-1}(B)) \subseteq B.$$

Proof. If $b \in f(f^{-1}(B))$, then $b = f(a)$ for some element a in $f^{-1}(B)$. From this, it follows that $f(a) \in B$, and consequently $b \in B$.

Corollary. If, in addition, f maps onto the set Y, then

$$f(f^{-1}(B)) = B.$$

Proof. In view of the inclusion proved in the theorem, we need only establish that, under the existing hypothesis, $B \subseteq f(f^{-1}(B))$. For this, let $b \in B$; then, as f is by supposition an onto function, $b = f(a)$ for some choice of a in X. Since $a \in f^{-1}(B)$,

$$f(a) \in f(f^{-1}(B)),$$

so that

$$b \in f(f^{-1}(B)).$$

Theorem 1–9. For each subset $A \subseteq X$,

$$A \subseteq f^{-1}(f(A)).$$

Proof. The proof is almost obvious, for, if $a \in A$, then $f(a) \in f(A)$; hence,

$$a \in f^{-1}(f(A)).$$

Corollary. If, in addition, f is a one-to-one function, then

$$A = f^{-1}(f(A)).$$

Proof. It plainly suffices to establish the one inclusion $f^{-1}(f(A)) \subseteq A$. To start with, let $a \in f^{-1}(f(A))$. We then have $f(a) \in f(A)$ and thus $f(a) = f(a')$ for some a' in A. Since f is assumed to be one-to-one, $a = a'$ and so $a \in A$.

Before terminating this section, it may be well to review, quickly, some of the facts from number theory which we shall require later. Most of these results depend on the so-called Well-Ordering Principle:

Well-Ordering Principle. Every nonempty subset S of nonnegative integers contains a smallest element; that is, there exists some (unique) element $a \in S$ with $a \leq b$ for all $b \in S$.

Let us start with the following result.

Theorem 1–10. If $a, b \in Z$, with $b > 0$, then there exist unique integers q and r such that

$$a = qb + r, \qquad 0 \leq r < b.$$

Proof. We begin by proving that the set,

$$S = \{a - xb \mid x \in Z; a - xb \geq 0\},$$

is not empty. Since $b \geq 1$, $|a|b \geq |a|$, and

$$a - (-|a|)b = a + |a|b \geq a + |a| \geq 0.$$

Hence, for $x = -|a|$, $a - xb \in S$. By the Well-Ordering Principle, S contains a smallest integer, say r. In other words, there is some $q \in Z$ for which

$$r = a - qb, \qquad r \geq 0.$$

We now show that $r < b$. In the contrary case, $r \geq b$ and

$$a - (q + 1)b = (a - qb) - b = r - b \geq 0,$$

which implies $r - b \in S$. Since $r - b < r$, this contradicts the choice of r as the smallest element in S; therefore, having reached a contradiction, $r < b$.

To prove the uniqueness of the integers q and r, suppose that

$$a = qb + r = q'b + r',$$

where $0 \le r < b$, $0 \le r' < b$. Then $r' - r = b(q - q')$, consequently

$$|r' - r| = b|q - q'|.$$

Adding the inequalities $-b < -r \le 0$ and $0 \le r' < b$, we obtain

$$-b < r' - r < b, \qquad \text{or} \qquad |r' - r| < b.$$

Hence, $b|q - q'| < b$, so that

$$0 \le |q - q'| < 1.$$

Since $|q - q'|$ is a nonnegative integer, it follows that $q = q'$, which in turn gives $r = r'$.

Corollary. (*Division Algorithm*). If $a, b \in Z$, with $b \ne 0$, then there exist unique integers q and r such that

$$a = qr + b, \qquad 0 \le r < |b|.$$

Proof. It suffices to consider the case where b is negative. Then $|b| > 0$ and the theorem yields unique integers q' and r for which

$$a = q'|b| + r, \qquad 0 \le r < |b|.$$

Since $|b| = -b$, we may take $q = -q'$ to get

$$a = qb + r, \qquad 0 \le r < |b|.$$

Let us now make the following definition.

Definition 1–15. Let $a, b \in Z$, with $a \ne 0$. The integer a is said to *divide* b, or a is a *divisor* of b, in symbols $a \mid b$, provided there exists some $c \in Z$ such that $b = ac$. If a does not divide b, then we write $a \nmid b$.

When the notation $a \mid b$ is employed, it is to be understood (even if not explicitly mentioned) that $a \ne 0$.

Some immediate consequences of this definition are noted below; the reader is asked to verify each of them.

Theorem 1–11. Let $a, b, c \in Z$. Then

1) $a \mid 0$, $1 \mid a$, $a \mid a$,
2) $a \mid \pm 1$ if and only if $a = \pm 1$,
3) if $a \mid b$, then $ac \mid bc$,

4) if $a \mid b$ and $b \mid c$, then $a \mid c$,

5) $a \mid b$ and $b \mid a$ if and only if $a = \pm b$,

6) if $c \mid a$ and $c \mid b$, then $c \mid (ax + by)$ for every $x, y \in Z$.

From (1) above, we see that every integer $a \neq 0$ is divisible by 1 and a, divisors which are frequently referred to as *improper* divisors. An integer $a > 1$ having no divisors other than the improper ones is said to be a *prime number*; an integer $a > 1$ that is not prime is termed *composite*. Thus, according to our definition, 1 is neither prime nor composite. In particular, an integer $a > 1$ is composite if and only if there exist integers b, c with $a = bc, 1 < b < a,$ $1 < c < a$.

If $a, b \in Z$, we say an integer d is a *common divisor* of a and b if $d \mid a$ and $d \mid b$. Also,

Definition 1–16. Let a and b be integers, not both of which are zero. The *greatest common divisor* of a and b, denoted by gcd (a, b), is the positive integer d such that

1) $d \mid a$ and $d \mid b$,

2) if $c \mid a$ and $c \mid b$, then $c \mid d$.

Briefly, gcd (a, b) is the largest integer in the set of all common divisors of a and b.

A natural question to ask is whether the integers a and b can possess two different greatest common divisors. For an answer, suppose there are two positive integers d and d' which satisfy the conditions of Definition 1–16. Then by (2), we must have $d \mid d'$ as well as $d' \mid d$, whence $d = \pm d'$ [Theorem 1–11(5)]. Since d and d' are both positive integers, it follows that $d = d'$. Thus, the greatest common divisor of a and b is unique, when it exists. The following theorem will prove that any two integers, which are not both zero, actually do have a greatest common divisor.

Theorem 1–12. If a, b are integers, not both of which are zero, then gcd (a, b) exists; in fact, there exist integers x and y such that

$$\text{gcd } (a, b) = ax + by.$$

Proof. First, define the set S by

$$S = \{au + bv \mid u, v \in Z; au + bv > 0\}.$$

This set S is not empty. For example, if $a \neq 0$, the integer $|a| = au + b0$ will lie in S, where we choose $u = 1$ or -1 according as a is positive or negative. By the Well-Ordering Principle, S must contain a smallest element $d > 0$; that is to say, there exist $x, y \in Z$ for which $d = ax + by$. We assert that $d = $ gcd (a, b).

From the Division Algorithm, one can obtain integers q and r such that $a = qd + r, 0 \le r < d$. But then r will be of the form

$$r = a - qd = a - q(ax + by)$$
$$= a(1 - qx) + b(-qy).$$

Were $r > 0$, this representation would imply $r \in S$, and contradict the fact that d is the least integer in S. Thus $r = 0$, so that $d \mid a$. A similar argument establishes that $d \mid b$, making d a common divisor of a and b. On the other hand, if $c \mid a$ and $c \mid d$, then by Theorem 1–11(6), $c \mid (ax + by)$, or rather, $c \mid d$. From these two statements, we conclude that d is the greatest common divisor of a and b.

It may be well to record the fact that the integers x and y in the representation gcd $(a, b) = ax + by$ are by no means unique. More concretely, if $a = 90$ and $b = 252$, then

$$\text{gcd } (90, 252) = 18 = (3)90 + (-1)252.$$

Among other possibilities, we also have

$$18 = (3 + 252)90 + (-1 - 90)252 = (255)90 + (-91)252.$$

There is a special case of Theorem 1–12 which will play an important role in the future; while it is, in effect, a corollary of the foregoing result, we shall single it out as a theorem. But first, a definition: two integers a and b, not both of which are zero, are said to be *relatively prime* (or prime to each other) if and only if gcd $(a, b) = 1$. For instance, the integers 8 and 15 are relatively prime, although neither is itself a prime.

Theorem 1–13. Let $a, b \in Z$, not both zero. Then a and b are relatively prime if and only if there exist integers x and y such that

$$1 = ax + by.$$

Proof. If a and b are relatively prime, so that gcd $(a, b) = 1$, Theorem 1–12 guarantees the existence of x and y satisfying $1 = ax + by$. Conversely, suppose $1 = ax + by$ for suitable $x, y \in Z$ and that $d = $ gcd (a, b). Since $d \mid a, d \mid b$, Theorem 1–11(6) implies $d \mid (ax + by)$, or rather $d \mid 1$. Because d is positive, this forces $d = 1$ [Theorem 1–11(2)], as desired.

In light of Theorem 1–13, one may easily prove

Theorem 1–14. (*Euclid's Lemma*). If $a \mid bc$, with a and b relatively prime, then $a \mid c$.

Proof. Since gcd $(a, b) = 1$, there exist integers x and y for which $1 = ax + by$. Multiplying by c, we obtain

$$c = (ax + by)c = a(cx) + (bc)y.$$

Now $a \mid a$ trivially and $a \mid bc$ by hypothesis, so that a must divide the sum $acx + bcy$; hence $a \mid c$, as asserted.

Corollary. If p is a prime and $p \mid (a_1a_2 \cdots a_n)$, then $p \mid a_k$ for some k, $1 \le k \le n$.

Proof. Our proof is by induction on n. For $n = 1$, the result obviously holds. Suppose, as the induction hypothesis, that $n > 1$ and that whenever p divides a product of less than n factors, then it divides at least one of the factors of this product. Now, let $p \mid (a_1a_2 \cdots a_n)$. If p divides a_1, there is nothing to prove. In the contrary case, p and a_1 are relatively prime; hence, by the theorem, $p \mid (a_2 \cdots a_n)$. Since the product $a_2 \cdots a_n$ contains $n - 1$ factors, the induction hypothesis implies $p \mid a_k$ for some k with $2 \le k \le n$.

Having developed the machinery, it might be of interest to give a proof of the Fundamental Theorem of Arithmetic.

Theorem 1–15. (*Fundamental Theorem of Arithmetic*). Every positive integer $a > 1$ can be expressed as a product of primes; this representation is unique, apart from the order in which the factors occur.

Proof. The first part of the proof—the existence of a prime factorization—is proved by induction on the values of a. The statement of the theorem is trivially true for the integer 2, since 2 is itself a prime. Assume the result holds for all positive integers $2 \le b < a$. If a is already a prime, we are through; otherwise, $a = bc$ for suitable integers b, c with $1 < b < a$, $1 < c < a$. By the induction hypothesis,

$$b = p_1 p_2 \cdots p_r, \qquad c = p_1' p_2' \cdots p_s',$$

with p_i, p_i' all primes. But then,

$$a = bc = p_1 \cdots p_r p_1' \cdots p_s'$$

is a product of primes.

To establish uniqueness, let us suppose the integer a can be represented as a product of primes in two ways, say

$$a = p_1 p_2 \cdots p_n = q_1 q_2 \cdots q_m,$$

where the p_i and q_i are primes. The argument proceeds by induction on the integer n. In the case $n = 1$, we have $a = p_1 = q_1(q_2 \cdots q_m)$. Since p_1 is prime, it possesses no proper factorization, so that $m = 1$ and $p_1 = q_1$.

Next, assume $n > 1$ and that whenever a can be expressed as a product of less than n factors, this representation is unique, except for the order of the factors. From the equality $p_1 p_2 \cdots p_n = q_1 q_2 \cdots q_m$, it follows that $p_1 \mid (q_1 q_2 \cdots q_m)$. Thus, by the preceding corollary, there is some prime q_k, $1 \le k \le m$, for which $p_1 \mid q_k$; relabeling, if necessary, we may suppose, $p_1 \mid q_1$. But then $p_1 = q_1$, for q_1 has no divisors other than 1 and itself. Canceling this common factor, we conclude $p_2 \cdots p_n = q_2 \cdots q_m$. According to the induction hypothesis, a product of $n - 1$ primes can be factored in essentially one way. Therefore, the primes $q_2, \ldots, q_m$ are simply a rearrangement of the primes $p_2, \ldots, p_n$. The two prime factorizations of a are thus identical, completing the induction step.

An immediate consequence of this theorem is the following:

Theorem 1–16. (*Euclid*). There are an infinite number of primes.

Proof. Assume the statement is false; that is, assume there are only a finite number of primes $p_1, p_2, \ldots, p_n$. Consider the positive integer

$$a = (p_1 p_2 \cdots p_n) + 1.$$

None of the primes p_i divides a. If a were divisible by p_1, for instance, we would then have $p_1 \mid (a - p_1 p_2 \cdots p_n)$ by Theorem 1–11(6), or $p_1 \mid 1$; this is impossible by part (2) of the same theorem. But, since $a > 1$, the Fundamental Theorem asserts it must have a prime factor. Accordingly, a is divisible by a prime which is not among our list of all primes. This argument shows there is no finite listing of the prime integers.

This completes our survey of some of the fundamental notions concerning sets, functions, and arithmetic in the integers. Although the treatment was purposely sketchy, it is hoped that the reader did not find it too superficial. In the subsequent chapters of the text, we shall utilize the foregoing concepts by applying these ideas to certain specific situations.

PROBLEMS

1. Let $f: X \to Y$ be an arbitrary function. Define a relation in the set X as follows: for any two elements $x, y \in X$, $x \sim y$ if and only if $f(x) = f(y)$. Verify that $\sim$ is an equivalence relation in X and describe its equivalence classes.

2. Show that the ordered triples (a, b, c) and (a', b', c') are equal if and only if $a = a'$, $b = b'$, $c = c'$.

3. Give an example of two functions f and g from $R^{\#}$ into $R^{\#}$ with $f \neq g$ for which $f \circ g = g \circ f$.

4. Determine $f \circ g$, $g \circ f$, and their respective domains, given that
   a) $f = \{(x, x^2 + x) \mid x \in R^{\#}\}$, $g = \{(x, 3x + 4) \mid x \in R^{\#}\}$,
   b) $f = \{(x, x/(x^2 + 1)) \mid x \in R^{\#}\}$, $g = \{(x, 1/x) \mid x \in R^{\#} - \{0\}\}$.

5. Let f, g and h be functions such that $R_h \subseteq D_g$ and $R_g \subseteq D_f$. Verify the law

$$f \circ (g \circ h) = (f \circ g) \circ h.$$

6. Let f, g and h be functions from $R^{\#}$ into $R^{\#}$ with $R_h \subseteq D_f \cap D_g$. Prove that

$$(f/g) \circ h = (f \circ h)/(g \circ h).$$

7. Determine which of the functions below are one-to-one. In those cases in which the function f is not one-to-one, exhibit two pairs (x_1, y_1), $(x_2, y_2) \in f$ such that $x_1 \neq x_2$ but $y_1 = y_2$.

a) $f = \{(x, x^2 + 1) \mid x \in R^{\#}\}$,
b) $f = \{(x, |x - 1|) \mid -2 \leq x \leq 2\}$,
c) $f = \{(x, 1/x) \mid x \in R^{\#}_+\}$.

8. For every pair of real numbers a and b, define a function $f_{ab} \colon R^{\#} \to R^{\#}$ by the formula $f_{ab}(x) = ax + b$ for each $x \in R^{\#}$.

a) Show that $f_{1b} \circ f_{a0} = f_{ab}$.
b) For $a \neq 0$, prove that f_{ab} is both one-to-one and onto.
c) For $a \neq 0$, obtain f_{ab}^{-1}.

9. Using functions $f \colon R^{\#} \to R^{\#}$, give an example of a function which is

a) one-to-one but not onto,
b) onto but not one-to-one.

10. For functions $g \colon X \to Y$ and $f \colon Y \to Z$, show that the following statements are true:

a) If $f \circ g$ is an onto function, then f is also.
b) If $f \circ g$ is a one-to-one function, then g is also.
c) If f and g are both one-to-one functions, then $f \circ g$ is also one-to-one and $(f \circ g)^{-1} = g^{-1} \circ f^{-1}$.

11. Establish the following characterizations for any function $f \colon X \to Y$:

a) f is onto Y if and only if for all functions g, $h \colon Y \to Z$, $g \circ f = h \circ f$ implies that $g = h$.
b) f is one-to-one if and only if for all functions g, $h \colon Z \to X$, $f \circ g = f \circ h$ implies that $g = h$.

12. If $f \colon X \to Y$, $g \colon Y \to Z$ and $A \subseteq X$, prove that

$$(g \circ f) \mid A = g \circ (f \mid A).$$

13. Given $f \colon X \to Y$ and $A, B \subseteq X$, show that

a) $f(A \cup B) = f(A) \cup f(B)$,
b) $f(A \cap B) \subseteq f(A) \cap f(B)$,
c) $f(A) - f(B) \subseteq f(A - B)$,
d) if $A \subseteq B$, then $f(A) \subseteq f(B)$.

14. Given $f \colon X \to Y$ and $A, B \subseteq Y$, show that

a) $f^{-1}(A \cup B) = f^{-1}(A) \cup f^{-1}(B)$,
b) $f^{-1}(A \cap B) = f^{-1}(A) \cap f^{-1}(B)$,
c) $f^{-1}(A) - f^{-1}(B) = f^{-1}(A - B)$,
d) if $A \subseteq B$, then $f^{-1}(A) \subseteq f^{-1}(B)$.

Comparing these results with those of Problem 13, one can see that inverse images are much better behaved than direct images.

15. If $f: X \rightarrow Y$, prove that f is a one-to-one function if and only if

$$f(A \cap B) = f(A) \cap f(B)$$

for all sets A, $B \subseteq X$.

16. Given integers a and b, which are not both zero, establish the following facts concerning gcd (a, b):

   a) gcd $(a, -b)$ = gcd $(-a, b)$ = gcd $(-a, -b)$,
   b) whenever $a \neq 0$, gcd $(a, 0)$ = $|a|$,
   c) gcd (a, b) = $|a|$ if and only if $a \mid b$,
   d) gcd (ca, cb) = $|c|$ gcd (a, b), provided $c \neq 0$,
   e) gcd (a, b) = gcd $(a, b + ca)$, for every $c \in Z$.

17. Prove that if a, b, c are integers, no two of which are zero, then

$$\gcd \big(\gcd (a, b), c\big) = \gcd \big(a, \gcd (b, c)\big)$$
$$= \gcd \big(\gcd (a, c), b\big).$$

18. Prove the two assertions below:

   a) If gcd (a, b) = gcd (a, c) = 1, then gcd (a, bc) = 1.
   b) If gcd (a, b) = 1, $a \mid c$ and $b \mid c$, then $ab \mid c$.

19. Let a and b be integers, not both zero. The *least common multiple* of a and b, denoted by lcm (a, b), is the positive integer e such that

   1) $a \mid e$ and $b \mid e$; that is, e is a multiple of both a and b,
   2) if $a \mid c$ and $b \mid c$, then $e \mid c$.

   Show that the least common multiple of a and b is related to the greatest common divisor of a and b by

$$(\text{lcm } (a, b))(\gcd (a, b)) = |ab|.$$

20. Let a, b, $c \in Z$, with a and b not both zero, and let d = gcd (a, b). Verify that there exist integers x and y such that

$$ax + by = c,$$

if and only if $d \mid c$.

CHAPTER 2

GROUP THEORY

2-1 DEFINITION AND EXAMPLES OF GROUPS

In this chapter, and throughout the remainder of the text, we shall deal with mathematical systems which are defined by a prescribed list of properties. Emphasis will be on deriving theorems that follow logically from the postulates and which, at the same time, help to describe the algebraic structure of the particular system under consideration. This axiomatic approach not only permits us to concentrate on essential ideas, but also unifies the presentation by showing the basic similarities of many diverse and apparently unrelated examples.

We first confine our attention to systems involving just one operation, since they are amenable to the simplest formal description. Despite this simplicity, the axioms permit the construction of a profuse and elegant theory in which one encounters many of the fundamental notions common to all algebraic systems.

Before beginning, however, it is necessary to arrive at some understanding concerning the use of the equivalence relation $=$. We will henceforth take the equality sign to mean, intuitively, "is the same as." In other words, the symbol $=$ asserts that the two particular expressions involved are merely different names for, or descriptions of, one and the same object; just one object is being considered, and it is named twice. To indicate that a and b are not the same object we shall, naturally enough, write $a \neq b$.

As a first step in our program, we introduce the concept of a binary operation. This idea is the cornerstone of all that follows.

Definition 2-1. Given a nonempty set S, any function from the Cartesian product $S \times S$ into S is called a *binary operation* on S.

A binary operation on S thus assigns to each ordered pair of elements of S a uniquely determined third element of the same set S. For instance, if $P(A)$ denotes the power set of a fixed set A, then both $\cup$ and $\cap$ are binary operations on $P(A)$. In practice, we shall generally use the symbol $*$ to represent a binary operation and write $a * b$, instead of $*((a, b))$, for its value at the ordered pair $(a, b) \in S \times S$. While this convention is at variance with the functional notation developed in the previous chapter, its use in the present situation is dictated by long-standing mathematical tradition. At the very least, it has the advantage of avoiding some rather clumsy notation.

From time to time, we shall permit ourselves to make such informal statements as "combine a with b" or "form $a * b$." In a precise sense, what is really meant of course is to apply the function $*$ to the ordered pair (a, b). The most useful aspect of a binary operation is that, having once formed the element $a * b$, we may in turn combine it with other members of S; the result of all such calculations again lies in S.

Needless to say, the particular notation used for the abstract product of two elements is of no great importance. On occasions some other symbol, as equally noncommittal as $*$, will be employed. Specifically, we will frequently choose to write $a \circ b$ in place of $a * b$ (in this context, the symbol $\circ$ is not intended to have any special connection with functional composition). In general, a and b will have no numerical value but will simply be arbitrary elements in our underlying set S, whatever this set may be, while $*$ may well be some law of composition which bears no resemblance to the usual operations of elementary algebra.

Closely allied to the notion of a binary operation is the so-called *closure condition*. For a formal statement of this property, suppose that $*$ is a binary operation on the set S and $A \subseteq S$; the subset A is said to be *closed* under the operation $*$ provided $a * b \in A$ whenever a and b are in A. The desirable feature here is that when A is closed under the operation $*$, the restriction of $*$ to the subset A is a binary operation on A as well as S.

Example 2–1. Ordinary subtraction is clearly a binary operation on the set Z of integers; the subset Z_+ of positive integers, however, is not closed under subtraction.

When the set S being considered has a relatively small number of elements, the results of applying the operation $*$ to its members may be conveniently represented in what might be called an *operation* or *multiplication table*. We construct this table by first listing the members of S in the same order both vertically and horizontally. The result $a * b$ then appears in the body of the table at the intersection of the row headed by a and the column headed by b. Conversely, such a table could equally well serve to define a binary operation on S, for the result of combining any pair of elements of S would be displayed somewhere in the table.

Example 2–2. A binary operation $*$ may be defined on the three-element set $S = \{1, 2, 3\}$ by means of the operation table below:

$*$	1	2	3
1	1	2	3
2	3	1	2
3	2	3	1

According to the table, the product $2 * 3$, for instance, is equal to the element 2, located at the intersection of the row marked 2 and the column marked 3.

Given an arbitrary binary operation $*$, there is certainly no reason to expect that $a * b$ will be the same as $b * a$ for all a and b. In fact, it can be seen in the above example that $1 * 2 = 2$, whereas $2 * 1 = 3$. One must consequently take care to refer to $a * b$ as the product of a and b and to $b * a$ as the product of b and a; the distinction is quite important. We should also point out that it is obviously possible to combine an element with itself. That is to say, $a * a$ can be defined.

Definition 2–2. By a *mathematical system* (or *mathematical structure*), we shall mean a nonempty set of elements together with one or more binary operations defined on this set.

A mathematical system consisting of the set S and a single binary operation $*$ will be denoted by the ordered pair $(S, *)$; analogously, a system consisting of the set S and two operations $*$ and $\circ$ will be represented by the ordered triple $(S, *, \circ)$.

Example 2–3. The pair $(S, \cdot)$, where the set $S = \{1, -1, i, -i\}$ and the operation is that of ordinary multiplication, is a mathematical system provided one defines $i^2 = -1$.

Example 2–4. If Z_e and Z_o denote the even and odd integers, respectively, then $(Z_e, +, \cdot)$ constitutes a mathematical system, while $(Z_o, +, \cdot)$ does not. In the latter case, the set Z_o is not closed under addition, since the sum of two odd integers is necessarily even.

The systems to be studied subsequently are classified according to the properties they possess or, to put it another way, according to the axioms they satisfy. Our object will be to present a sequential development of the principal mathematical systems of modern algebra, beginning with those involving relatively few axioms and progressing to systems satisfying more detailed hypotheses.

The axioms which form the starting point of the abstract theory can be, by nature, rather varied. The growing tendency of modern mathematics is to isolate almost any convenient set of properties from its original context, to define a particular system, and to develop the corresponding abstract theory through logical deduction. Some of these formal axiomatic theories, such as the notion of a group, have a fundamental importance to the whole of mathematics and have been instrumental in unifying various apparently unrelated branches; other theories, while satisfying the esthetic and inquisitive needs of the mathematician, are limited in the extent of their applicability. We do not mean to create the impression that it is the usual practice for one to define a new system by arbitrarily (apart from logical considerations) writing down axioms. Although there is no particular necessity for the model to precede the theoretical development, in most cases the axioms are the abstract realization of the properties common to a variety of specific examples. With these general remarks out of the way, let us get down to work.

A set on which a single unrestricted binary operation is defined does not by itself yield a structure rich enough for our purposes; the concept, being too general, is poor in content. Certain reasonable limitations must be imposed on the operation if one is to obtain useful results. In the following paragraphs, some of the more basic requirements are named and briefly examined. For conciseness, we shall hereafter omit the word "binary" inasmuch as every operation to be considered will necessarily be binary.

Given a mathematical system $(S, *)$, the symbol $a * b * c$ is at the moment completely meaningless, since the operation $*$ has only been defined for pairs of elements of S. If, however, we make the stipulation that whenever quantities are enclosed in parentheses these are to be evaluated first, then both the expressions $a * (b * c)$ and $(a * b) * c$ make sense. Namely, $a * (b * c)$ is to be interpreted as: combine a with what results from combining b with c; while $(a * b) * c$ is to be interpreted as: first combine a with b and then combine the result with c. Of course, the resulting elements $a * (b * c)$ and $(a * b) * c$ will not necessarily be the same.

Definition 2–3. The operation $*$ defined on the set S is said to be *associative* if

$$a * (b * c) = (a * b) * c \qquad \text{(associative law)},$$

for every triple, distinct or not, of elements a, b, and c of S.

Example 2–5. The operation of subtraction on the set $R^\#$ of real numbers is not associative, since in general

$$a - (b - c) \neq (a - b) - c.$$

Example 2–6. An associative operation $*$ may be defined on Z, the set of integers, by taking $a * b = a + b + ab$. (We shall frequently delete the dot and write the product of a and b under ordinary multiplication simply as ab.) Then

$$a * (b * c) = a * (b + c + bc)$$
$$= a + (b + c + bc) + a(b + c + bc),$$

while

$$(a * b) * c = (a + b + ab) * c$$
$$= (a + b + ab) + c + (a + b + ab)c.$$

The equality of these two expressions follows in part from the fact that addition and multiplication are themselves associative in Z.

When dealing with a system whose operation is defined by a multiplication table rather than a formula, it is generally quite tedious to establish the associativity of the operation, for one must compute all possible threefold products. On the other hand, it may be far easier to show that the operation is not associative, as all we need do in this case is find three particular elements from the underlying set for which the associative law fails.

Example 2–7. Consider the operation $*$ defined on the set $S = \{1, 2, 3\}$ by the operation table:

$$
\begin{array}{c|ccc}
* & 1 & 2 & 3 \\
\hline
1 & 1 & 2 & 3 \\
2 & 3 & 1 & 2 \\
3 & 2 & 3 & 1 \\
\end{array}
$$

From this table, we see that $2 * (1 * 3) = 2 * 3 = 2$, whereas $(2 * 1) * 3 = 3 * 3 = 1$; that is,

$$2 * (1 * 3) \neq (2 * 1) * 3.$$

The associative law thus fails to hold in the system $(S, *)$.

The mathematical system which we shall use to build up more complicated algebraic structures is known as a semigroup.

Definition 2–4. A *semigroup* is a pair $(S, *)$ consisting of a nonempty set S together with an associative (binary) operation $*$ defined on S.

Let us stress that it is an abuse of language to say a certain set alone is a semigroup without also specifying the operation involved, as it may be quite possible to equip the same set with several associative operations. For this reason, we have utilized the ordered pair notation to indicate both the operation and the underlying set of elements.

Observe that since any three elements from the set of a semigroup always associate, there is no particular reason for parentheses. Consequently, when dealing with such a system, the symbol $a * b * c$ has meaning in the sense that we are free to interpret it either as $a * (b * c)$ or as $(a * b) * c$. More generally, the notation $a_1 * a_2 * \cdots * a_m$ is unambiguous, for it can be shown that all ways of inserting parentheses so as to give this expression a value yield the same result (Theorem 2–4). An operation which is not associative has the decided disadvantage that the notation for multiple-factored products can become quite unwieldy as a result of the constant need for parentheses.

In order to solidify the notion of a semigroup, we present several examples.

Example 2–8. There are several semigroups with which the reader is already familiar. If, for instance, Z_+ denotes the set of all positive integers, then both the pairs $(Z_+, +)$ and $(Z_+, \cdot)$ form semigroups. Similar statements hold for the sets Z, Q, and $R^{\#}$.

Example 2–9. Define the operation $*$ on the real numbers by the rule

$$a * b = \max \{a, b\}, \qquad a, b \in R^{\#}.$$

That is, $a * b$ is the larger of the two numbers a and b, or either one if $a = b$. Here, we have

$$a * (b * c) = \max \{a, b, c\} = (a * b) * c,$$

so that $(R^{\#}, *)$ satisfies the requirements of a semigroup.

Example 2–10. For any set X, each of the systems $(P(X), \cup)$ and $(P(X), \cap)$ constitutes a semigroup (Theorem 1–2).

Example 2–11. Let X be a nonempty set and S be the collection of all functions $f : X \to X$. If $\circ$ denotes functional composition, then the pair $(S, \circ)$ provides another illustration of a semigroup (Problem 5, Section 1–2).

As we shall subsequently see, the relevance of the semigroup concept lies in the fact that many important systems contain the semigroup structure as a subsystem.

We have already indicated that the order in which elements occur in a product is quite essential. If it is possible to interchange the order of combining any two elements from our set without affecting the result, then the operation is termed commutative.

Definition 2–5. The operation $*$ defined on the set S is called *commutative* if

$$a * b = b * a \qquad \text{(commutative law)},$$

for every pair of elements $a, b \in S$.

Examples 2–8, 2–9 and 2–10 are of *commutative semigroups* (semigroups whose operation is commutative), while in Example 2–11 functional composition is not, in general, a commutative operation. Although the commutative law may fail to hold throughout an entire system, it may still be valid for particular pairs of elements; accordingly, it will be convenient to make the following definition.

Definition 2–6. Two elements a and b are said to *commute* or *permute* (with each other) provided $a * b = b * a$.

Employing this terminology, we observe that the operation of the system $(S, *)$ is commutative if and only if every pair of elements of S commute.

Once an operation has been defined on a set, one finds that certain elements play special roles; there may exist identity elements and inverse elements.

Definition 2–7. The system $(S, *)$ is said to have a (two-sided) identity element for the operation $*$ if there exists an element e in S such that

$$a * e = e * a = a$$

for every $a \in S$. An element e having this property is called an *identity element* (unit element, neutral element) for $(S, *)$.

An identity element thus causes each element of the set S to remain stationary under the operation. In particular, notice that $e * e = e$. Of course, for a given system, an identity element may or may not exist; in case an identity does exist, it must be unique, as the theorem below shows.

Theorem 2–1. A mathematical system $(S, *)$ has at most one identity element.

Proof. For the proof, let us suppose that $(S, *)$ has two identity elements e and e'. Since $e * a = a$ for each $a \in S$, then in particular $e * e' = e'$. But on the other hand, e' is also an identity element, so we must have $e * e' = e$. We thus obtain $e = e * e' = e'$ and consequently $e = e'$; that is, if the system actually has an identity, then there is precisely one element with this property.

It follows from Theorem 2–1 that, whenever $(S, *)$ has an identity, we are justified in using the expression "the identity element of $(S, *)$"; the symbol e will be reserved exclusively for this identity.

Definition 2–8. A semigroup $(S, *)$ is said to be a *semigroup with identity* if there exists a (unique) identity element for $(S, *)$.

Example 2–12. The semigroup $(Z_+, \cdot)$ possesses an identity element, namely, the positive integer 1. On the other hand, the semigroup $(Z_+, +)$ has none, since $0 \notin Z_+$.

Example 2–13. Both the semigroups $(P(X), \cup)$ and $(P(X), \cap)$ have identities. Here, the empty set $\emptyset$ is the identity element for the union operation, since

$$A \cup \emptyset = \emptyset \cup A = A \quad \text{for each set} \quad A \subseteq X.$$

As is easy to see, the universal set X acts as the identity element for the operation of intersection, since

$$A \cap X = X \cap A = A \quad \text{for each set} \quad A \subseteq X.$$

Example 2–14. To record one more example of a semigroup with identity, consider the set of numbers

$$S = \{a + b\sqrt{2} \mid a, b \in Z\},$$

and the operation of ordinary multiplication. First, one is obliged to check that S is actually closed under multiplication; this is fairly clear, for if $a + b\sqrt{2}$ and $c + d\sqrt{2}$ are arbitrary members of S, then

$$(a + b\sqrt{2})(c + d\sqrt{2}) = (ad + 2bd) + (ad + bc)\sqrt{2} \in S.$$

It is not particularly difficult to establish that the pair $(S, \cdot)$ is a commutative semigroup with identity element $1 = 1 + 0\sqrt{2}$; we omit the argument.

When working with an operation which has an identity element, it is natural to inquire which elements of the underlying set, if any, have inverses.

Definition 2–9. Let $(S, *)$ be a mathematical system with identity element e. An element $a \in S$ is said to have a (two-sided) inverse under the operation $*$ if there exists some member a' of S such that

$$a * a' = a' * a = e.$$

An element a' having this property is called an *inverse* of a and is customarily denoted by a^{-1}.

An inverse has the effect of reducing a given element, under the operation, to the identity element. In particular, since $e * e = e$, we may infer that $e^{-1} = e$.

It will be established shortly that, for a semigroup with identity, each element has at most one inverse relative to the unique identity element. (The reader might try to work out the proof for himself.) Thus, when dealing with such a system, there is no ambiguity of meaning in the symbol a^{-1} and, if it exists, we are free to speak of "the inverse of an element."

Example 2–15. Let S be the set of all ordered pairs of nonzero real numbers and $*$ the binary operation defined by

$$(a, b) * (c, d) = (ac, bd).$$

Then the system $(S, *)$ forms a (commutative) semigroup with identity, with the pair $(1, 1)$ serving as its identity element. For $(a, b) \in S$, we evidently have $(a, b)^{-1} = (1/a, 1/b)$, since

$$(a, b) * (1/a, 1/b) = \bigl(a(1/a), b(1/b)\bigr) = (1, 1).$$

Example 2–16. Let X be a nonempty set and S be the collection of all functions $f: X \to X$. It is easy to see that the system $(S, \circ)$ is a semigroup with identity, having as its identity the identity map i_X. A function $f \in S$ will possess an inverse relative to the operation of composition if and only if f is a one-to-one mapping from X onto itself; in this event, the inverse of f (under $\circ$) is the usual inverse function f^{-1}:

$$f \circ f^{-1} = i_X = f^{-1} \circ f.$$

Example 2–17. As a further illustration of these ideas, let us return to the semigroup $\bigl(P(X), \cup\bigr)$ of Example 2–13. In this case, just the empty set $\emptyset$ possesses an inverse; for if $A \in P(X)$, with $A \neq \emptyset$, there is no subset A^{-1} of X such that $A \cup A^{-1} = \emptyset$. Likewise, in regard to the semigroup $\bigl(P(X), \cap\bigr)$, the only member of $P(X)$ which has an inverse is the universal set X.

There is a mathematical system, known as a group, which displays most of the properties we have so far discussed.

Definition 2–10. The pair $(G, *)$ is a *group* if and only if $(G, *)$ is a semigroup with identity in which each element of G has an inverse.

While the above definition is perfectly acceptable, we prefer to rephrase it in the following more detailed form, merely as a matter of convenience.

Definition 2–11. A group is a pair $(G, *)$ consisting of a nonempty set G and a binary operation $*$ defined on G, satisfying the four requirements:

1) G is closed under the operation $*$,
2) the operation $*$ is associative,
3) G contains an identity element e for the operation $*$, and
4) each element a of G has an inverse $a^{-1} \in G$, relative to $*$.

This definition calls for several remarks. For one thing, the first of the requirements cited above could easily have been omitted, since any set is closed with respect to a binary operation defined on it. (We merely wish to emphasize that one must always check the closure condition.) Observe particularly that commutativity is not required in the definition. If it happens that the group operation satisfies this additional hypothesis, then $(G, *)$ is referred to as a *commutative* or *abelian group*. Let us also point out that it is possible to give a less redundant version of the group axioms from which the present axioms follow as logical consequences; for this, we refer the reader to Problem 14 at the end of the section.

When the group operation is clearly understood, one often identifies the group with its underlying set of elements and refers to the group as G rather than as $(G, *)$. For further simplicity, many authors drop the star notation and write ab in place of $a * b$. While we shall continue to adhere to the $a * b$ convention, we will nonetheless adopt some of the terminology of ordinary multiplication and talk of forming products, multiplying elements together, etc. At times, we shall also be somewhat imprecise and speak loosely about the elements of the group $(G, *)$, when we really mean the elements of the underlying set G; however, this should cause no particular confusion.

In order that the reader fully appreciate the generality of the concept of a group and at the same time gain some familiarity with this idea, we pause to offer a selection of examples. Further examples appear in the exercises.

Example 2–18. Let a be any nonzero real number and consider the set G of integral multiples of a:

$$G = \{na \mid n \in Z\}.$$

The pair $(G, +)$, where, as usual, $+$ indicates ordinary addition, forms a commutative group. In this case, the identity is $0 = 0a \in G$, while the inverse of an arbitrary element na of G is $-(na) = (-n)a \in G$.

Example 2–19. Consider the set of ordered pairs,

$$G = \{(0, 0), (0, 1), (1, 0), (1, 1)\},$$

and the operation $*$ defined by Table 2–1. In this group, the identity element is the pair $(0, 0)$, and every element is its own inverse. Here the verification of the associative law becomes a process of detailed enumeration of all possible cases that could arise.

Table 2–1

$*$	$(0, 0)$	$(0, 1)$	$(1, 0)$	$(1, 1)$
$(0, 0)$	$(0, 0)$	$(0, 1)$	$(1, 0)$	$(1, 1)$
$(0, 1)$	$(0, 1)$	$(0, 0)$	$(1, 1)$	$(1, 0)$
$(1, 0)$	$(1, 0)$	$(1, 1)$	$(0, 0)$	$(0, 1)$
$(1, 1)$	$(1, 1)$	$(1, 0)$	$(0, 1)$	$(0, 0)$

Since the entire table is symmetric about the main diagonal (upper left to lower right), the group operation $*$ is commutative. Note that each element of G appears once and only once in each row and column of the table. Indeed, any multiplication table for a group has this feature.

Example 2–20. Let $P(X)$ be the power set of some fixed nonempty set X. As we have seen, the systems $(P(X), \cup)$ and $(P(X), \cap)$ possess identity elements $\emptyset$ and X, respectively, but neither system has inverses for any elements other than their respective identities. Consequently, $P(X)$ does not constitute a group with regard to the formulation of either unions or intersections. It is possible, however, to remedy this deficiency by defining another operation on $P(X)$ in terms of union and intersection which will result in a group structure.

More specifically, consider the operation $\triangle$ (the symbol is traditional) given by the formula

$$A \triangle B = (A - B) \cup (B - A),$$

for

$$A, B \in P(X).$$

Figure 2–1

This operation, known as the *symmetric difference* of A and B, yields the set which is represented by the shaded area in Fig. 2–1. We shall leave as an exercise the verification that the symmetric difference operation is commutative and associative.

It is easy to see that for any set $A \subseteq X$ (that is, for any element of $P(X)$),

$$A \triangle \emptyset = (A - \emptyset) \cup (\emptyset - A) = A \cup \emptyset = A,$$

which proves that the empty set $\emptyset$ serves as an identity element for $\triangle$. Moreover,

$$A \triangle A = (A - A) \cup (A - A) = \emptyset \cup \emptyset = \emptyset.$$

This implies that each element of $P(X)$ is its own inverse. Consequently, the mathematical system $(P(X), \Delta)$ is a commutative group.

Example 2–21. As a simple example of a noncommutative group, let the set G consist of all ordered pairs of real numbers with nonzero first component:

$$G = \{(a, b) \mid a, b \in R^{\#}, a \neq 0\}.$$

Define the operation $*$ on G by the formula

$$(a, b) * (c, d) = (ac, bc + d).$$

The associativity of the operation follows from the familiar properties of the real numbers, for we have

$$
\begin{aligned}
[(a, b) * (c, d)] * (e, f) &= (ac, bc + d) * (e, f) \\
&= ((ac)e, (bc + d)e + f) \\
&= (a(ce), b(ce) + (de + f)) \\
&= (a, b) * (ce, de + f) \\
&= (a, b) * [(c, d) * (e, f)].
\end{aligned}
$$

It is readily verified that the pair $(1, 0)$ serves as the identity element, while the inverse of $(a, b) \in G$ is $(1/a, -b/a)$. To see that the group $(G, *)$ is not commutative, merely consider the elements $(1, 2)$ and $(3, 4)$ of G:

$$(1, 2) * (3, 4) = (3, 10) \neq (3, 6) = (3, 4) * (1, 2).$$

Example 2–22. For another example of a noncommutative group, take the set G as consisting of the six functions $f_1, f_2, \ldots, f_6$, where for

$$x \in R^{\#} - \{0, 1\},$$

we define

$$f_1(x) = x, \qquad f_2(x) = \frac{1}{x},$$

$$f_3(x) = 1 - x, \qquad f_4(x) = \frac{x - 1}{x},$$

$$f_5(x) = \frac{x}{x - 1}, \qquad f_6(x) = \frac{1}{1 - x}.$$

Let the group operation be that of functional composition.

Thus, as an illustration, we have

$$(f_2 \circ f_6)(x) = f_2(f_6(x)) = f_2\left(\frac{1}{1 - x}\right) = \frac{1}{1/(1 - x)}$$

$$= 1 - x = f_3(x),$$

which implies that $f_2 \circ f_6 = f_3$. On the other hand,

$$(f_6 \circ f_2)(x) = f_6(f_2(x))$$

$$= f_6\left(\frac{1}{x}\right) = \frac{1}{1 - 1/x}$$

$$= \frac{x}{x - 1} = f_5(x),$$

Table 2–2

$\circ$	f_1	f_2	f_3	f_4	f_5	f_6
f_1	f_1	f_2	f_3	f_4	f_5	f_6
f_2	f_2	f_1	f_6	f_5	f_4	f_3
f_3	f_3	f_4	f_1	f_2	f_6	f_5
f_4	f_4	f_3	f_5	f_6	f_2	f_1
f_5	f_5	f_6	f_4	f_3	f_1	f_2
f_6	f_6	f_5	f_2	f_1	f_3	f_4

so that $f_6 \circ f_2 = f_5$, which shows that the operation $*$ is not commutative. The multiplication for $(G, \circ)$ in this case is given by Table 2–2. Since functional composition is associative (Theorem 1–7), the system $(G, \circ)$ is certainly a semigroup. The operation table shows that f_1 is the identity element and the respective inverses are

$$f_1^{-1} = f_1, \qquad f_2^{-1} = f_2, \qquad f_3^{-1} = f_3,$$
$$f_4^{-1} = f_6, \qquad f_5^{-1} = f_5, \qquad f_6^{-1} = f_4.$$

To encompass all the different groups above in a single concept obviously requires the formulation of the underlying group concept in the most general terms. This is precisely the point we hope to convey to the reader; the value of contemporary mathematics lies in its power to abstract and thus to lay bare the structurally essential relations between superficially distinct entities.

Historically, the notion of a group arose early in the nineteenth century out of attempts to solve polynomial equations. Galois was the first to use the word "group" in any technical sense when he considered the group of permutations of the roots of such equations. A major achievement in the evolution of the theory was Klein's classification, in the 1870's, of the various branches of geometry according to groups of transformations under which certain geometric properties remain invariant. It remained some time, however, before satisfactory group postulates, free of redundancy, were stated. Definition 2–11, first formulated in 1902, is attributed to the American mathematician E. V. Huntington.

In the twentieth century, group theory has embraced all branches of mathematics and, indeed, a wide variety of other fields. It is difficult to give examples without becoming too technical, but the theory of groups is now employed in the study of quantum mechanics, general relativity, and crystallography. In these areas, group theory is not only a tool with which calculations are made but also a source of concepts and principles for the formulation of new theories. A recent example can be found in the physics of fundamental particles with the discovery of a new "elementary particle" whose existence had been predicted from a classification scheme based on groups. It is certainly appropriate to begin our investigation of mathematical systems with this concept.

PROBLEMS

1. Determine which of the following binary operations on the set Q are associative and which are commutative.

   a) $a * b = 0$ b) $a * b = \frac{1}{2}(a + b)$

   c) $a * b = b$ d) $a * b = a + b - 1$

2. Suppose the system $(S, *)$ has an identity element; show that if the equation

$$(a * b) * (c * d) = (a * c) * (b * d)$$

   holds for all possible choices of elements a, b, c and d of S, then the operation $*$ is both associative and commutative.

3. Prove that the set of ordered pairs of real numbers together with the operation $*$ defined on S by
$$(a, b) * (c, d) = (a + c, b + d + 2bd)$$

   constitutes a commutative semigroup with identity.

4. Let us define a binary operation $*$ on the set $S = \{1, 2, 3, 4, 6\}$ as follows:

$$a * b = \gcd (a, b).$$

   For example, $6 * 4 = 2$, $3 * 4 = 1$, etc. Show that $(S, *)$ is a commutative semigroup. [*Hint:* Problem 17, Section 1–2.]

5. Consider the three-element set $S = \{a, b, c\}$ and the operation $*$ given by the multiplication table below:

$*$	a	b	c
a	a	b	c
b	b	a	c
c	c	c	c

   Verify that the pair $(S, *)$ is a commutative semigroup with identity, but not a group.

6. In the following instances, determine whether the systems $(G, *)$ described are commutative groups. For those systems failing to be so, indicate which axioms are not satisfied.

   a) $G = Z_+$, $a * b = \max \{a, b\}$,

   b) $G = Z$, $a * b = \min \{a, b\}$ (the smaller of a and b),

   c) $G = R^\#$, $a * b = a + b - ab$,

   d) $G = Z_+$, $a * b = \max \{a, b\} - \min \{a, b\}$,

   e) $G = Z \times Z$, $(a, b) * (c, d) = (a + c, b + d)$,

   f) $G = R^\# \times R^\#$, $(a, b) * (c, d) = (ac + bd, ad + bd)$,

   g) $G = R^\# \times R^\# - (0, 0)$, $(a, b) * (c, d) = (ac - bd, ad + bc)$.

7. Suppose that $a \in R^\# - \{0, 1\}$ and consider the set G of integral powers of a: $G = \{a^k \mid k \in Z\}$. If $\cdot$ denotes ordinary multiplication, prove that $(G, \cdot)$ is a group.

An inspection of the proof shows that we have established a little more than is indicated by the statement of the theorem. We have, in fact, shown that if an element of a semigroup with identity has an inverse, then it must be unique.

Corollary. Each element of a semigroup with identity has at most one inverse.

A further useful conclusion to be drawn from Theorem 2–2 is that $(a^{-1})^{-1} = a$. This stems from the observation that $(a^{-1})^{-1}$ is an element of G for which

$$a^{-1} * (a^{-1})^{-1} = (a^{-1})^{-1} * a^{-1} = e.$$

Since a itself has this property, and since inverses have just been seen to be unique, the element a must be the inverse of a^{-1}. For the proof of the next theorem, we shall require a preliminary lemma.

Lemma. If $a, b, c, d \in G$ and $(G, *)$ is a semigroup, then

$$(a * b) * (c * d) = a * ((b * c) * d).$$

Proof. Let us temporarily denote the product $c * d$ by x. Then, since the operation $*$ is associative, we have

$$\begin{aligned} a * ((b * c) * d) &= a * (b * (c * d)) \\ &= a * (b * x) \\ &= (a * b) * x \\ &= (a * b) * (c * d). \end{aligned}$$

Theorem 2–3. If $(G, *)$ is a group and $a, b \in G$, then $(a * b)^{-1} = b^{-1} * a^{-1}$. That is, the inverse of a product of group elements is the product of their inverses in reverse order.

Proof. According to the definition of inverse, all we need to show is that

$$(a * b) * (b^{-1} * a^{-1}) = (b^{-1} * a^{-1}) * (a * b) = e,$$

where e is the group identity. From the uniqueness of the inverse of $a * b$, we would then conclude that

$$(a * b)^{-1} = b^{-1} * a^{-1}.$$

Using the above lemma, we have

$$\begin{aligned} (a * b) * (b^{-1} * a^{-1}) &= a * ((b * b^{-1}) * a^{-1}) \\ &= a * (e * a^{-1}) = a * a^{-1} \\ &= e. \end{aligned}$$

A similar argument establishes that $(b^{-1} * a^{-1}) * (a * b) = e$.

Corollary. If a and b are invertible elements of a semigroup with identity, then

$$(a * b)^{-1} = b^{-1} * a^{-1}.$$

To be sure, if the operation $*$ is commutative, then we do have

$$(a * b)^{-1} = a^{-1} * b^{-1};$$

however, in the absence of this hypothesis there is no guarantee that the inverse of a product is equal to the product of the respective inverses. The next example should help to make these notions clearer.

Example 2–23. Let G denote the set of all ordered pairs of real numbers with nonzero first component. If the binary operation $*$ is defined on the set G by the rule

$$(a, b) * (c, d) = (ac, bc + d),$$

then $(G, *)$ is a noncommutative group [Example 2–21]. The identity element of the group is the pair $(1, 0)$; the inverse of an element $(a, b) \in G$ is $(1/a, -b/a)$. A direct computation shows that

$$((1, 3) * (2, 4))^{-1} = (2, 10)^{-1} = (\tfrac{1}{2}, -5),$$

while

$$(2, 4)^{-1} * (1, 3)^{-1} = (\tfrac{1}{2}, -2) * (1, -3) = (\tfrac{1}{2}, -5).$$

Thus $((1, 3) * (2, 4))^{-1} = (2, 4)^{-1} * (1, 3)^{-1}$, as is guaranteed by Theorem 2–3. However, computing the product of the inverses in the order

$$(1, 3)^{-1} * (2, 4)^{-1},$$

we obtain

$$(1, 3)^{-1} * (2, 4)^{-1} = (1, -3) * (\tfrac{1}{2}, -2) = (\tfrac{1}{2}, -\tfrac{7}{2}),$$

so that

$$((1, 3) * (2, 4))^{-1} \neq (1, 3)^{-1} * (2, 4)^{-1}.$$

For this group then, the inverse of a product of elements is not equal to the product of their respective inverses in direct order. This should not be particularly surprising inasmuch as the group $(G, *)$ is noncommutative.

The previous lemma is actually a special case of a result mentioned earlier which in effect asserts that parentheses are superfluous in a product of group elements, and consequently that their omission can lead to no misunderstanding. The exact story is told in the next theorem.

First, however, let us introduce some auxiliary notation: suppose $(S, *)$ is a semigroup and the elements $a_1, a_2, \ldots, a_n$ belong to S (where $n > 1$). Their *standard product*, symbolized by $a_1 * a_2 * \cdots * a_n$, is defined recursively as

$$a_1 * a_2 * \cdots * a_n = (a_1 * a_2 * \cdots * a_{n-1}) * a_n.$$

When $n = 4$, for instance, $a_1 * a_2 * a_3 * a_4$ will turn out to be

$$a_1 * a_2 * a_3 * a_4 = (a_1 * a_2 * a_3) * a_4$$
$$= ((a_1 * a_2) * a_3) * a_4.$$

In essence, we are using induction to define a particular grouping of parentheses and therefore a particular element of S.

With this definition in mind, we now show that a product is determined solely by the order of its factors, and not on the manner of distributing parentheses.

Theorem 2–4. (*Generalized Associative Law*). Let $(S, *)$ be a semigroup and $a_1, a_2, \ldots, a_n$ be a set of $n \geq 3$ elements of S. Then all possible products of $a_1, a_2, \ldots, a_n$, taken in that order and arrived at by placing parentheses in any meaningful position, yield one and the same result.

Proof. The strategy we shall employ is to prove all products of the elements $a_1, a_2, \ldots, a_n$ are equal to their standard product $a_1 * a_2 * \cdots * a_n$; our argument proceeds by induction on n, where $n \geq 3$. In the case $n = 3$, the result follows directly from the associativity of $*$:

$$a_1 * (a_2 * a_3) = (a_1 * a_2) * a_3 = a_1 * a_2 * a_3.$$

Next, assume that the assertion holds for all products of m factors, where $3 \leq m < n$, and let x be any product involving n factors.

Since x is obtained by successive applications of the operation $*$, there must be a final multiplication between two expressions having less than n factors. By the induction hypotheses, each of these two expressions equals the standard product, so that x may be written as

$$x = (a_1 * a_2 * \cdots * a_k) * (a_{k+1} * a_{k+2} * \cdots * a_n), \qquad 1 \leq k < n.$$

By definition of the standard product,

$$a_{k+1} * a_{k+2} * \cdots * a_n = (a_{k+1} * a_{k+2} * \cdots * a_{n-1}) * a_n,$$

whence

$$x = (a_1 * a_2 * \cdots * a_k) * [(a_{k+1} * a_{k+2} * \cdots * a_{n-1}) * a_n].$$

The usual associative law now yields

$$x = [(a_1 * a_2 * \cdots * a_k) * (a_{k+1} * a_{k+2} * \cdots * a_{n-1})] * a_n.$$

Applying first our induction assumption to the expression in brackets (which certainly contains less than n factors) and then the definition of the standard product again, we infer that

$$x = (a_1 * a_2 * \cdots * a_{n-1}) * a_n = a_1 * a_2 * \cdots * a_n.$$

This completes the induction step and therefore the proof of the theorem.

Given four elements a_1, a_2, a_3, $a_4 \in S$, parentheses can be legally inserted and the elements multiplied (in the given order) five different ways. Theorem 2–4 permits us to conclude that all these products are equal:

$$
\begin{aligned}
(((a_1 * a_2) * a_3) * a_4) &= (a_1 * (a_2 * a_3)) * a_4 \\
&= a_1 * ((a_2 * a_3) * a_4) \\
&= a_1 * (a_2 * (a_3 * a_4)) \\
&= (a_1 * a_2) * (a_3 * a_4).
\end{aligned}
$$

As a matter of notation, it will be our tendency to omit parentheses in writing products; the exception to this will be found on those occasions when we wish to emphasize the associative law or a certain grouping of elements.

Theorem 2–5. (*Cancellation Law*). If a, b, and c are elements of a group $(G, *)$ such that either $a * c = b * c$ or $c * a = c * b$, then $a = b$.

Proof. Since $c \in G$, c^{-1} exists in G. Multiplying the equation $a * c = b * c$ on the right side by c^{-1}, we obtain

$$(a * c) * c^{-1} = (b * c) * c^{-1}.$$

Then, by the associative law, this becomes

$$a * (c * c^{-1}) = b * (c * c^{-1}),$$

or $a * e = b * e$. Therefore $a = b$. Similarly, we can show that $c * a = c * b$ implies $a = b$.

Corollary. The only solution of the group equation $x * x = x$ is $x = e$.

Proof. The conclusion is an immediate consequence of the cancellation law and the fact that $x * x = x * e$.

In a system $(S, *)$, an element $x \in S$ is said to be *idempotent* provided $x * x = x$. What we have just shown is that a group possesses exactly one idempotent element, namely the group identity. For an illustration of a system in which every element is idempotent the student is referred to Problem 4, Section 2–1.

This last theorem allows us to cancel, from the same side, in equations involving group elements. We cannot conclude, however, that $a * c = c * b$ implies $a = b$, unless the group is known to be commutative.

An arbitrary binary operation need not satisfy the cancellation law. To see this, we consider the set $G = \{1, 2, 3\}$ under the following multiplication table:

*	1	2	3
1	1	2	3
2	2	1	2
3	3	2	1

On examining the table, we observe that $2 * 1 = 2 * 3$; but obviously $1 \neq 3$. The failure of the cancellation law in this instance results from the fact that when we multiply both sides of the equation $2 * 1 = 2 * 3$ by $2^{-1} = 2$, the element 2 does not associate with the product $2 * 3$; that is,

$$2 * (2 * 3) \neq (2 * 2) * 3.$$

Theorem 2–6. In a group $(G, *)$, the equations $a * x = b$ and $y * a = b$ have unique solutions.

Proof. First, $x = a^{-1} * b$ satisfies the group equation $a * x = b$, since

$$a * (a^{-1} * b) = (a * a^{-1}) * b$$
$$= e * b$$
$$= b.$$

This shows that there is at least one solution in G; it remains for us to show that there is only one. Suppose there is some other element $x' \in G$ such that $a * x' = b$. Then

$$a * x' = a * (a^{-1} * b),$$

so that by the cancellation law,

$$x' = a^{-1} * b, \quad \text{or} \quad x' = x.$$

The second part of the theorem may be proved in an analogous manner.

Corollary. In a multiplication table for a group, each element appears exactly once in each row and column.

Proof. For a proof by contradiction, suppose that the element b occurred twice in the row headed by a. There would then exist elements x_1 and x_2, with $x_1 \neq x_2$, such that

$$a * x_1 = b \quad \text{and} \quad a * x_2 = b.$$

However, this situation is plainly incompatible with the above theorem which asserts that there is one and only one solution of the equation $a * x = b$. A proof for columns can be obtained by imitating the argument for rows.

It can be shown that all groups with fewer than six elements are commutative; thus a noncommutative group must necessarily contain at least six elements. The proof of this fact is somewhat lengthy, although the actual details are not by themselves particularly difficult. The subsequent lemma will serve to isolate the most tedious aspect of the theorem.

Lemma. If a and b are noncommuting elements of a group $(G, *)$—that is, $a * b \neq b * a$—then the elements of the set,

$$\{e, a, b, a * b, b * a\},$$

are all distinct.

Proof. The basic idea of the proof is to examine the members of the set $\{e, a, b, a * b, b * a\}$ two at a time, and show that each of the ten possible equalities leads to a contradiction of the hypothesis

$$a * b \neq b * a.$$

On several occasions, the cancellation law is used without explicit reference. The argument runs as follows:

1) $e = a$ implies $a * b = e * b = b = b * e = b * a$,

2) $e = b$ implies $a * b = a * e = a = e * a = b * a$,

3) $e = a * b$ implies $a * e = e * a = (a * b) * a = a * (b * a)$, so that $e = b * a$ or $a * b = b * a$,

4) $e = b * a$ implies $e * a = a * e = a * (b * a) = (a * b) * a$, so that $e = a * b$ or $b * a = a * b$,

5) $a = b$ implies $a * b = a * a = b * a$,

6) $a = a * b$ implies $e = b$, reducing to case (2),

7) $a = b * a$ implies $e = b$, reducing to case (2),

8) $b = a * b$ implies $e = a$, reducing to case (1),

9) $b = b * a$ implies $e = a$, reducing to case (1),

10) $a * b = b * a$ contradicts the hypothesis.

The proof of the lemma is now complete.

Theorem 2–7. Any noncommutative group has at least six elements.

Proof. If $(G, *)$ is a noncommutative group, it must have a pair of noncommuting elements a and b. According to the lemma, the set $\{e, a, b, a * b, b * a\}$ then consists of distinct members. We now proceed to establish that one of the group elements $a * a$ or $a * b * a$ is distinct from these five; however, it is not possible to specify abstractly whether it is $a * a$ or $a * b * a$.

With the aid of the lemma, we first show that $a * a$ is different from each member of $\{a, b, a * b, b * a\}$. To start with, observe that

a) $a * a = a$ implies $a = e$, reducing to case (1) of the lemma,
b) $a * a = b$ implies $a * b = a * (a * a) = (a * a) * a = b * a$,
c) $a * a = a * b$ implies $a = b$, reducing to case (5),
d) $a * a = b * a$ implies $a = b$, reducing to case (5).

Thus, either $a * a \neq e$, in which case $a * a$ is the sixth distinct element of G or else $a * a = e$.

In this latter instance, we can show $a * b * a$ to be distinct from each of e, a, b, $a * b$, $b * a$ and consequently to be the required sixth element. The reasoning here depends on the fact that

$$a * (a * b * a) = (a * a) * (b * a) = e * (b * a) = b * a.$$

e) $a * b * a = e$ implies $b * a = a * (a * b * a) = a * e = a$, reducing to case (7),
f) $a * b * a = a$ implies $a * b = e$, reducing to case (3),
g) $a * b * a = b$ implies $a * b = a * (a * b * a) = b * a$,
h) $a * b * a = a * b$ implies $a = e$, reducing to case (1),
i) $a * b * a = b * a$ implies $a = e$, reducing to case (1),

which establishes the result. An alternative proof will be presented in Section 2–5.

The generalized associative law insures that the product $a * a * \cdots * a$ has an unambiguous meaning irrespective of how the factors are parenthesized. Designating the foregoing product by the symbol a^k (assuming there are k factors), we may introduce the notion of the positive powers of a. The next definition extends this idea to arbitrary integral powers.

Definition 2–12. In any group $(G, *)$, the *integral powers* of an element $a \in G$ are defined by

$$a^k = a * a * \cdots * a \quad \text{(k factors),}$$
$$a^0 = e,$$
$$a^{-k} = (a^{-1})^k,$$

where $k \in Z_+$.

With these conventions, the customary laws of exponents have their counterpart in group theory.

Theorem 2–8. Let $(G, *)$ be a group, $a \in G$, and $m, n \in Z$. The powers of a obey the following laws of exponents:

1) $a^n * a^m = a^{n+m} = a^m * a^n$,   2) $(a^n)^m = a^{nm} = (a^m)^n$,

3) $a^{-n} = (a^n)^{-1}$,   4) $e^n = e$.

The detailed proof of these statements requires a breakdown into "cases" and can safely be left as an exercise. We caution the reader that the property $(a * b)^n = a^n * b^n$ is not to be expected in an arbitrary group (a moment's reflection should convince one of this).

We shall now conclude this section with two particularly important examples of groups, since we shall have frequent occasion to refer to them in the future.

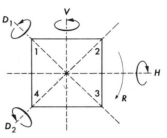

Figure 2–2

Example 2–24. The group to be introduced here is known as the *group of symmetries of a square.* Imagine a cardboard square having its sides parallel to the axes of a coordinate system and its center at the origin (Fig. 2–2).

The elements of the set G are taken to be certain rigid motions of the square. Permitted motions are the following: clockwise rotations R_{90}, R_{180}, R_{270}, and R_{360} about the center through angles of 90, 180, 270, and 360 degrees, respectively; reflections (flips out of the plane and back into it) H and V about the horizontal and vertical lines through the center; reflections D_1 and D_2 about the indicated diagonals. We can *multiply* two such motions by performing them in succession, beginning with the one on the right. Thus $X * Y$ means the motion that achieves the same result as Y followed by X.

For example, $H * R_{90}$ is that element of G which has the same net effect as R_{90} (a rotation clockwise through 90°) followed by H (a horizontal flip). By observing the manner in which the numbered corners of the square are shifted around, we see that $H * R_{90}$ produces the same result as the single motion D_2; so $H * R_{90} = D_2$. A similar analysis shows $R_{90} * H = D_1$ from which we infer that our multiplication is not commutative.

Table 2–3

*	R_{90}	R_{180}	R_{270}	R_{360}	H	V	D_1	D_2
R_{90}	R_{180}	R_{270}	R_{360}	R_{90}	D_1	D_2	V	H
R_{180}	R_{270}	R_{360}	R_{90}	R_{180}	V	H	D_2	D_1
R_{270}	R_{360}	R_{90}	R_{180}	R_{270}	D_2	D_1	H	V
R_{360}	R_{90}	R_{180}	R_{270}	R_{360}	H	V	D_1	D_2
H	D_2	V	D_1	H	R_{360}	R_{180}	R_{270}	R_{90}
V	D_1	H	D_2	V	R_{180}	R_{360}	R_{90}	R_{270}
D_1	H	D_2	V	D_1	R_{90}	R_{270}	R_{360}	R_{180}
D_2	V	D_1	H	D_2	R_{270}	R_{90}	R_{180}	R_{360}

The complete multiplication table for the operation $*$ is shown in Table 2–3. Note that R_{360} serves as the identity element and each of R_{180}, R_{360}, H, V, D_1, and D_2 is its own inverse, whereas R_{90} and R_{270} are inverses of each other.

The associative law also holds, but this is not immediately obvious. We shall see later that the symmetries of the square are equivalent to a group of permutations of the set $\{1, 2, 3, 4\}$ (observe that a symmetry is completely described by its effect on the vertices) and associativity therefore follows from the associativity of functional composition. Granting this for the moment, the proof that $(G, *)$ constitutes a group is complete.

Similar groups may be defined for other geometric figures; in fact, for any regular n-sided polygon. Problem 14 at the end of this section deals with the group of symmetries of the equilateral triangle.

Example 2–25. Let $(G, *)$ be an arbitrary group. For a fixed element $a \in G$, define the *left-multiplication function* $f_a \colon G \to G$ by

$$f_a(x) = a * x \qquad \text{for each} \qquad x \in G.$$

That is, f_a multiplies (or translates) each element of G by a on the left. If $x \in G$, then

$$x = a * (a^{-1} * x) = f_a(a^{-1} * x),$$

so that f_a maps G onto itself. Moreover, f_a is one-to-one, for if $x, y \in G$ with $f_a(x) = f_a(y)$, then $a * x = a * y$. From the cancellation law, we conclude that $x = y$.

Suppose we combine two of these mappings, say f_a and f_b, under the usual composition of functions. For any $x \in G$, we see that

$$(f_a \circ f_b)(x) = f_a(f_b(x)) = f_a(b * x) = a * (b * x)$$
$$= (a * b) * x = f_{a*b}(x).$$

This means that $f_a \circ f_b = f_{a*b}$, so that the set of all such functions is closed under the operation of functional composition.

For the sake of notation, set $F_G = \{f_a \mid a \in G\}$. Our aim is to show that the pair $(F_G, \circ)$ is actually a group.

Indeed, if e is the identity element for $(G, *)$, then f_e acts as the identity for $(F_G, \circ)$, since

$$f_a \circ f_e = f_{a*e} = f_a = f_{e*a} = f_e \circ f_a.$$

Moreover, $(f_a)^{-1} = f_{a^{-1}}$, for we have

$$f_a \circ f_{a^{-1}} = f_{a*a^{-1}} = f_e = f_{a^{-1}*a} = f_{a^{-1}} \circ f_a.$$

We already know that composition of functions is associative (Theorem 1–7), so it follows that $(F_G, \circ)$ forms a group.

PROBLEMS

1. Given that a, b, c, and d are elements of the semigroup $(G, *)$, prove that

$$((a * b) * c) * d = a * (b * (c * d)).$$

2. Complete the proof of Theorem 2–8.

3. Prove the theorem: A group $(G, *)$ is commutative if and only if $(a * b)^{-1} = a^{-1} * b^{-1}$ for every $a, b \in G$.

4. Given a and b are elements of a group $(G, *)$, with $a * b = b * a$, show that $(a * b)^k = a^k * b^k$ for every integer $k \in Z$.

5. Let $(G, *)$ be a group such that $(a * b)^2 = a^2 * b^2$ for every $a, b \in G$. Prove that the group is commutative.

6. Given $a^2 = e$ for every element a of the group $(G, *)$, show that the group must be commutative.

7. A group $(G, *)$ is said to be *cyclic* if there exists an element $a \in G$ such that every element of G is of the form a^k for some integer k (positive, negative, or zero). Such an element a is called a *generator* of the group.

    a) Prove that any cyclic group is commutative.

    b) Given $G = \{1, -1, i, -i\}$, with $i^2 = -1$, show that $(G, \cdot)$ is a cyclic group. Which of its elements are generators?

8. Prove that if a and b are elements of a group $(G, *)$ with the property

$$a^{-1} * b * a = b^{-1} \quad \text{and} \quad b^{-1} * a * b = a^{-1},$$

then $a^4 = e = b^4$.

9. Prove that if $(G, *)$ is a group having more than two elements, then there exist $a, b \in G$, with $a \neq b$, $a \neq e$, $b \neq e$, such that $a * b = b * a$.

10. If $(S, *)$ is a semigroup with identity and G the set of all elements of S having inverses with respect to the operation $*$, verify that the pair $(G, *)$ is a group.

11. Prove that a group may alternatively be defined as a semigroup $(G, *)$ in which, for all $a, b \in G$, each of the equations $a * x = b$ and $y * a = b$ has a solution in G. [*Hint:* Use the characterization of a group given in Problem 14, Section 2–1.]

12. Show that any semigroup $(S, *)$ with a finite number of elements possesses an idempotent element. [*Hint:* For $n > 1$, proceed by induction on n, the number of elements of S; given $a \in S$, let $A = \{a^k \mid k = 2, 3, \ldots\}$, and argue according to whether or not A contains the element a.]

13. For any system $(S, *)$, define the set

$$A = \{a \in S \mid a * (b * c) = (a * b) * c \text{ for all } b, c \in S\}.$$

If $A \neq \emptyset$, prove that the pair $(A, *)$ is a semigroup.

14. Let the set G consist of certain rigid motions of an equilateral triangle. Permitted motions are three clockwise rotations R_{120}, R_{240}, and R_{360} about the center through angles of 120, 240, and 360 degrees, respectively, and three reflections L_1, L_2, and L_3 about lines l_1, l_2, and l_3 as indicated (Fig. 2–3). As usual, define the operation $*$ on G to be one motion followed by another. Prove that the system $(G, *)$ is a group.

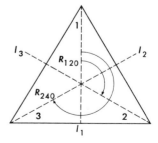

Figure 2–3

15. Let $(G, *)$ and $(H, \circ)$ be two distinct groups. Define a binary operation $\cdot$ on the Cartesian product

$$G \times H = \{(g, h) \mid g \in G, h \in H\},$$

as follows: for

$$(g_1, h_1), (g_2, h_2) \in G \times H,$$

set

$$(g_1, h_1) \cdot (g_2, h_2) = (g_1 * g_2, h_1 \circ h_2).$$

Prove that $(G \times H, \cdot)$ is a group, called the *direct product group* of $(G, *)$ and $(H, \circ)$; show further that this group is commutative whenever the original groups are commutative.

2-3 TWO IMPORTANT GROUPS

This section is devoted to an examination of two important and frequently used groups: the group of integers modulo n and the group of permutations of the elements of a set (the so-called symmetric group). While these groups are of some interest per se, our main purpose in introducing them is to provide two more concrete examples to illustrate concepts which will be developed subsequently.

We begin with an investigation of the notion of congruence, in terms of which the group of integers modulo n will be formulated.

Definition 2-13. Let n be a fixed positive integer. Two integers a and b are said to be *congruent modulo n*, written

$$a \equiv b \pmod{n},$$

if and only if the difference $a - b$ is divisible by n. That is, $a \equiv b \pmod{n}$ if and only if $a - b = kn$ for some integer k.

For instance, if $n = 7$, we have

$$3 \equiv 24 \pmod{7},$$

$$-5 \equiv 2 \pmod{7},$$

$$-8 \equiv -50 \pmod{7}, \quad \text{etc}.$$

If $a - b$ is not divisible by n, we say that a is incongruent to b modulo n and, in this case, write $a \not\equiv b \pmod{n}$.

It is noteworthy that every pair of integers are congruent modulo 1, while a pair of integers are congruent modulo 2 provided they are both even or both odd.

Our first theorem provides a useful characterization of congruence modulo n in terms of remainders on division by n.

Theorem 2-9. Let n be a fixed positive integer and a, b be arbitrary integers. Then $a \equiv b \pmod{n}$ if and only if a and b have the same remainder when divided by n.

Proof. Suppose first $a \equiv b \pmod{n}$, so that $a = b + kn$ for some integer k. On division by n, b leaves a certain remainder r:

$$b = qn + r, \qquad \text{where} \qquad 0 \le r < n.$$

Thus, $a = b + kn = (q + k)n + r$, which shows a has the same remainder as b.

On the other hand, let $a = q_1 n + r$ and $b = q_2 n + r$, with the same remainder r ($0 \le r < n$). Then

$$a - b = (q_1 n + r) - (q_2 n + r) = (q_1 - q_2)n,$$

with $q_1 - q_2$ an integer. Hence, n is a factor of $a - b$ and so $a \equiv b \pmod{n}$.

Congruence may be viewed as a type of equality in the sense that its behavior with respect to addition and multiplication is reminiscent of ordinary equality. Some of the elementary properties of equality which also carry over to congruences are listed in the next theorem.

Theorem 2–10. Let n be a fixed positive integer and a, b, c be arbitrary integers. Then

1) $a \equiv a \pmod{n}$,
2) if $a \equiv b \pmod{n}$, then $b \equiv a \pmod{n}$,
3) if $a \equiv b \pmod{n}$ and $b \equiv c \pmod{n}$, then $a \equiv c \pmod{n}$,
4) if $a \equiv b \pmod{n}$ and $c \equiv d \pmod{n}$,
   then $a + c \equiv b + d \pmod{n}$, $ac \equiv db \pmod{n}$,
5) if $a \equiv b \pmod{n}$, then $ac \equiv bc \pmod{n}$,
6) if $a \equiv b \pmod{n}$, then $a^k \equiv b^k \pmod{n}$ for every positive integer k.

Proof. For any integer a, $a - a = 0n$, so that $a \equiv a \pmod{n}$ by Definition 2–13. If $a \equiv b \pmod{n}$, then $a - b = kn$ for some integer k. Hence

$$b - a = (-k)n,$$

where $-k$ is an integer. This yields (2).

To obtain (3), suppose that $a \equiv b \pmod{n}$ and $b \equiv c \pmod{n}$. Then

$$a - b = kn \qquad \text{and} \qquad b - c = hn$$

for some integers k, h. Therefore,

$$a - c = (a - b) + (b - c) = kn + hn = (k + h)n,$$

which implies $a \equiv c \pmod{n}$.

Similarly, if $a \equiv b \pmod{n}$ and $c \equiv d \pmod{n}$, then there exist integers k_1, k_2 such that

$$a - b = k_1 n \qquad \text{and} \qquad c - d = k_2 n.$$

Consequently,

$$(a + c) - (b + d) = (a - b) + (c - d) = k_1n + k_2n$$
$$= (k_1 + k_2)n,$$

or

$$a + c \equiv b + d \ (\text{mod } n).$$

Also,

$$ac = (b + k_1n)(d + k_2n) = bd + (bk_2 + dk_1 + k_1k_2n)n.$$

Since $bk_2 + dk_1 + k_1k_2n$ is an integer, $ac - bd$ is divisible by n, so that

$$ac \equiv bd \ (\text{mod } n).$$

This establishes (4).

Property (5) follows directly from the second part of (4), since $c \equiv c \ (\text{mod } n)$.

Finally, we prove (6) by an inductive argument. The statement is certainly true for $k = 1$. Assuming it holds for an arbitrary k, we must show that it also holds for $k + 1$. But this is immediate from (4), since $a^k \equiv b^k \ (\text{mod } n)$ and $a \equiv b \ (\text{mod } n)$ imply $a^k a \equiv b^k b \ (\text{mod } n)$, or $a^{k+1} \equiv b^{k+1} \ (\text{mod } n)$.

In the foregoing theorem we saw that if $a \equiv b \ (\text{mod } n)$, then $ca \equiv cb \ (\text{mod } n)$ for any integer c. It is interesting to note that the converse of this statement fails to be true. For instance, $2 \cdot 4 \equiv 2 \cdot 1 \ (\text{mod } 6)$, yet $4 \not\equiv 1 \ (\text{mod } 6)$. To put it another way, one cannot unrestrictedly apply the cancellation law in the algebra of congruences. The only positive assertion that can be made in this regard is embodied in the following theorem.

Theorem 2–11. If $ca \equiv cb \ (\text{mod } n)$ and c is relatively prime to n, then $a \equiv b \ (\text{mod } n)$.

Proof. By hypothesis, $c(a - b) = kn$ for some integer k. Since c is prime to n, it follows that n must divide $a - b$ [Theorem 1–14]; hence, $a \equiv b \ (\text{mod } n)$.

Definition 2–14. For an arbitrary integer a, let $[a]$ denote the set of all integers congruent to a modulo n:

$$[a] = \{x \in Z \mid x \equiv a \ (\text{mod } n)\}$$
$$= \{x \in Z \mid x = a + kn \text{ for some integer } k\}.$$

We call $[a]$ the *congruence class*, modulo n, determined by a and refer to a as a *representative* of this class.

By way of illustration, suppose that we are dealing with congruence modulo 3. Then

$$[0] = \{x \in Z \mid x = 3k \text{ for some } k \in Z\}$$
$$= \{\ldots, -9, -6, -3, 0, 3, 6, 9, \ldots\}.$$

Also

$$[1] = \{x \in Z \mid x = 1 + 3k \text{ for some } k \in Z\}$$
$$= \{\ldots, -8, -5, -2, 1, 4, 7, 10, \ldots\}.$$

Similarly,

$$[2] = \{\ldots, -7, -4, -1, 2, 5, 8, 11, \ldots\}.$$

Observe that every integer lies in one of these three classes. Integers in the same congruence class are congruent modulo 3, while integers in different classes are incongruent modulo 3.

A particular congruence class may be designated in a variety of ways by merely changing its representative. In the above illustration, for instance,

$$[-7] = [2] = [11] = [35] = \cdots$$

It suffices to remark that the characteristic feature of these various representatives is that, in this case, they all differ from each other by multiples of 3, and in general, differ by multiples of n. For convenience, one often selects the smallest nonnegative integer from each congruence class to represent it; in practice, we shall adhere to this notational convention.

To return to the general case of congruence modulo n, let

$$Z_n = \{[0], [1], [2], \ldots, [n-1]\}.$$

Several properties of the collection Z_n which we shall later require appear in the next theorem.

Theorem 2–12. Let n be a positive integer and Z_n be as defined above. Then

1) for each $[a] \in Z_n$, $[a] \neq \emptyset$,
2) if $[a] \in Z_n$ and $b \in [a]$, then $[b] = [a]$; that is, any element of the congruence class $[a]$ determines the class,
3) for any $[a]$, $[b] \in Z_n$ where $[a] \neq [b]$, $[a] \cap [b] = \emptyset$,
4) $\cup\{[a] \mid a \in Z\} = Z$.

Proof. The first three assertions of Theorem 2–10 indicate that the relation $a \equiv b \pmod{n}$ forms an equivalence relation in the set Z of integers. Indeed, the congruence classes as defined in Definition 2–14 are simply the equivalence classes for this equivalence relation. Viewed in this light, the statement of Theorem 2–12 is a translation of Theorem 1–5 into the language of "congruence modulo n."

The set Z_n, whose elements are the congruence classes modulo n, is traditionally known as the set of *integers modulo n*. It may strike the reader that this terminology is somewhat inappropriate for, precisely speaking, the elements of Z_n are not single integers, but rather infinite sets of integers. Moreover, the set Z_n is not infinite, like the integers, but is a finite set with n elements. While this is not quite in accord with our intuition, we bow to long-standing custom and shall continue to refer to Z_n as the integers modulo n.

By a partition of the set S, we mean a family of nonempty subsets of S which are pairwise disjoint and whose union is all of S. It follows from Theorem 2–12 that, for each $n \in Z_+$, the integers modulo n constitute a partition of the set Z.

Definition 2–15. A binary operation $+_n$ may be defined on Z_n as follows: for each $[a]$, $[b] \in Z_n$, let $[a] +_n [b] = [a + b]$.

Definition 2–15 asserts that the modular sum of two congruence classes $[a]$ and $[b]$ is the unique member of Z_n which contains the ordinary sum $a + b$. However, there is a subtle problem connected with this definition. Inasmuch as addition of congruence classes in Z_n is defined in terms of representatives from these classes, we must show that the operation $+_n$ does not depend on the two representatives chosen. It must be proved formally, that if $[a'] = [a]$ and $[b'] = [b]$, then $[a'] +_n [b'] = [a] +_n [b]$, or rather, $[a' + b'] = [a + b]$. Now $a' \in [a'] = [a]$ and $b' \in [b'] = [b]$, which implies

$$a' \equiv a \;(\mathrm{mod}\; n) \qquad \text{and} \qquad b' \equiv b \;(\mathrm{mod}\; n).$$

By virtue of Theorem 2–10(4), it follows that

$$a' + b' \equiv a + b \;(\mathrm{mod}\; n), \qquad \text{or} \qquad a' + b' \in [a + b].$$

Theorem 2–12(2) then indicates that $[a' + b'] = [a + b]$, as desired. Thus the operation $+_n$ is unambiguously defined, independent of the arbitrary choice of representatives.

Example 2–26. Suppose we consider congruence modulo 7 and the typical addition

$$[3] +_7 [6] = [3 + 6] = [9].$$

Since $[3] = [10]$ and $[6] = [-15]$, the same answer should be obtained if one used

$$[10] +_7 [-15] = [10 - 15] = [-5].$$

While these results appear superficially different, both congruence classes $[9]$ and $[-5]$ may be expressed more simply as $[2]$. Thus, although written in terms of different representatives, either modular addition gives the same sum, $[2]$. Other possible choices $[-4] +_7 [-8] = [-12]$, $[17] +_7 [6] = [23]$, $[3] +_7 [13] = [16]$, also yield the sum $[2]$.

We are now in a position to prove one of the principal theorems of this section.

Theorem 2–13. For each positive integer n, the mathematical system $(Z_n, +_n)$ forms a commutative group, known as the *group of integers modulo n*.

Proof. The associativity and commutativity of the operation $+_n$ are a direct consequence of the same properties of the integers under ordinary addition.

Indeed, if $[a]$, $[b]$, $[c] \in Z_n$, then

$$\begin{aligned}
[a] +_n ([b] +_n [c]) &= [a] +_n [b + c] \\
&= [a + (b + c)] \\
&= [(a + b) + c] \\
&= [a + b] +_n [c] \\
&= ([a] +_n [b]) +_n [c].
\end{aligned}$$

Similarly,

$$[a] +_n [b] = [a + b] = [b + a] = [b] +_n [a].$$

By definition of $+_n$, it is clear that $[0]$ is the identity element. Finally, if $[a] \in Z_n$, then $[n - a] \in Z_n$ and

$$[a] +_n [n - a] = [a + (n - a)] = [n] = [0],$$

so that $[a]^{-1} = [n - a]$. This completes the proof that $(Z_n, +_n)$ is a commutative group.

Incidentally, Theorem 2–13 also shows that for every positive integer n there exists at least one commutative group with n elements.

If we adopt the convention of designating each congruence class by its smallest nonnegative representative, then the operation table for, say $(Z_4, +_4)$, looks like

$+_4$	$[0]$	$[1]$	$[2]$	$[3]$
$[0]$	$[0]$	$[1]$	$[2]$	$[3]$
$[1]$	$[1]$	$[2]$	$[3]$	$[0]$
$[2]$	$[2]$	$[3]$	$[0]$	$[1]$
$[3]$	$[3]$	$[0]$	$[1]$	$[2]$

For simplicity, it is convenient to remove the brackets in the designation of the congruence classes of Z_n. Thus we often write $Z_n = \{0, 1, 2, \ldots, n - 1\}$. With this notation, the above operation table assumes the form

$+_4$	0	1	2	3
0	0	1	2	3
1	1	2	3	0
2	2	3	0	1
3	3	0	1	2

For the second of our two examples, let us turn to the study of permutation groups. To this end, suppose that N is a finite set having n elements which, for simplicity, we take to be the first n natural numbers; that is to say,

$$N = \{1, 2, \ldots, n\}.$$

Definition 2–16. By a *permutation* of the set N is meant any one-to-one mapping of N onto itself.

In what follows, the totality of all permutations of the set N will be denoted by the symbol S_n. Since the number of different permutations of n objects is $n!$, the first thing to note is that S_n is itself a finite set with $n!$ distinct elements. Next, any permutation $f \in S_n$ may be described by

$$f = \{(1, f(1)), (2, f(2)), \ldots, (n, f(n))\}.$$

While this is the acceptable functional notation, it will prove to be more convenient to represent f in a *two-line form*

$$f = \begin{pmatrix} 1 & 2 & \cdots & n \\ f(1) & f(2) & \cdots & f(n) \end{pmatrix},$$

where the corresponding images appear below each integer. Clearly, the order of the elements in the top row of this symbol is immaterial, for the columns may be rearranged without affecting the nature of the function. Precisely speaking, if g is an arbitrary permutation of the integers, $1, 2, \ldots, n$, then f could equally well be given by

$$f = \begin{pmatrix} g(1) & g(2) & \cdots & g(n) \\ f(g(1)) & f(g(2)) & \cdots & f(g(n)) \end{pmatrix}.$$

From this, we infer that each of the $n!$ permutations in S_n may be written in $n!$ different ways. For instance, the following two symbols both represent the same element of S_4:

$$\begin{pmatrix} 1 & 2 & 3 & 4 \\ 2 & 4 & 3 & 1 \end{pmatrix}, \qquad \begin{pmatrix} 2 & 1 & 4 & 3 \\ 4 & 2 & 1 & 3 \end{pmatrix}.$$

Permutations, being functions, may be *multiplied* under the operation of functional composition. Thus, for permutations $f, g \in S_n$,

$$f \circ g = \begin{pmatrix} 1 & 2 & \cdots & n \\ f(1) & f(2) & \cdots & f(n) \end{pmatrix} \circ \begin{pmatrix} 1 & 2 & \cdots & n \\ g(1) & g(2) & \cdots & g(n) \end{pmatrix}$$

$$= \begin{pmatrix} g(1) & g(2) & \cdots & g(n) \\ f(g(1)) & f(g(2)) & \cdots & f(g(n)) \end{pmatrix} \circ \begin{pmatrix} 1 & 2 & \cdots & n \\ g(1) & g(2) & \cdots & g(n) \end{pmatrix}$$

$$= \begin{pmatrix} 1 & 2 & \cdots & n \\ f(g(1)) & f(g(2)) & \cdots & f(g(n)) \end{pmatrix}.$$

What we have done is to rearrange the columns of the first (left) permutation until its top row is the same as the bottom row of the second (right) permutation; the product $f \circ g$ is then the permutation whose top row is the top row of the second factor and whose bottom row is the bottom row of the first factor. With a little practice one can evaluate products without having to write out this intermediate preparation. Many authors prefer to carry out the multiplication of permutations in the opposite order (that is, they apply the factors in a product from left to right), and the reader should be particularly watchful for this.

Before stating a theorem which indicates the algebraic nature of S_n under this method of composition, we hope to clarify some of the foregoing points with an example.

Example 2–27. If the set N consists of the integers 1, 2, 3, then there are $3! = 6$ permutations in S_3, namely,

$$f_1 = \begin{pmatrix} 1 & 2 & 3 \\ 1 & 2 & 3 \end{pmatrix}, \quad f_2 = \begin{pmatrix} 1 & 2 & 3 \\ 2 & 3 & 1 \end{pmatrix}, \quad f_3 = \begin{pmatrix} 1 & 2 & 3 \\ 3 & 1 & 2 \end{pmatrix},$$

$$f_4 = \begin{pmatrix} 1 & 2 & 3 \\ 1 & 3 & 2 \end{pmatrix}, \quad f_5 = \begin{pmatrix} 1 & 2 & 3 \\ 2 & 1 & 3 \end{pmatrix}, \quad f_6 = \begin{pmatrix} 1 & 2 & 3 \\ 3 & 2 & 1 \end{pmatrix}.$$

A typical multiplication, say $f_4 \circ f_6$, proceeds as follows:

$$f_4 \circ f_6 = \begin{pmatrix} 1 & 2 & 3 \\ 1 & 3 & 2 \end{pmatrix} \circ \begin{pmatrix} 1 & 2 & 3 \\ 3 & 2 & 1 \end{pmatrix}$$

$$= \begin{pmatrix} 3 & 2 & 1 \\ 2 & 3 & 1 \end{pmatrix} \circ \begin{pmatrix} 1 & 2 & 3 \\ 3 & 2 & 1 \end{pmatrix} = \begin{pmatrix} 1 & 2 & 3 \\ 2 & 3 & 1 \end{pmatrix} = f_2.$$

On the other hand, we have

$$f_6 \circ f_4 = \begin{pmatrix} 1 & 2 & 3 \\ 3 & 2 & 1 \end{pmatrix} \circ \begin{pmatrix} 1 & 2 & 3 \\ 1 & 3 & 2 \end{pmatrix}$$

$$= \begin{pmatrix} 1 & 3 & 2 \\ 3 & 1 & 2 \end{pmatrix} \circ \begin{pmatrix} 1 & 2 & 3 \\ 1 & 3 & 2 \end{pmatrix} = \begin{pmatrix} 1 & 2 & 3 \\ 3 & 1 & 2 \end{pmatrix} = f_3,$$

so that multiplication of permutations is not commutative.

Theorem 2–14. The pair $(S_n, \circ)$ forms a group, known as the *symmetric group on n symbols*, which is noncommutative for $n \geq 3$.

The proof of this fact is omitted inasmuch as a more general version of the theorem will be given shortly. In passing, it is only necessary to note that the identity element for $(S_n, \circ)$ is the permutation

$$\begin{pmatrix} 1 & 2 & \ldots & n \\ 1 & 2 & \ldots & n \end{pmatrix},$$

while the multiplicative inverse of any permutation $f \in S_n$ is described by

$$f^{-1} = \begin{pmatrix} f(1) & f(2) & \ldots & f(n) \\ 1 & 2 & \ldots & n \end{pmatrix}.$$

Parenthetically, we might observe that the group of symmetries of the square (Example 2–24) can be subsumed under the theory of permutation groups, for these symmetries really do nothing more than map the four vertices of the square in a one-to-one fashion onto themselves. This particular group is obviously not equal to the symmetric group $(S_4, \circ)$, since the set S_4 must contain $4! = 24$ elements; indeed, one can easily find permutations in S_4 which do not correspond to any symmetry of the square. Rather, we have an example of what is called a subgroup of the group $(S_4, \circ)$.

In the following somewhat technical definition, we introduce a special type of permutation called a cycle.

Definition 2–17. Let $n_1, n_2, \ldots, n_k$ be k distinct integers between 1 and n. If a permutation $f \in S_n$ is such that

$$f(n_i) = n_{i+1} \quad \text{for} \quad 1 \le i < k,$$

$$f(n_k) = n_1, \quad \text{and}$$

$$f(n) = n \quad \text{for} \quad n \notin \{n_1, n_2, \ldots, n_k\},$$

then f is said to be a k-*cycle*, or a *cycle of length* k.

Simply put, a cycle replaces n_1 by n_2, n_2 by n_3, $\ldots$, and finally n_k by n_1, while leaving all other elements fixed. For cycles, a more condensed notation than the usual two-line form is to write $(n_1, n_2, \ldots, n_k)$, indicating that each integer is to be replaced by its successor on the right and the last integer by the first. In the symmetric group $(S_5, \circ)$, for example, we have

$$\begin{pmatrix} 1 & 2 & 3 & 4 & 5 \\ 1 & 5 & 2 & 4 & 3 \end{pmatrix} = (2 \quad 5 \quad 3).$$

Of course, each integer which is omitted in this cycle notation is presumed to map onto itself under the permutation. A given cycle may clearly be represented in more than one way, since any of its elements can be put in the first position of the one-line form, as with

$$(2 \quad 5 \quad 3) = (5 \quad 3 \quad 2) = (3 \quad 2 \quad 5).$$

A final comment, before we formulate a significant result on the factorization of permutations, is that one multiplies cycles by multiplying the permutations they represent. Thus, in $(S_5, \circ)$ again,

$$(2 \quad 5 \quad 3) \circ (1 \quad 2 \quad 4 \quad 3) = \begin{pmatrix} 1 & 2 & 3 & 4 & 5 \\ 1 & 5 & 2 & 4 & 3 \end{pmatrix} \circ \begin{pmatrix} 1 & 2 & 3 & 4 & 5 \\ 2 & 4 & 1 & 3 & 5 \end{pmatrix}$$

$$= \begin{pmatrix} 1 & 2 & 3 & 4 & 5 \\ 5 & 4 & 1 & 2 & 3 \end{pmatrix}.$$

Theorem 2–15. Every permutation $f \in S_n$ can be written as a commutative product of cycles, no two of which have an element in common.

Proof. First, consider the set of images of the integer 1 under successive powers of f: $\{f(1), f^2(1), f^3(1), \ldots\}$. As usual, by f^m we mean $f \circ f \circ \cdots \circ f$, m times. Since the domain of f is finite, $f^i(1) = f^j(1)$ for some $i < j$, whence $f^{j-i}(1) = 1$. This in turn implies that there exists a least positive integer k $(1 \leq k \leq n)$ for which $f^k(1) = 1$. Let $(1, f(1), f^2(1), \cdots, f^{k-1}(1))$ be the first cycle of the permutation f. If the element 2 is not found in this cycle, repeat the foregoing argument to obtain another cycle $(2, f(2), f^2(2), \ldots, f^{j-1}(2))$, where j is the smallest positive integer such that $f^j(2) = 2$. In at most n such steps, this procedure must terminate. The order of multiplication of the resulting cycles is immaterial, for they clearly have no elements in common.

To illustrate Theorem 2–15, let us return momentarily to the permutation considered above; in this case,

$$\begin{pmatrix} 1 & 2 & 3 & 4 & 5 \\ 5 & 4 & 1 & 2 & 3 \end{pmatrix} = (1 \quad 5 \quad 3) \circ (2 \quad 4),$$

since

$$f(1) = 5, \qquad f^2(1) = f(5) = 3, \qquad f^3(1) = f(3) = 1,$$

and

$$f(2) = 4, \qquad f^2(2) = f(4) = 2.$$

The simplest of permutations are undoubtably the 2-cycles, for they just interchange two elements and leave all others fixed. It is customary to refer to such cycles as *transpositions.*

Corollary. Every permutation may be expressed as the product of transpositions.

Proof. In light of the preceding result, it suffices to write any k-cycle as a product of transpositions. A direct computation shows that this can be done rather simply in the following manner:

$$(1 \quad 2 \quad \ldots \quad k) = (1 \quad k) \circ (1 \quad k-1) \circ \cdots \circ (1 \quad 2).$$

As the above transpositions have an integer in common, they do not, in general, commute. Furthermore, the decomposition is by no means unique. For instance,

$$(1 \quad 2 \quad 3) = (1 \quad 3) \circ (1 \quad 2) = (2 \quad 1) \circ (2 \quad 3).$$

While a given permutation may be factored into a product of transpositions in a variety of ways, the number of transpositions involved will always have the same parity. That is, if one factorization has an even (odd) number of transpositions, then every factorization must have an even (odd) number of transpositions.

The notion of permutation as presented in Definition 2–16 is not sufficiently general for all our purposes, since it restricts us to finite sets only. It would seem more natural to define this concept for arbitrary sets, finite or infinite, as follows.

Definition 2–18. If G is any nonempty set, then a *permutation* of G is a one-to-one function from the set G onto itself.

We represent the set of all permutations of G by the symbol, sym G (the reason for this choice will be clear in a moment). To be sure, if G is a finite set having n elements, then sym $G = S_n$.

In this general framework, it is possible to prove a structure theorem from which Theorem 2–14 will follow as a special case.

Theorem 2–16. For a nonempty set G, the pair (sym G, $\circ$) constitutes a group, called the *symmetric group* of G.

Proof. The first thing to be done is to show that $\circ$ is actually a binary operation on sym G. Given arbitrary permutations f, $g \in$ sym G, the composition $f \circ g$ is obviously a function from G into G. If the element $c \in G$, then there exists some $b \in G$ such that $f(b) = c$; similarly, there is an element a in G for which $g(a) = b$. Hence,

$$(f \circ g)(a) = f(g(a)) = f(b) = c,$$

which shows that $f \circ g$ is an onto function.

By definition, both f and g are one-to-one functions; we would like to conclude that the composition $f \circ g$ also has this property. For this purpose, consider arbitrary elements a, $b \in G$ with $a \neq b$. Since g is one-to-one, the images $g(a)$ and $g(b)$ are necessarily distinct in G. But then, the one-to-one character of f implies $f(g(a)) \neq f(g(b))$. In other words, $(f \circ g)(a) \neq (f \circ g)(b)$, which establishes the desired one-to-oneness of $f \circ g$. From the preceding remarks, we infer that $f \circ g \in$ sym G whenever f and g are in sym G, making $\circ$ a binary operation of the set sym G.

The associativity of functional composition follows from Theorem 1–7. Plainly, the identity function i_G is a permutation of G and is such that

$$f \circ i_G = f = i_G \circ f,$$

for any $f \in$ sym G, showing i_G to be an identity element for the system (sym G, $\circ$). If $f \in$ sym G, the inverse function f^{-1} exists, is a one-to-one function, and maps the set G onto itself. Moreover, f^{-1} is the inverse of f with respect to composition. All of which justifies the statement that (sym G, $\circ$) is a group.

PROBLEMS

1. Prove that if $a \equiv b$ (mod n), then $ca \equiv cb$ (mod cn).

2. a) Find all solutions x, where $0 \leq x < 15$, of the equation $3x \equiv 6$ (mod 15).
   b) Prove that $6^n \equiv 6$ (mod 10) for any $n \in Z_+$.

3. Describe the partition of Z determined by the integers modulo 5.

4. Let $P(x)$ be a polynomial in x with integral coefficients. If n is a solution of the equation $P(x) \equiv 0$ (mod n), and $a \equiv b$ (mod n), prove that b is also a solution.

5. Show that the pair $(\{0, 4, 8, 12\}, +_{16})$ is a group.

6. Use the fact that $10 \equiv 1$ (mod 9) to prove that an integer is divisible by 9 if and only if the sum of its digits is divisible by 9. [*Hint:* Express the integer in decimal form as a sum of powers of 10.]

7. For any integer n, prove that either $n^2 \equiv 0$ (mod 4) or $n^2 \equiv 1$ (mod 4).

8. a) Determine solutions of the congruence equations $x^2 \equiv -1$ (mod 5) and $x^2 \equiv -1$ (mod 13). This shows, loosely speaking, that the square of an integer in Z_n may be negative.
   b) If the equation $x^2 \equiv a$ (mod n) has a solution x_1, show $x_2 = n - x_1$ is also a solution.

9. Suppose $a^2 \equiv b^2$ (mod n), where n is a prime number. Prove that either $a \equiv b$ (mod n) or $a \equiv -b$ (mod n).

10. a) Prove the symmetric group on two symbols, $(S_2, \circ)$, is commutative.
    b) Demonstrate that the group $(S_3, \circ)$, and hence any larger symmetric group, is noncommutative by considering the permutations

$$\begin{pmatrix} 1 & 2 & 3 \\ 2 & 3 & 1 \end{pmatrix} \quad \text{and} \quad \begin{pmatrix} 1 & 2 & 3 \\ 3 & 2 & 1 \end{pmatrix}.$$

11. Express the following permutations as (a) products of cycles having no elements in common, (b) products of transpositions.

$$\begin{pmatrix} 1 & 2 & 3 & 4 & 5 & 6 \\ 3 & 6 & 4 & 1 & 2 & 5 \end{pmatrix}, \quad \begin{pmatrix} 1 & 2 & 3 & 4 & 5 & 6 & 7 \\ 5 & 7 & 6 & 2 & 1 & 3 & 4 \end{pmatrix}$$

12. Show that the cycle (1 2 3 4 5) may be written as a product of 3-cycles.

13. Verify the relation $(1\ 2\ 3\ \ldots\ n)^{-1} = (n\ n-1\ \ldots\ 2\ 1)$; in particular deduce that every transposition is its own inverse.

14. The symmetries of the square (Example 2–24) may be interpreted as permutations of the vertices. Represent each of these symmetries by a corresponding permutation.

15. Consider the set G consisting of the four permutations

$$\begin{pmatrix} 1 & 2 & 3 & 4 \\ 1 & 2 & 3 & 4 \end{pmatrix}, \quad \begin{pmatrix} 1 & 2 & 3 & 4 \\ 2 & 1 & 4 & 3 \end{pmatrix}, \quad \begin{pmatrix} 1 & 2 & 3 & 4 \\ 3 & 4 & 1 & 2 \end{pmatrix}, \quad \begin{pmatrix} 1 & 2 & 3 & 4 \\ 4 & 3 & 2 & 1 \end{pmatrix}.$$

Show that $(G, \circ)$ constitutes a commutative group.

16. Form the set $G = \{f, f^2, f^3, f^4, f^5, f^6\}$, where f is the permutation

$$f = \begin{pmatrix} 1 & 2 & 3 & 4 & 5 & 6 \\ 2 & 3 & 4 & 5 & 6 & 1 \end{pmatrix},$$

and prove that the pair $(G, \circ)$ is a commutative group.

2–4 SUBGROUPS

There are two standard techniques in attacking the problem of the structure of a particular group. One method calls for finding all the subgroups of the group, with the hope of gaining information about the parent group through its local structure. The other approach is to determine all homomorphisms from the given group into a more familiar group; the idea here is that the images will reflect some of the algebraic properties of the original group. On closer scrutiny, we shall see that while these lines of investigation aim in different directions, they are not entirely unrelated, but rather aspects of the same problem. For the moment, however, our attention is focused on analyzing a group by means of its subgroups; the question of structure-preserving mappings is a more subtle matter and will be deferred to a later section.

From various examples and exercises, the reader may have noticed that certain subsets of the elements of a group lead to new groups when one restricts the group operation to these subsets. It is this situation in which we shall be primarily interested.

Definition 2–19. Let $(G, *)$ be a group and $H \subseteq G$ be a nonempty subset of G. The pair $(H, *)$ is said to be a *subgroup* of $(G, *)$ if $(H, *)$ is itself a group.

Each group $(G, *)$ has two obvious subgroups. For, if $e \in G$ is the identity element of the group $(G, *)$, then both $(\{e\}, *)$ and $(G, *)$ are subgroups of $(G, *)$. These two subgroups are often referred to as the *trivial* subgroups of $(G, *)$; all subgroups between these two extremes are called nontrivial subgroups. Any subgroup different from $(G, *)$ is termed *proper*.

Example 2–28. If Z_e and Z_o denote the sets of even and odd integers, respectively, then $(Z_e, +)$ is a subgroup of the group $(Z, +)$, while $(Z_o, +)$ is not.

Example 2–29. Consider $(Z_6, +_6)$, the group of integers modulo 6. If

$$H = \{0, 2, 4\},$$

then $(H, +_6)$, whose operation table is given below, is a subgroup of $(Z_6, +_6)$.

$+_6$	0	2	4
0	0	2	4
2	2	4	0
4	4	0	2

Example 2–30. Let $(G, *)$ be the group of symmetries of the square (see Example 2–24), where $G = \{R_{90}, R_{180}, R_{270}, R_{360}, H, V, D_1, D_2\}$ and the operation $*$ consists of following one motion by another. This group contains eight nontrivial subgroups. We leave it to the reader to verify that the following sets comprise the elements of these subgroups:

$$\{R_{90}, R_{180}, R_{270}, R_{360}\}, \qquad \{R_{180}, R_{360}, H, V\},$$
$$\{R_{180}, R_{360}, D_1, D_2\}, \qquad \{R_{180}, R_{360}\}, \qquad \{R_{360}, D_1\},$$
$$\{R_{360}, D_2\}, \qquad \{R_{360}, H\}, \qquad \{R_{360}, V\}.$$

Suppose $(H, *)$ is a subgroup of the group $(G, *)$. Since the identity element of $(H, *)$ satisfies the equation $x * x = x$, it must be the same as the identity of the parent group $(G, *)$, for otherwise we would have two idempotent elements in G, contrary to Theorem 2–5. The identity element of a group thus also serves as the identity element for any of its subgroups. Moreover, the uniqueness of the inverse elements in a group implies the inverse of an element $h \in H$ in the subgroup $(H, *)$ is the same as its inverse in the whole group $(G, *)$.

To establish that a given subset H of G, along with the induced operation of $(G, *)$, constitutes a subgroup, we must verify that all the conditions of Definition 2–11 are satisfied. However, the associativity of the operation $*$ in H is an immediate consequence of its associativity in G, since $H \subseteq G$. It is necessary then to show only the following:

1) $a, b \in H$ implies $a * b \in H$ (closure),
2) $e \in H$, where e is the identity element of $(G, *)$,
3) $a \in H$ implies $a^{-1} \in H$.

Needless to say, the saving in not having to check the associative law can prove to be considerable.

A theorem which establishes a single convenient criterion for determining subgroups is given below.

Theorem 2–17. Let $(G, *)$ be a group and $\emptyset \neq H \subseteq G$. Then $(H, *)$ is a subgroup of $(G, *)$ if and only if $a, b \in H$ implies $a * b^{-1} \in H$.

Proof. If $(H, *)$ is a subgroup and $a, b \in H$, then $b^{-1} \in H$, and so $a * b^{-1} \in H$ by the closure condition. Conversely, suppose H is a nonempty subset of G

which contains the element $a * b^{-1}$ whenever a, $b \in H$. Since H contains at least one element b, we may take $a = b$ to see that $b * b^{-1} = e \in H$. Also, $b^{-1} = e * b^{-1} \in H$ for every b in H, applying the hypothesis to the pair e, $b \in H$. Finally, if a and b are any two members of the set H, then by what was just proved b^{-1} also belongs to H, so that $a * b = a * (b^{-1})^{-1} \in H$; in other words, the set H is closed with respect to the operation $*$. Because $*$ is an associative operation in G, H inherits the associative law as a subset of G. All the group axioms are satisfied and the system $(H, *)$ is therefore a subgroup of $(G, *)$.

Definition 2–20. The *center* of a group $(G, *)$, denoted by cent G, is the set

$$\text{cent } G = \{c \in G \mid c * x = x * c \text{ for all } x \in G\}.$$

Thus cent G consists of those elements which commute with every element of G. For example, in the group of symmetries of the square,

$$\text{cent } G = \{R_{180}, R_{360}\}.$$

The reader may already have deduced that a group $(G, *)$ is commutative if and only if cent $G = G$.

As illustrations of the use of Theorem 2–17 in determining when a subset of the elements of a group is the set of elements of a subgroup, we present the following two theorems.

Theorem 2–18. The pair (cent G, $*$) is a subgroup of each group $(G, *)$.

Proof. We first observe that cent G is nonempty, for at the very least $e \in$ cent G. Now consider any two elements a, $b \in$ cent G. By the definition of center, we know that $a * x = x * a$ and $b * x = x * b$ for every element x of G. Thus, if $x \in G$,

$$\begin{aligned}
(a * b^{-1}) * x &= a * (b^{-1} * x) \\
&= a * (x^{-1} * b)^{-1} \\
&= a * (b * x^{-1})^{-1} \\
&= a * (x * b^{-1}) \\
&= (a * x) * b^{-1} \\
&= (x * a) * b^{-1} = x * (a * b^{-1}),
\end{aligned}$$

which implies $a * b^{-1} \in$ cent G. According to Theorem 2–17, this is a sufficient condition for (cent G, $*$) to be a subgroup of $(G, *)$.

Theorem 2–19. If $(H_i, *)$ is an arbitrary indexed collection of subgroups of the group $(G, *)$, then $(\cap H_i, *)$ is also a subgroup.

Proof. Since the sets H_i all contain the identity element of $(G, *)$, the intersection $\cap H_i \neq \emptyset$. Next, suppose a and b are any two elements of $\cap H_i$; then

a, $b \in H_i$, where i ranges over the index set. The pair $(H_i, *)$ being a subgroup, it follows that the product $a * b^{-1}$ also belongs to H_i. As this is true for every index i, $a * b^{-1} \in \cap H_i$, which implies $(\cap H_i, *)$ is a subgroup of $(G, *)$.

In regard to the group of symmetries of the square, we could take

$$H_1 = \{R_{90}, R_{180}, R_{270}, R_{360}\},$$
$$H_2 = \{R_{180}, R_{360}, D_1, D_2\}.$$

The system $(H_1 \cap H_2, *) = (\{R_{180}, R_{360}\}, *)$ is obviously a subgroup of this group, for its elements comprise the center of the group.

In general, without further restriction on the subgroups $(H_i, *)$, it is not true that the pair $(\cup H_i, *)$ will again be a subgroup of $(G, *)$. One simply cannot guarantee that $\cup H_i$ will contain products whose factors come from different H_i. To give a concrete illustration, both $(\{0, 6\}, +_{12})$ and $(\{0, 4, 8\}, +_{12})$ are subgroups of $(Z_{12}+_{12})$, yet on taking the union, $(\{0, 4, 6, 8\}, +_{12})$ fails to be so. The difficulty in this case is that the modular sums $4 +_{12} 6$ and $6 +_{12} 8$ do not belong to the set $\{0, 4, 6, 8\}$.

By the way of an analog to Theorem 2–19, we have:

Theorem 2–20. Let $(H_i, *)$ be an indexed collection of subgroups of the group $(G, *)$. Suppose the family of subsets $\{H_i\}$ has the property that for any two of its members H_i and H_j there exists a set H_k (depending on i and j) in $\{H_i\}$ such that $H_i \subseteq H_k$ and $H_j \subseteq H_k$. Then $(\cup H_i, *)$ is also a subgroup of $(G, *)$.

Proof. By now the pattern of proof should be clear. We assume that a and b are arbitrary elements of $\cup H_i$ and show that $a * b^{-1} \in \cup H_i$. If a, $b \in \cup H_i$, then there exist subsets H_i, H_j containing a and b, respectively. According to our hypothesis, $H_i \subseteq H_k$ and $H_j \subseteq H_k$ for some choice of H_k in $\{H_i\}$. Since $(H_k, *)$ is a subgroup and both a, $b \in H_k$, it follows that the product $a * b^{-1}$ belongs to H_k. Accordingly, $a * b^{-1} \in \cup H_i$ as was claimed at the beginning.

As a particular case of the foregoing result, consider just two subgroups $(H_1, *)$ and $(H_2, *)$. Theorem 2–20 may be interpreted as asserting that $(H_1 \cup H_2 *)$ will again be a subgroup of $(G, *)$ provided either $H_1 \subseteq H_2$ or $H_2 \subseteq H_1$. What is rather interesting is that this condition is necessary, as well as sufficient. The next theorem gives the details.

Theorem 2–21. Let $(H_1, *)$ and $(H_2, *)$ be subgroups of the group $(G, *)$. The pair $(H_1 \cup H_2,)$ is also a subgroup if and only if $H_1 \subseteq H_2$ or $H_2 \subseteq H_1$.

Proof. In view of the preceding remarks, it is enough to show that if $(H_1 \cup H_2, *)$ is a subgroup, then one of the sets H_1 or H_2 must be contained in the other. Suppose to the contrary that this assertion were false: that is, $H_1 \nsubseteq H_2$ and $H_2 \nsubseteq H_1$. Then there would exist elements $a \in H_1 - H_2$ and $b \in H_2 - H_1$.

Now, if the product $a * b$ were a member of the set H_1, we could infer that

$$b = a^{-1} * (a * b) \in H_1,$$

which is clearly not true. On the other hand, the possibility $a * b \in H_2$ yields the equally false conclusion

$$a = (a * b) * b^{-1} \in H_2.$$

That is, the elements a, $b \in H_1 \cup H_2$, but $a * b \notin H_1 \cup H_2$. This conclusion is obviously untenable, for it contradicts the fact $(H_1 \cup H_2, *)$ is a group. Having arrived at a contradiction, the proof is complete.

The next topic of interest concerns cyclic subgroups. To facilitate this discussion, we first introduce some special notation.

Definition 2–21. If $(G, *)$ is an arbitrary group and $\emptyset \neq S \subseteq G$, then the symbol (S) will represent the set

$$(S) = \cap\{H \mid S \subseteq H; (H, *) \text{ is a subgroup of } (G, *)\}.$$

The set (S) clearly exists, for G itself is a member of the family appearing on the right; that is, $(G, *)$ is a (trivial) subgroup of $(G, *)$ and $S \subseteq G$. In addition, since S is contained in each of the sets being intersected, we always have the inclusion $S \subseteq (S)$.

Theorem 2–22. The pair $((S), *)$ is a subgroup of $(G, *)$, known either as the *enveloping subgroup* for S or the *subgroup generated by the set* S.

Proof. The proof is an immediate consequence of Theorem 2–19.

Definition 2–21 implies that whenever $(H, *)$ is a subgroup of the group $(G, *)$ with $S \subseteq H$, then $(S) \subseteq H$. For this reason, one speaks informally of $((S), *)$ as being the smallest subgroup which contains the set S. Of course, it may well happen that $(S) = G$, and in such a situation, the group $(G, *)$ is said to be *generated* by the subset S. For example, it is easy to see that the group $(Z, +)$ is generated by Z_o, the set of odd integers.

We shall give an alternative description of the subset (S) which is frequently easier to work with than Definition 2–21. In what follows, the symbol S^{-1} is used to indicate the collection of inverses of elements in S: $S^{-1} = \{a^{-1} \mid a \in S\}$. The result we propose to obtain is that

$$(S) = \{a_1 * a_2 * \cdots * a_n \mid a_1, \ldots, a_n \in S \cup S^{-1}; n \in Z_+\}.$$

Although the notation is self explanatory, it would be helpful to explicitly point out that the set on the right consists of all finite products whose factors are either elements in S or inverses of elements in S. Let us temporarily designate this set of products by $[S]$.

An abbreviated proof of the assertion above might run as follows: The system $([S], *)$ is a subgroup of the group $(G, *)$ with the property $S \subseteq [S]$. As $((S), *)$ is the smallest such subgroup, it follows that $(S) \subseteq [S]$. The reverse inclusion is justified by the fact that any subgroup which contains the set S must necessarily contain all the elements of $[S]$.

A case of special importance arises when S consists of a single element a. In this situation, it is usual to write (a) instead of $(\{a\})$ and refer to the associated subgroup $((a), *)$ as the *cyclic subgroup generated by* a. The subset (a) is rather easy to describe; as all its products involve the element a or its inverse, (a) simply reduces to the integral powers of a:

$$(a) = \{a^n \mid n \in Z\}.$$

It is entirely possible that the group $(G, *)$ is equal to one of its cyclic subgroups, that is, for some choice of $a \in G$, $(a) = G$. Under these circumstances, the group $(G, *)$ is referred to as a *cyclic group* with *generator* a. Thus, to say a group is cyclic means that each of its members can be expressed as an integral power of some fixed element of the group.

A cyclic group may possess several different generators; indeed, one always has $(a) = (a^{-1})$. Notice in addition that, as a consequence of the law of exponents, any cyclic group must be commutative.

To make these notions clearer, let us pause to examine several examples.

Example 2–31. First consider the group of integers $(Z, +)$. In this case, since the group operation is that of addition, the abstract product $a * a * \cdots * a$ is replaced by the ordinary sum $a + a + \cdots + a$. Accordingly, the subset generated by the element a takes the form

$$(a) = \{na \mid n \in Z\}.$$

Using this notation, $\{0\} = (0)$, $Z = (1)$, while $Z_e = (2)$. We may thus conclude that both the groups $(Z, +)$ and $(Z_e, +)$ are cyclic, with the integers 1 and 2 as their respective generators.

Example 2–32. Another illustration is furnished by $(Z_{12}, +_{12})$, the group of integers modulo 12. Note that we now write $a +_{12} a +_{12} \cdots +_{12} a$ for $a * a * \cdots * a$. The cyclic subgroup generated by, say 3, is $(\{0, 3, 6, 9\}, +_{12})$, for here,

$$(3) = \{3n \;(\text{mod } 12) \mid n \in Z\} = \{0, 3, 6, 9\}.$$

As $(1) = Z_{12}$, the group $(Z_{12}, +_{12})$ is itself cyclic; other possible generators of $(Z_{12}, +_{12})$ are 5, 7 and 11. It is not difficult to see that, in general, the group of integers modulo n is cyclic with 1 as a generator.

Example 2–33. The group of symmetries of the square is not cyclic, for cyclic groups are necessarily commutative. Save for the identity, the distinct powers of any of its elements comprise the members of a nontrivial cyclic sub-group. The rotation R_{90}, in particular, generates the subgroup whose elements are $\{R_{90}, R_{180}, R_{270}, R_{360}\}$.

By a *finite group*, we mean any group whose underlying set of elements is a finite set. The *order* of a finite group is defined to be the number of its elements. Analogously, a group with an infinite number of elements is said to have infinite order.

In the following theorems, we shall see that finite cyclic groups have a particularly simple structure. For one thing, the elements of a finite cyclic group with generator a are just $e, a, a^2, \ldots, a^{n-1}$, where n is the order of the group. All other powers of a are superfluous, since they merely repeat these.

Theorem 2–23. If $((a), *)$ is a finite cyclic group of order n, then

$$(a) = \{e, a, a^2, \ldots, a^{n-1}\}.$$

Proof. As the set (a) is finite, not all the powers of the generator a are distinct. There must be some repetition $a^i = a^j$ with $i < j$. On multiplying this equation by $a^{-i} = (a^i)^{-1}$, it follows that $a^{j-i} = e$. Thus the set of positive integers k for which $a^k = e$ is nonempty. Suppose m is the smallest positive integer with this property; that is, $a^m = e$, while $a^k \neq e$ for $0 < k < m$.

The set $S = \{e, a, a^2, \ldots, a^{m-1}\}$ consists of distinct elements of (a). For $a^r = a^s$, with $0 \le r < s \le m - 1$, implies that $a^{s-r} = e$, contrary to the minimality of m. To complete the proof, it remains to show each member a^k of the group $((a), *)$ is equal to an element of S. Now, by the division algorithm, we may write $k = qm + r$ for some integers q and r with $0 \le r < m$. Hence,

$$a^k = (a^m)^q * a^r = e * a^r = a^r \in S.$$

This means the set $(a) \subseteq S$, yielding $(a) = \{e, a, a^2, \ldots, a^{m-1}\}$ and the subsequent equality $m = n$.

If a is an element of the group $(G, *)$, we define the *order of a* to be the order of the cyclic subgroup $((a), *)$ generated by a. The last result permits an alternative viewpoint: the order of a is the least positive integer n, provided it exists, such that $a^n = e$. Of course, if no such integer exists, a is of infinite order. As an illustration, consider the group $(Z_4, +_4)$; here, the element 0 has order 1, 1 has order 4, 2 has order 2, while 3 has order 4.

In certain cases (unfortunately, far too few), it is possible to characterize completely the subgroups of a given group. To cite one instance, in the additive group of integers $(Z, +)$, the subgroups are all of the form $((n), +)$ for some nonnegative integer n. Actually, the situation is somewhat more general, for it can be shown that any subgroup of a cyclic group is again cyclic; we shall discuss this next.

Theorem 2–24. Every subgroup of a cyclic group is cyclic.

Proof. Let $((a), *)$ be a cyclic group generated by the element a and let $(H, *)$ be one of its subgroups. If $H = \{e\}$, the theorem is trivially true, for $(\{e\}, *)$ is the cyclic subgroup generated by the identity element. We may thus suppose the set $H \neq \{e\}$. If $a^m \in H$, where $m \neq 0$, then a^{-m} is also an element of H; hence, H must contain positive powers of a. Let n be the smallest positive integer such that $a^n \in H$. We propose to show $H = (a^n)$.

To establish the inclusion $H \subseteq (a^n)$, let a^k be an arbitrary element in the set H. The division algorithm implies there exist integers q and r for which

$$k = qn + r, \qquad 0 \leq r < n.$$

Since both a^n and a^k are elements of H,

$$a^r = a^{k-qn} = a^k * (a^n)^{-q} \in H.$$

If $r > 0$, we have a contradiction to the assumption that a^n is the minimal positive power of a in H. Accordingly, $r = 0$ and $k = qn$. Thus, only powers of a^n lie in H, indicating $H \subseteq (a^n)$.

On the other hand, since the set H is closed under the group operation, any power of a^n must again be a member of H. Consequently, $(a^n) \subseteq H$. The two inclusions demonstrate that $H = (a^n)$.

Corollary. If $(H, *)$ is a subgroup of $((a), *)$ and $H \neq \{e\}$, then $H = (a^n)$ where n is the least positive integer such that $a^n \in H$.

We shall return to a further discussion of cyclic groups at the appropriate place in the sequel. For the moment, though, let us indicate another useful method for manufacturing new subgroups from given ones. For this, some special terminology is required.

Definition 2–22. Let $(G, *)$ be a group and H, K be nonempty subsets of G. The *product* of H and K, in that order, is the set

$$H * K = \{h * k \mid h \in H, k \in K\}.$$

A brief comment on notation that should be made is that the usual custom is to write the product $H * H$ merely as H^2 and, if one of the sets consists of a single element a, simplify $\{a\} * H$ to $a * H$.

At first sight, the reader might reasonably conjecture that whenever $(H, *)$ and $(K, *)$ are both subgroups of $(G, *)$, then $(H * K, *)$ will also be a subgroup. The group of symmetries of the square, however, shows that such a simple outcome is not to be expected. Here, it is enough to consider the subgroups having elements $H = \{R_{360}, D_1\}$ and $K = \{R_{360}, V\}$. A quick check establishes that there is no subgroup whose members comprise the product set

$$H * K = \{R_{360} * R_{360}, R_{360} * V, D_1 * R_{360}, D_1 * V\} = \{R_{360}, V, D_1, R_{270}\}.$$

In fact, the set $H * K$ isn't even closed under the group operation. One need not be dismayed by this state of affairs, for an additional assumption on the subsets H and K readily overcomes the difficulty.

Theorem 2–25. If $(H, *)$ and $(K, *)$ are subgroups of the group $(G, *)$ such that $H * K = K * H$, then the pair $(H * K, *)$ is also a subgroup.

Proof. Innocuous as the equality $H * K = K * H$ appears, it is nonetheless the source of some difficulty. This notation does not mean each element of H commutes with each element of K; all it signifies is that whenever h and k are arbitrary members of H and K, then there exist elements $h' \in H$, $k' \in K$ for which $h * k = k' * h'$. Bearing this in mind, let us proceed with the proof proper.

Plainly, the product set $H * K$ is nonempty, for $e = e * e \in H * K$. Now, let a and b be any pair of elements in $H * K$. Then $a = h * k$ and $b = h_1 * k_1$ for suitable choice of h, $h_1 \in H$ and k, $k_1 \in K$. As usual, our aim in what follows is to show that the product $a * b^{-1}$ lies in $H * K$. This is achieved through first noting

$$a * b^{-1} = (h * k) * (h_1 * k_1)^{-1} = h * ((k * k_1^{-1}) * h_1^{-1}).$$

Since K is closed under $*$, the element $k * k_1^{-1}$ belongs to K and consequently

$$(k * k_1^{-1}) * h_1^{-1} \in K * H.$$

By virtue of the condition $K * H = H * K$, there exist elements $h_2 \in H$ and $k_2 \in K$ satisfying

$$(k * k_1^{-1}) * h_1^{-1} = h_2 * k_2.$$

We may thus conclude that

$$a * b^{-1} = h * (h_2 * k_2) = (h * h_2) * k_2 \in H * K,$$

for the closure of the set H insures $h * h_2$ also is a member of it. To complete the proof, it suffices to invoke Theorem 2–17.

Corollary. If $(H, *)$ and $(K, *)$ are subgroups of the commutative group $(G, *)$ then $(H * K, *)$ is again a subgroup.

The utility of Theorem 2–25 lies in the fact that it permits another characterization of the subgroup generated by a union of sets. What happens is this: if the pair $(H * K, *)$ forms a subgroup of $(G, *)$, it must in fact be the subgroup generated by $H \cup K$; in symbols,

$$(H * K, *) = ((H \cup K), *).$$

Let us briefly outline the argument involved. To start with, the two inclusions

$$H = H * e \subseteq H * K \qquad \text{and} \qquad K = e * K \subseteq H * K$$

indicate $H \cup K \subseteq H * K$. We have already observed that the subgroup generated by $H \cup K$ is the smallest subgroup to contain this union. Thus, whenever $(H * K, *)$ is a subgroup, it follows that $(H \cup K) \subseteq H * K$. On the other hand, the set $(H \cup K)$ by definition must contain all products of the form $h * k$ with $h \in H$, $k \in K$. This results in the reverse inclusion $H * K \subseteq (H \cup K)$ and the subsequent equality $H * K = (H \cup K)$.

The significant point in this discussion is that we have gained a great deal of insight into the structure of the group generated by the union $H \cup K$, where $(H, *)$ and $(K, *)$ are both subgroups of the group $(G, *)$. To be specific, in the event the condition $H * K = K * H$ holds, each member of $((H \cup K), *)$ is expressible as the product of an element of H with an element of K. This statement obviously applies in the case where the parent group $(G, *)$ is commutative.

Example 2–34. For purposes of illustrating the above remarks, let us return again to the commutative group $(Z_{12}, +_{12})$ and the two subgroups $(\{0, 6\}, +_{12})$ and $(\{0, 4, 8\}, +_{12})$. To obtain the smallest subgroup which contains $\{0, 6\}$ and $\{0, 4, 8\}$, it suffices merely to compute the product of these subsets:

$$\{0, 6\} +_{12} \{0, 4, 8\} = \{0 +_{12} 0, 0 +_{12} 4, 0 +_{12} 8, 6 +_{12} 0, 6 +_{12} 4, 6 +_{12} 8\}$$
$$= \{0, 4, 8, 6, 10, 2\}.$$

Hence, the subgroup of $(Z_{12}, +_{12})$ generated by the union $\{0, 6\} \cup \{0, 4, 8\}$ is just $(\{0, 2, 4, 6, 8, 10\}, +_{12})$.

PROBLEMS

1. In each of the following cases, establish that $(H, \cdot)$ is a subgroup of the group $(G, \cdot)$:
   a) $H = \{1, -1\}$, $G = \{1, -1, i, -i\}$, where $i^2 = -1$;
   b) $H = \{2^n \mid n \in Z\}$, $G = Q - \{0\}$;
   c) $H = Q - \{0\}$, $G = R^\# - \{0\}$;
   d) $H = \{(1 + 2n)/(1 + 2m) \mid n, m \in Z\}$, $G = Q - \{0\}$.

2. Prove that $(\{0, 4, 8, 12\}, +_{16})$ is a subgroup of $(Z_{16}, +_{16})$, the group of integers modulo 16.

3. In the symmetric group $(S_n, \circ)$, let H denote the set of permutations leaving the integer n fixed:
$$H = \{f \in S_n \mid f(n) = n\}.$$

Show that the pair $(H, \circ)$ is a subgroup of $(S_n, \circ)$.

4. Prove that if $(H, *)$ is a subgroup of the group $(G, *)$ and $(K, *)$ is a subgroup of $(H, *)$, then $(K, *)$ is also a subgroup of $(G, *)$.

5. Let $(H, *)$ be a subgroup of the group $(G, *)$. We say that two elements a and b of G are *congruent modulo* H, written $a \equiv b \pmod{H}$, if and only if $a * b^{-1} \in H$. Establish that congruence modulo H is an equivalence relation in G.

Observe that in the additive group of integers $(Z, +)$, where the subgroups are of the form $((n), +)$, n a nonnegative integer, this relation reduces to congruence modulo n.

6. Suppose that $(G, *)$ is a group and $a \in G$. Let $C(a)$ denote the set of all elements of G which commute with a:

$$C(a) = \{x \in G \mid a * x = x * a\}.$$

Prove that the pair $(C(a), *)$ is a subgroup of $(G, *)$, known as the *centralizer* of a in G. Also verify the equality, cent $G = \bigcap_{a \in G} C(a)$.

7. Given $(G, *)$ is a finite group, prove that
   a) there exists a positive integer n such that $a^n = e$ for all $a \in G$,
   b) if H is a nonempty subset of G which is closed under the operation $*$, then $(H, *)$ is a subgroup of $(G, *)$.

8. In the commutative group $(G, *)$, define the set H by

$$H = \{a \in G \mid a^k = e \text{ for some } k \in Z\}.$$

Determine whether the pair $(H, *)$ is a subgroup of $(G, *)$.

9. Let $(G, *)$ be a group and $a, b \in G$. Establish the following facts regarding the order of an element.
   a) The elements a, a^{-1} and $b * a * b^{-1}$ all have the same order.
   b) Both the products $a * b$ and $b * a$ have the same order. [*Hint:* Write $a * b = a * (b * a) * a^{-1}$ and use (a).]
   c) If a is of order n, then $a^i = a^j$ if and only if $i \equiv j \pmod{n}$.

10. Determine the cyclic subgroup of $(S_5, \circ)$, the symmetric group on five symbols, generated by the cycle (1 3 5 2 4).

11. Prove that a group of even order contains an element $a \neq e$ such that $a^2 = e$. [*Hint:* If $a \neq a^{-1}$ for all a, the group contains an odd number of elements.]

12. Let $(H, *)$ be a subgroup of the group $(G, *)$ such that $H \neq G$. Prove that the subgroup generated by the complement $G - H$ is the group $(G, *)$ itself.

13. Suppose $(G, *)$ is a group and S is a nonempty subset of G. If the elements of S all commute, show that the subgroup generated by S, $((S), *)$ is a commutative group.

14. Given a group $(G, *)$ and $\emptyset \neq H \subseteq G$, verify that the following statements are equivalent:
    a) $(H, *)$ is a subgroup of $(G, *)$.
    b) $H * H \subseteq H$ and $H^{-1} \subseteq H$.
    c) $H * H^{-1} \subseteq H$.

15. If $(H, *)$ is a subgroup of the group $(G, *)$ and $\emptyset \neq K \subseteq G$, prove $H * K \subseteq H$ implies $K \subseteq H$.

16. Let $(H, *)$ and $(K, *)$ be subgroups of the commutative group $(G, *)$ with orders n and m, respectively. Assuming $H \cap K = \{e\}$, verify that the order of the group $(H * K, *)$ is nm.

17. Consider the group of symmetries of the square. Use Theorem 2–25 to obtain the subgroup generated by $H \cup K$, where $H = \{R_{180}, R_{360}\}$, $K = \{R_{360}, D_1\}$.

18. Let $(G, *)$ be a group of order n, where n is odd. Prove that each element of G is a square (i.e., if $x \in G$, then $x = y^2$ for some y in G).

2–5 NORMAL SUBGROUPS AND QUOTIENT GROUPS

Although we have derived some interesting results concerning subgroups, this concept, if unrestricted, is too general for many purposes. To obtain certain highly desirable conclusions, additional assumptions that go beyond Definition 2–19 must be imposed.

Thus, in the present section, we narrow the field and focus attention on a restricted class of subgroups which we shall refer to as normal subgroups. From a conceptual point of view, such groups are "normal" in the sense that they make the resulting theory so much richer than would otherwise be the case. While not every subgroup need be of this type, normal subgroups occur nonetheless with considerable frequency. It will soon become apparent that for the major part of our work, the significant aspect of this class of subgroups resides in the fact that they permit the construction of algebraic structures known as quotient groups.

Having already divulged some of the content of this section, let us now proceed to develop these ideas in detail. As a starting point, we prove a sequence of theorems leading to the conclusion that each subgroup induces a decomposition of the elements of the parent group into disjoint subsets known as *cosets*.

Definition 2–23. Let $(H, *)$ be a subgroup of the group $(G, *)$ and let $a \in G$. The set

$$a * H = \{a * h \mid h \in H\}$$

is called a *left coset* of H in G. The element a is a *representative* of $a * H$.

In a similar fashion, we can define the right cosets $H * a$ of H. The right cosets of the same subgroup are in general different from the left cosets. If the group operation $*$ of $(G, *)$ is commutative, then clearly $a * H = H * a$ for all $a \in G$. In the subsequent discussions, we will generally consider only left cosets of a subgroup. It is obvious that a parallel theory for right cosets may be developed.

Before proceeding to an example, we shall make several simple observations. First, if e is the identity element of $(G, *)$, then

$$e * H = \{e * h \mid h \in H\} = \{h \mid h \in H\} = H,$$

so that H itself is a left coset of H. Moreover, since $e \in H$, we have

$$a = a * e \in a * H,$$

that is, every element a of G belongs to some left coset of H, and more specifically, to the coset $a * H$. We shall make use of this fact in a little while.

We note further that there is a one-to-one correspondence between the
elements of H and those of any coset of H. Indeed, if $a * H$ is a left coset of H,
we may define a mapping $f: H \rightarrow a * H$ by $f(h) = a * h$. This function maps
onto $a * H$, since every element of $a * H$ is of the form $a * h$ for some choice
of $h \in H$. In addition f is a one-to-one function, for if $a * h_1 = a * h_2$, where
$h_1, h_2 \in H$, the cancellation law for groups yields $h_1 = h_2$. That is, $f(h_1) = f(h_2)$
implies $h_1 = h_2$. If the group $(G, *)$ has a finite number of elements, we may
therefore conclude that any two left cosets of H have the same number of
elements, namely, the number of elements in H.

Example 2–35. Returning once again to the group of symmetries of the
square, let us select the subgroup $(S, *)$, where $S = \{R_{360}, V\}$. The task of
computing the left cosets of S is straightforward, since we have the operation
table for this group at our disposal (see Example 2–24).

$$R_{90} * S = \{R_{90} * R_{360}, R_{90} * V\} = \{R_{90}, D_2\},$$

$$R_{180} * S = \{R_{180} * R_{360}, R_{180} * V\} = \{R_{180}, H\},$$

$$R_{270} * S = \{R_{270} * R_{360}, R_{270} * V\} = \{R_{270}, D_1\},$$

$$R_{360} * S = \{R_{360} * R_{360}, R_{360} * V\} = \{R_{360}, V\},$$

$$H * S = \{H * R_{360}, H * V\} = \{H, R_{180}\},$$

$$V * S = \{V * R_{360}, V * V\} = \{V, R_{360}\},$$

$$D_1 * S = \{D_1 * R_{360}, D_1 * V\} = \{D_1, R_{270}\},$$

$$D_2 * S = \{D_2 * R_{360}, D_2 * V\} = \{D_2, R_{90}\}.$$

From a quick inspection, the reader will observe that there are only four
distinct cosets,

$$\{R_{90}, D_2\}, \quad \{R_{180}, H\}, \quad \{R_{270}, D_1\}, \quad \text{and} \quad \{R_{360}, V\} = S.$$

These cosets are disjoint and their union is the underlying set of elements of
the whole group. As we shall see, this is always the case. Also, for this subgroup the notions of left and right cosets do not agree, since

$$D_1 * S = \{D_1, R_{270}\} \neq \{D_1, R_{90}\} = S * D_1.$$

Theorem 2–26. If $(H, *)$ is a subgroup of the group $(G, *)$, then $a * H = H$
if and only if $a \in H$.

Proof. Suppose first that $a * H = H$. As we have just remarked, the fact that
the identity e is a member of H implies that the element a belongs to $a * H$,
and thus by hypothesis to H also. On the other hand, if $a \in H$, then $a * H \subseteq H$,

since the set H, being the set of elements of a subgroup, is closed under the group operation $*$. The opposite inclusion is obtained by noting that each element $h \in H$ may be written as

$$h = a * (a^{-1} * h).$$

Here, $a^{-1} * h \in H$, since both a, $h \in H$ and $(H, *)$ is a subgroup of $(G, *)$. This implies that $h \in a * H$ and consequently $H \subseteq a * H$.

Our next theorem provides a simple criterion for the equality of two left cosets, when a representative of each is known.

Theorem 2–27. If $(H, *)$ is a subgroup of the group $(G, *)$, then

$$a * H = b * H,$$

if and only if $a^{-1} * b \in H$.

Proof. Assume that $a * H = b * H$. Then, if $a * h_1$ is an arbitrary element of $a * H$, there must exist an $h_2 \in H$ such that $a * h_1 = b * h_2$. From this we conclude that

$$a^{-1} * b = h_1 * h_2^{-1},$$

and, since the product $h_1 * h_2^{-1}$ belongs to H, that $a^{-1} * b \in H$.

Conversely, if $a^{-1} * b \in H$, then by Theorem 2–26 we have

$$(a^{-1} * b) * H = H.$$

This implies that any element $h_1 \in H$ can be expressed as

$$h_1 = (a^{-1} * b) * h_2$$

for some $h_2 \in H$, from which we infer that $a * h_1 = b * h_2$. Thus each product $a * h_1$ in the coset $a * H$ is equal to an element of the form $b * h_2$, and consequently lies in the coset $b * H$. Since this statement also holds, with a and b interchanged,

$$a * H = b * H.$$

Remark. When working with right cosets, the requirement $a^{-1} * b \in H$ must be replaced by $a * b^{-1} \in H$; that is, $H * a = H * b$ if and only if $a * b^{-1} \in H$.

As an immediate consequence of the last theorem, we see that any element a_1 of the left coset $a * H$ determines this coset. For if $a_1 \in a * H$, then $a_1 = a * h_1$ for suitable $h_1 \in H$. Thus $a^{-1} * a_1 \in H$, so that by the theorem, $a * H = a_1 * H$. This means that each element of a coset can be thought of as a representative of that coset. In a certain sense we are being prejudiced whenever we denote a coset by $a * H$, for someone else might choose to call it $b * H$ where $b \neq a$, but $a^{-1} * b \in H$.

We are now in a position to prove a fundamental result concerning cosets to the effect that if two left cosets have an element in common, then they are precisely the same set.

Theorem 2–28. If $(H, *)$ is a subgroup of the group $(G, *)$ then either the cosets $a * H$ and $b * H$ are disjoint or else $a * H = b * H$.

Proof. Suppose that $a * H$ and $b * H$ contain some element c in common. Since c is in $a * H$, there exists an $h_1 \in H$ such that $c = a * h_1$. Similarly, we have $c = b * h_2$ for some element $h_2 \in H$. It follows then that

$$a * h_1 = b * h_2, \quad \text{or} \quad a^{-1} * b = h_1 * h_2^{-1}.$$

Since $(H, *)$ is a subgroup, the product $h_1 * h_2^{-1}$, and thus $a^{-1} * b$, must lie in the set H. One need only apply Theorem 2–27 to conclude

$$a * H = b * H.$$

We saw earlier that each element $a \in G$ is a member of some left coset of H in G, namely, the coset $a * H$; that is, G is exhausted by its left cosets. Theorem 2–28 indicates that an element can belong to one and only one left coset of H. Thus the set G is partitioned by H into disjoint sets, each of which has exactly as many elements as H. For ease of future reference let us summarize these remarks in the following theorem.

Theorem 2–29. If $(H, *)$ is a subgroup of the group $(G, *)$, the left (right) cosets of H in G form a partition of the set G.

Example 2–36. Consider $(Z_{12}, +_{12})$, the group of integers modulo 12. If we take $\{0, 4, 8\}$ for the set H, then $(\{0, 4, 8\}, +_{12})$ is evidently a subgroup of $(Z_{12}, +_{12})$. The left cosets of H in Z_{12} are

$$0 +_{12} H = \{0, 4, 8\} = 4 +_{12} H = 8 +_{12} H,$$
$$1 +_{12} H = \{1, 5, 9\} = 5 +_{12} H = 9 +_{12} H,$$
$$2 +_{12} H = \{2, 6, 10\} = 6 +_{12} H = 10 +_{12} H,$$
$$3 +_{12} H = \{3, 7, 11\} = 7 +_{12} H = 11 +_{12} H.$$

In this case, the coset decomposition of Z_{12} relative to the subset H is just

$$Z_{12} = \{0, 4, 8\} \cup \{1, 5, 9\} \cup \{2, 6, 10\} \cup \{3, 7, 11\}.$$

Suppose now that $(G, *)$ is a finite group, say of order n, and $(H, *)$ is a subgroup of $(G, *)$ of order k. We can then decompose the set G into a union of a finite number of disjoint left cosets of H:

$$G = (a_1 * H) \cup (a_2 * H) \cup \cdots \cup (a_r * H).$$

The number r of distinct left cosets appearing in this decomposition is called the *index* of H in G. Since each coset in the above decomposition has k elements, the set G itself must have $r \cdot k$ elements; hence $n = r \cdot k$ or

$$\text{order } G = (\text{index } H) \cdot (\text{order } H).$$

This establishes the following classical result due to Lagrange.

Theorem 2–30. (*Lagrange*). The order and index of any subgroup of a finite group divides the order of the group.

There is a corollary to Theorem 2–30 which is of some intrinsic interest.

Corollary. If $(G, *)$ is a group of order n, then the order of any element $a \in G$ is a factor of n; in addition, $a^n = e$.

Proof. Let the element a have order k. By definition, the cyclic subgroup $((a), *)$ generated by a must also be of order k. According to the conclusion of Lagrange's Theorem, k is a divisor of n; that is, $n = rk$ for some $r \in Z_+$. Hence,

$$a^n = a^{rk} = (a^k)^r = e^r = e,$$

completing the proof of both assertions.

From Lagrange's Theorem, we are able to conclude that any finite group of prime order has no nontrivial subgroups. Actually a stronger statement can be made:

Theorem 2–31. If $(G, *)$ is a finite group of composite order, then $(G, *)$ has nontrivial subgroups.

Proof. If the group $(G, *)$ is not cyclic, any element $a \in G$ with $a \neq e$ generates a nontrivial cyclic subgroup $((a), *)$. Thus, it suffices to consider cyclic groups of composite order. To this end, suppose $G = (a)$ where the generator a has order nm $(n, m \neq 1)$. Then $(a^n)^m = e$, while $(a^n)^{m'} \neq e$ for $0 < m' < m$. From this, it is obvious that $((a^n), *)$ is a nontrivial cyclic subgroup of $(G, *)$ with order m.

Corollary. Every group $(G, *)$ of prime order is cyclic.

Proof. Consider the cyclic subgroup $((a), *)$ generated by any $a \in G$, with $a \neq e$. Now, the order of $((a), *)$ must divide the order of $(G, *)$, a prime; since (a) contains more than one element, order $(a) = $ order G, whence $(a) = G$.

As a further application of Lagrange's Theorem, we can now give a simplified proof of Theorem 2–7:

Theorem 2–7. (*Revisited*). Any noncommutative group has at least six elements.

Proof. A group of prime order, being a cyclic group, is necessarily commutative. Accordingly, any group having order 2, 3, or 5 will be commutative. Suppose next that $(G, *)$ is a group of order 4. By Lagrange's Theorem, each element of G distinct from the identity has order 2 or 4. If one of them has order 4, then $(G, *)$ is a cyclic group of order 4 and therefore commutative. On the other hand, a group each of whose elements other than the identity has order 2 must be commutative by Problem 6, Section 2–2. This argument establishes that all groups of order less than 6 are commutative groups.

Incidentally, the implication of Lagrange's Theorem cannot be reversed; that is to say, a group of order n need not have a subgroup of order k, where k is a divisor of n. To be more specific, a group of order 12 exists which has no subgroups of order 6. The particular group we are referring to happens to be a subgroup of the symmetric group $(S_4, \circ)$ and has as its elements:

$$\begin{pmatrix} 1 & 2 & 3 & 4 \\ 1 & 2 & 3 & 4 \end{pmatrix}, \quad \begin{pmatrix} 1 & 2 & 3 & 4 \\ 1 & 3 & 4 & 2 \end{pmatrix}, \quad \begin{pmatrix} 1 & 2 & 3 & 4 \\ 1 & 4 & 2 & 3 \end{pmatrix},$$

$$\begin{pmatrix} 1 & 2 & 3 & 4 \\ 2 & 1 & 4 & 3 \end{pmatrix}, \quad \begin{pmatrix} 1 & 2 & 3 & 4 \\ 2 & 4 & 3 & 1 \end{pmatrix}, \quad \begin{pmatrix} 1 & 2 & 3 & 4 \\ 2 & 3 & 1 & 4 \end{pmatrix},$$

$$\begin{pmatrix} 1 & 2 & 3 & 4 \\ 3 & 4 & 1 & 2 \end{pmatrix}, \quad \begin{pmatrix} 1 & 2 & 3 & 4 \\ 3 & 2 & 4 & 1 \end{pmatrix}, \quad \begin{pmatrix} 1 & 2 & 3 & 4 \\ 3 & 1 & 2 & 4 \end{pmatrix},$$

$$\begin{pmatrix} 1 & 2 & 3 & 4 \\ 4 & 1 & 3 & 2 \end{pmatrix}, \quad \begin{pmatrix} 1 & 2 & 3 & 4 \\ 4 & 2 & 1 & 3 \end{pmatrix}, \quad \begin{pmatrix} 1 & 2 & 3 & 4 \\ 4 & 3 & 2 & 1 \end{pmatrix}.$$

This permutation group does, however, have subgroups of orders 2, 3, and 4.

We shall introduce next a particularly important class of subgroups which we shall refer to as normal subgroups.

Definition 2–24. A subgroup $(H, *)$ of the group $(G, *)$ is said to be *normal* (or invariant) in $(G, *)$ if and only if every left coset of H in G is also a right coset of H in G.

Thus, if $(H, *)$ is normal and $a * H$ is any left coset of H in G, there exists some element $b \in G$ such that

$$a * H = H * b.$$

Since a is in the left coset $a * H$, this means that a is also a member of the right coset $H * b$. The cosets $H * b$ and $H * a$ have the element a in common; so the analog of Theorem 2–28 for right cosets implies that

$$H * b = H * a.$$

In other words, if $a * H$ happens to be a right coset of H, then it must be the right coset $H * a$. This observation allows us to reformulate Definition 2–24 as follows.

Definition 2–25. A subgroup $(H, *)$ is normal in the group $(G, *)$ if and only if $a * H = H * a$ for every $a \in G$.

For a normal subgroup $(H, *)$, we may thus speak simply of the cosets of H in G without specifying right or left. The trivial subgroups are obviously normal. More generally, every subgroup of a commutative group is a normal subgroup.

We will sometimes speak of a *simple* group (in the technical sense), meaning thereby that it has no normal subgroups other than the two trivial ones. For instance, the finite cyclic groups of prime order are simple groups.

Definition 2–25 indicates that normality of a subgroup $(H, *)$ guarantees a weak form of commutativity relative to H. For, if $h \in H$, while it cannot in general be concluded that $a * h = h * a$ for any $a \in G$, we do know that there exists an element $h' \in H$ such that

$$a * h = h' * a.$$

It would be gratifying to have a less cumbersome procedure than to compute cosets for determining whether a given subgroup is in fact a normal subgroup. Just such a criterion is given in the next theorem, and we shall have frequent occasion to make use of it.

Theorem 2–32. The subgroup $(H, *)$ is a normal subgroup of the group $(G, *)$ if and only if for each element $a \in G$,

$$a * H * a^{-1} \subseteq H.$$

Proof. First, assume that $a * H * a^{-1} \subseteq H$ for every $a \in G$. We must prove that in this case $a * H = H * a$. Let $a * h$ be an arbitrary element of $a * H$. Since $a * H * a^{-1} \subseteq H$, $a * h * a^{-1} = h_1$ for some $h_1 \in H$. Thus

$$a * h = (a * h * a^{-1}) * a = h_1 * a.$$

The product $h_1 * a$ lies in the right coset $H * a$, so we conclude that

$$a * H \subseteq H * a.$$

We obtain the opposite inclusion, $H * a \subseteq a * H$, by a similar argument upon observing that our hypothesis also implies

$$a^{-1} * H * a = a^{-1} * H * (a^{-1})^{-1} \subseteq H.$$

Conversely, suppose $a * H = H * a$ for each $a \in G$. Let $a * h_1 * a^{-1}$ be any element in $a * H * a^{-1}$. Then, since $a * H = H * a$, there exists an element

$h_2 \in H$ such that
$$a * h_1 = h_2 * a.$$

Consequently,
$$a * h_1 * a^{-1} = (h_2 * a) * a^{-1} = h_2,$$

which implies $a * H * a^{-1} \subseteq H$.

To demonstrate the convenience of this result, we now prove the following assertion:

(cent G, *) is a normal subgroup of each group $(G, *)$.

In terms of elements, it must be shown that if $c \in$ cent G and a is arbitrary in G, then $a * c * a^{-1} \in$ cent G. But this is fairly obvious, since from the definition of the center of a group, $a * c = c * a$. It follows at once that
$$a * c * a^{-1} = c * a * a^{-1} = c * e = c \in \text{cent } G.$$

Example 2–37. Let us return to the noncommutative group $(G, \circ)$ of order 6 presented in Example 2–22. The reader may recall that the elements of G are functions $f_1, f_2, \ldots, f_6$, while the group operation is functional composition. For convenience, the operation table is reproduced below:

$\circ$	f_1	f_2	f_3	f_4	f_5	f_6
f_1	f_1	f_2	f_3	f_4	f_5	f_6
f_2	f_2	f_1	f_6	f_5	f_4	f_3
f_3	f_3	f_4	f_1	f_2	f_6	f_5
f_4	f_4	f_3	f_5	f_6	f_2	f_1
f_5	f_5	f_6	f_4	f_3	f_1	f_2
f_6	f_6	f_5	f_2	f_1	f_3	f_4

If we take as H the subset $\{f_1, f_4, f_6\}$, then it is easily verified that the pair $(H, \circ)$ is a normal subgroup of $(G, \circ)$. The coset breakdown for the subgroup in question is
$$f_k \circ H = \{f_1, f_4, f_6\} = H \circ f_k \qquad \text{for} \quad k = 1, 4, 6,$$
$$f_k \circ H = \{f_2, f_3, f_5\} = H \circ f_k \qquad \text{for} \quad k = 2, 3, 5.$$

On the other hand, the subgroup $(\{f_1, f_2\}, \circ)$ is not normal; a short computation indicates why the criterion of Theorem 2–32 fails to be satisfied:
$$f_4 \circ f_2 \circ f_4^{-1} = f_4 \circ f_2 \circ f_6 = f_5 \notin \{f_1, f_2\}.$$

The significance of normal subgroups—indeed, our main purpose for introducing them—is that they enable us to define new groups which are associated in a natural way with the original group. More specifically, we shall show that the set of cosets of a normal subgroup is itself the set of elements of a group.

If $(H, *)$ is a normal subgroup of the group $(G, *)$, then we shall denote the collection of distinct cosets of H in G by G/H:

$$G/H = \{a * H \mid a \in G\}.$$

These are also right cosets, since the definition of a normal subgroup guarantees that $a * H = H * a$ for every $a \in G$.

A rule of composition $\otimes$ may be defined on G/H by the formula

$$(a * H) \otimes (b * H) = (a * b) * H.$$

Since this definition is stated in terms of coset representatives, we must first show that the multiplication of cosets under $\otimes$ is unambiguously defined, independent of the arbitrary choice of representatives from these sets. That is, it must be shown that if

$$a * H = a_1 * H \qquad \text{and} \qquad b * H = b_1 * H,$$

then also

$$(a * b) * H = (a_1 * b_1) * H.$$

According to Theorem 2–27, it is enough merely to prove that the product

$$(a * b)^{-1} * (a_1 * b_1)$$

is a member of H. Now, $a * H = a_1 * H$ and $b * H = b_1 * H$ imply both $a^{-1} * a_1, b^{-1} * b_1 \in H$. Since $(H, *)$ is normal in $(G, *)$, we know that

$$x * H * x^{-1} \subseteq H$$

for every $x \in G$. In particular,

$$b^{-1} * H * b = b^{-1} * H * (b^{-1})^{-1} \subseteq H.$$

From this we conclude $b^{-1} * (a^{-1} * a_1) * b \in H$ and, since H is closed, that

$$(a * b)^{-1} * (a_1 * b_1) = (b^{-1} * (a^{-1} * a_1) * b) * (b^{-1} * b_1) \in H.$$

The above argument shows $\otimes$ to be a *well-defined* binary operation on G/H in the sense that the product of two cosets depends only on the cosets involved and in no way on the representative elements chosen from them; any other choice would have yielded the same product.

Having thus prepared the way, we now state and prove the principal result of this section.

Theorem 2–33. If $(H, *)$ is a normal subgroup of the group $(G, *)$, then the system $(G/H, \otimes)$ forms a group, known as the *quotient group* of G by H.

Proof. First, let us observe that the associativity of the operation $\otimes$ is a direct consequence of the associativity of $*$ in G:

$$
\begin{aligned}
[(a * H) \otimes (b * H)] \otimes (c * H) &= ((a * b) * H) \otimes (c * H) \\
&= ((a * b) * c) * H \\
&= (a * (b * c)) * H \\
&= (a * H) \otimes ((b * c) * H) \\
&= (a * H) \otimes [(b * H) \otimes (c * H)].
\end{aligned}
$$

The coset $H = e * H$ is the identity element for the operation $\otimes$, since

$$
\begin{aligned}
(a * H) \otimes (e * H) &= (a * e) * H \\
&= a * H \\
&= (e * a) * H \\
&= (e * H) \otimes (a * H).
\end{aligned}
$$

It is equally easy to see that the inverse of the coset $a * H$ is $a^{-1} * H$, where a^{-1} denotes the inverse of a in $(G, *)$. This is evident from the computation

$$
\begin{aligned}
(a * H) \otimes (a^{-1} * H) &= (a * a^{-1}) * H \\
&= e * H \\
&= (a^{-1} * a) * H \\
&= (a^{-1} * H) \otimes (a * H).
\end{aligned}
$$

Hence all the group postulates are fulfilled and the proof is complete.

Example 2–38. Once again we fall back on the group of symmetries of the square for an illustration. Here, the subgroup

$$(S, *) = (\{R_{180}, R_{360}\}, *)$$

is normal, being the center of the group. Its distinct cosets, that is, the elements of G/S, are

$$G/S = \{\{R_{180}, R_{360}\}, \{R_{90}, R_{270}\}, \{V, H\}, \{D_1, D_2\}\}.$$

A typical coset multiplication proceeds as follows:

$$
\begin{aligned}
\{D_1, D_2\} \otimes \{R_{90}, R_{270}\} &= (D_1 * S) \otimes (R_{90} * S) \\
&= (D_1 * R_{90}) * S \\
&= H * S \\
&= \{V, H\}.
\end{aligned}
$$

To multiply two cosets under $\otimes$, all we really need to do is select an arbitrary representative from each coset, multiply these elements under the group operation $*$ and determine to which coset the resulting product belongs.

The operation table for the quotient group $(G/S, \otimes)$ is shown in Table 2–4.

Table 2–4

$\otimes$	$\{R_{180}, R_{360}\}$	$\{R_{90}, R_{270}\}$	$\{V, H\}$	$\{D_1, D_2\}$
$\{R_{180}, R_{360}\}$	$\{R_{180}, R_{360}\}$	$\{R_{90}, R_{270}\}$	$\{V, H\}$	$\{D_1, D_2\}$
$\{R_{90}, R_{270}\}$	$\{R_{90}, R_{270}\}$	$\{R_{180}, R_{360}\}$	$\{D_1, D_2\}$	$\{V, H\}$
$\{V, H\}$	$\{V, H\}$	$\{D_1, D_2\}$	$\{R_{180}, R_{360}\}$	$\{R_{90}, R_{270}\}$
$\{D_1, D_2\}$	$\{D_1, D_2\}$	$\{V, H\}$	$\{R_{90}, R_{270}\}$	$\{R_{180}, R_{360}\}$

Example 2–39. A simple, but useful example to keep in mind when working with quotient groups is furnished by the additive group of integers $(Z, +)$. It has been previously established that the (normal) subgroups of $(Z, +)$ are the cyclic subgroups $((n), +)$, n a nonnegative integer. The cosets of (n) in Z take the form

$$a + (n) = \{a + kn \mid k \in Z\} = [a].$$

In other words, the cosets of (n) are merely the congruence classes modulo n. Coset multiplication in $Z/(n)$, moreover, is given by

$$(a + (n)) \otimes (b + (n)) = a + b + (n),$$

or, with a judicious change of notation,

$$[a] \otimes [b] = [a + b].$$

We thus deduce that the quotient group of Z by (n) is none other than the group of integers modulo n,

$$(Z/(n), \otimes) = (Z_n +_n).$$

Among other things, this indicates that had we so desired, the study of the integers modulo n could have been subsumed under the more general theory of quotient groups.

It is a simple matter to see that any quotient group of a commutative group is necessarily commutative. A natural question is whether a noncommutative group can possess commutative quotient groups and, more pointedly, what conditions (if any at all) would insure their existence. As a concluding topic in this section, we investigate this particular situation. Our analysis begins with a basic definition.

Definition 2–26. Given a group $(G, *)$ and elements a, $b \in G$, the *commutator* of a and b is defined to be the product $a * b * a^{-1} * b^{-1}$.

To simplify matters, the symbol $[a, b]$ will be used to represent the commutator of two elements a and b; any other symbol would do as well, but this notation is standard. Inasmuch as $[a, b]$ satisfies the identity

$$a * b = [a, b] * b * a,$$

one may view the commutator of a and b as a measure of the extent to which $a * b$ differs from $b * a$. Indeed, the elements a and b commute if and only if $[a, b] = e$.

In general, the commutators do not by themselves form the elements of a subgroup, since they fail to be closed under multiplication. The usual procedure for bypassing this difficulty is to work instead with the subgroup generated by all the commutators $[a, b]$, $a, b \in G$. The resulting subgroup is known either as the *derived subgroup* or *commutator subgroup* of $(G, *)$ and may be denoted simply by $([G, G], *)$.

Now, the inverse of a commutator is again a commutator: $[a, b]^{-1} = [b, a]$. There is no necessity then of explicitly considering inverses in the definition of the set $[G, G]$; its elements consist merely of products of finitely many commutators of G. That is,

$$[G, G] = \{\textstyle\prod [a_i, b_i] \mid a_i, b_i \in G\},$$

where the symbol $\prod$ should be construed as representing a finite product with one or more factors.

With these preparatory remarks out of the way, we proceed to establish some of the special properties of the commutator subgroup.

Theorem 2–34. The group $([G, G], *)$ is a normal subgroup of $(G, *)$.

Proof. The proof proceeds along the usual line. Namely, it must be shown that for $c \in [G, G]$ and a in G, $a * c * a^{-1}$ lies in $[G, G]$. But,

$$a * c * a^{-1} = (a * c * a^{-1} * c^{-1}) * c = [a, c] * c.$$

The element $[a, c] * c$ is a finite product of commutators and accordingly belongs to $[G, G]$.

The quotient group $(G/[G, G], \otimes)$, which exists by virtue of Theorem 2–34, is called the *commutator quotient group* or *abelianized group*. The motivation for this latter choice of terminology will only become apparent after the next result.

Theorem 2–35. Let $(H, *)$ be a normal subgroup of the group $(G, *)$. The quotient group $(G/H, \otimes)$ is commutative if and only if $[G, G] \subseteq H$.

Proof. Suppose $a * H$ and $b * H$ are two arbitrary elements in G/H. Since the coset $H = e * H$ is the identity element of $(G/H, \otimes)$, the group operation

$\otimes$ will be commutative if and only if

$$H = [a * H, b * H] = (a * H) \otimes (b * H) \otimes (a * H)^{-1} \otimes (b * H)^{-1},$$

or, what amounts to the same thing,

$$H = (a * b * a^{-1} * b^{-1}) * H.$$

But, Theorem 2–26 tells us a necessary and sufficient condition for the last equality to hold is that

$$[a, b] = a * b * a^{-1} * b^{-1} \in H.$$

In other words, commutativity of the quotient group $(G/H, \otimes)$ is equivalent to requiring that the subgroup $(H, *)$ contain all the commutators of G. As $([G, G], *)$ is by definition the smallest subgroup with this property, the latter condition may be replaced by $[G, G] \subseteq H$.

A special case, but itself of interest, occurs on taking $H = [G, G]$:

Corollary. For any group $(G, *)$, the commutator quotient group $(G/[G, G], \otimes)$ is commutative.

The foregoing theorem says, in effect, that the commutator group is the smallest (again, in the sense of inclusion) normal subgroup whose associated quotient group is commutative. The transition from a group to its commutator quotient group is referred to as the *abelization* of the group and provides a convenient means of manufacturing commutative groups from noncommutative ones.

PROBLEMS

1. If $H = \{0, 6, 12, 18\}$, show that $(H, +_{24})$ is a cyclic subgroup of $(Z_{24}, +_{24})$. Also, list the elements of each coset of H in Z_{24}.

2. In the symmetric group $(S_4, \circ)$, let the set H consist of the four permutations

$$\begin{pmatrix} 1 & 2 & 3 & 4 \\ 1 & 2 & 3 & 4 \end{pmatrix}, \quad \begin{pmatrix} 1 & 2 & 3 & 4 \\ 2 & 1 & 4 & 3 \end{pmatrix}, \quad \begin{pmatrix} 1 & 2 & 3 & 4 \\ 3 & 4 & 1 & 2 \end{pmatrix}, \quad \begin{pmatrix} 1 & 2 & 3 & 4 \\ 4 & 3 & 2 & 1 \end{pmatrix}.$$

List the elements of each coset of H in S_4.

3. Assume $(H, *)$ is a subgroup of $(G, *)$.

a) Show that every left coset of H has the same number of elements as every right coset.

b) Prove that $(c * a) * H = (c * b) * H$ implies $a * H = b * H$.

c) Show that there exists a one-to-one correspondence between the left cosets of H in G and the right cosets of H in G. [*Hint:* $a * H \to H * a^{-1}$.]

4. Determine the left coset decomposition of the group of symmetries of the square with respect to the subgroup $(\{R_{360}, D_1\}, *)$.

5. In the group of symmetries of the equilateral triangle, find:
   a) all subgroups,
   b) all normal subgroups,
   c) the center of the group.

6. Show that if the cyclic group $((a), *)$ is infinite, then a and a^{-1} are its only generators, and all subgroups except $(\{e\}, *)$ are infinite.

7. Let $(H, *)$ be a subgroup of index 2 in the group $(G, *)$. Prove that $(H, *)$ is a normal subgroup. [*Hint:* $H \cup (a * H) = G = H \cup (H * a)$ for any $a \in G - H$.]

8. Given that $(H_1, *)$ and $(H_2, *)$ are both normal subgroups of the group $(G, *)$, prove that the subgroup $(H_1 \cap H_2, *)$ is also normal.

9. Let $(H, *)$ be a subgroup of the group $(G, *)$ and the set $N(H)$ be defined by

$$N(H) = \{a \in G \mid a * H * a^{-1} = H\}.$$

   a) Prove that the pair $(N(H), *)$ is a subgroup of $(G, *)$, called the *normalizer* of H in G.
   b) Prove that $(H, *)$ is normal if and only if $N(H) = G$.

10. Suppose that $(H, *)$ and $(K, *)$ are normal subgroups of the group $(G, *)$, with $H \cap K = \{e\}$. By considering elements of the form $h * k * h^{-1} * k^{-1}$, show that $h * k = k * h$ for all $h \in H, k \in K$.

11. Given $(H, *)$ and $(K, *)$ are subgroups of the group $(G, *)$ and one of these subgroups is normal, prove that the pair $(H * K, *)$ is a subgroup of $(G, *)$; when both are normal subgroups, show the group $(H * K, *)$ is also normal.

12. Find an example of a group $(G, *)$ having a subgroup $(H, *)$ for which the product of two left cosets of H in G need not be a left coset of H.

13. Describe the quotient group of
    a) $(Z_e, +)$ in $(Z, +)$,   b) $(\{0, 2, 4, 6, 8\}, +_{10})$ in $(Z_{10}, +_{10})$,
    c) $(Z, +)$ in $(Q, +)$,   d) $(\{1, -1\}, \cdot)$ in $(\{1, -1, i, -i\}, \cdot)$.

14. Let $(G, *)$ be a cyclic group with generator a and $(H, *)$ be any subgroup of $(G, *)$. Prove that the quotient group $(G/H, \otimes)$ is also cyclic with the coset $a * H$ as a generator.

15. Given $(H, *)$ is a normal subgroup of the group $(G, *)$, prove that the quotient group $(G/H, \otimes)$ is commutative whenever $(G, *)$ is commutative.

16. For any group $(G, *)$, describe the quotient groups of the trivial normal subgroups $(\{e\}, *)$ and $(G, *)$.

17. Consider the cyclic group $((a), *)$ of order 15 and the subgroup $((a^3), *)$. List the elements of each coset of (a^3) and construct the multiplication table for the quotient group $((a)/(a^3), \otimes)$.

18. In the commutative group $(G, *)$, let the set H consist of all elements of G with finite order. Prove that
    a) $(H, *)$ is a normal subgroup of $(G, *)$, called the *torsion subgroup*,
    b) the quotient group $(G/H, \otimes)$ is *torsion-free;* that is, none of its elements other than the identity are of finite order.

19. Show that a group $(G, *)$ is commutative if and only if $[G, G] = \{e\}$.

20. For any group $(G, *)$, let $(H, *)$ be the subgroup generated by the set of squares of elements of G. Establish the following:
    a) $(H, *)$ is a normal subgroup of $(G, *)$.
    b) The quotient group $(G/H, \otimes)$ is commutative.   [*Hint:* $[G, G] \subseteq H$, since $[a, b] = (a * b)^2 * (b^{-1} * a^{-1} * b)^2 * b^{-2}$.]

21. Let $(H_i, *)$ be a collection of nontrivial normal subgroups of the group $(G, *)$ such that $G = \cup H_i$. Assume further that $H_i \cap H_j = \{e\}$ for $i \neq j$. Prove that the parent group $(G, *)$ is necessarily commutative. [*Hint:* Let $a \in H_i$ and $b \in H_j$. For $i \neq j$, use Problem 10. In case $i = j$, choose any element $c \in G - H_i$. Then c and $c * a$ commute with every element of H_i; in particular, $e = [c * a, b * a] = [a, b]$.]

22. Prove that if the quotient group $(G/\mathrm{cent}\ G, \otimes)$ is cyclic, then $(G, *)$ is a commutative group.

2-6 HOMOMORPHISMS

Up to this point in the text, we have not considered mappings from one group to another; indeed, any knowledge of functions was irrelevant to most of the topics considered. They now enter in an essential way, for we wish to introduce a concept—the idea of algebraically indistinguishable systems—which will be of fundamental importance throughout the remainder of the book and which is, in fact, one of the most important notions in mathematics.

This section begins, however, with an analysis of a class of functions which preserve algebraic structure.

Definition 2-27. Let $(G, *)$ and $(G', \circ)$ be two groups and f a function from G into G', $f: G \to G'$. Then f is said to be a *homomorphism* (or operation-preserving function) from $(G, *)$ into $(G', \circ)$ if and only if

$$f(a * b) = f(a) \circ f(b)$$

for every pair of elements $a, b \in G$.

A few remarks are in order before considering any examples. First, notice that on the left-hand side of the above equation, the product $a * b$ is computed in G, while on the right side the product $f(a) \circ f(b)$ is that of elements of G'. The functions indicated in this definition have the characteristic property of carrying products into products. A common way of expressing the situation is to say that the image of a product under f is equal to the product of the images.

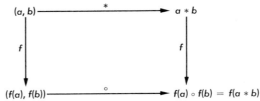

Another viewpoint is perhaps beneficial. The requirement that $f(a * b) = f(a) \circ f(b)$ for every pair of elements $a, b \in G$ is sometimes described by saying that the diagram of mappings on page 89 is commutative. For this condition asserts that if we start with elements a, b of G and move them to G' by either of the two routes indicated by the arrows—by first forming the product $a * b$ and then applying f to it or by first obtaining the images $f(a)$ and $f(b)$ and then taking their product—the result will be the same.

It may also strike the reader that the language in which Definition 2–27 is couched is open to criticism. To speak of a homomorphism from a group $(G, *)$ into a group $(G', \circ)$ is somewhat imprecise, since the mapping concerned is actually between their underlying sets of elements. This linguistic convention has the decided advantage, however, of indicating the operations preserved as well as the domain and range of the function.

Example 2–40. For an arbitrary group $(G, *)$, define the function $f: G \to G$ by taking $f = i_G$, the identity map on G. It is a triviality to check that f is a homomorphism from the group $(G, *)$ into itself, as

$$f(a * b) = a * b = f(a) * f(b).$$

Example 2–41. Suppose that $(G, *)$ and $(G', \circ)$ are two groups with identity elements e and e', respectively. The function $f: G \to G'$ given by $f(a) = e'$ for each $a \in G$ is a homomorphism:

$$f(a * b) = e' = e' \circ e' = f(a) \circ f(b).$$

This particular mapping (the so-called *trivial homomorphism*) is the only constant function which satisfies Definition 2–27.

Example 2–42. Consider the two groups $(R^\#, +)$ and $(R^\# - \{0\}, \cdot)$, where as usual, $+$ and $\cdot$ denote ordinary addition and multiplication. For $a \in R^\#$, define the function f by $f(a) = 2^a$. To show that the mapping f is operation-preserving, we must establish whether $f(a + b) = f(a) \cdot f(b)$. This is readily verified, since

$$f(a + b) = 2^{a+b} = 2^a \cdot 2^b = f(a) \cdot f(b).$$

Example 2–43. Let $(Z, +)$ be the group of integers under addition and $(Z_n, +_n)$ be the group of integers modulo n. Define $f: Z \to Z_n$ by $f(a) = [a]$; that is, map each integer into the congruence class containing it. That f is a homomorphism follows directly from the definition of modular addition:

$$f(a + b) = [a + b] = [a] +_n [b] = f(a) +_n f(b).$$

For future use, we shall label the set of all homomorphisms from the group $(G, *)$ into itself (the so-called *endomorphisms*) by the symbol hom G; a frequently used alternative notation is to write end G. Both notations have a certain suggestive power, and it reduces to a matter of personal preference.

Interestingly enough, the set hom G can be endowed with an algebraic structure:

Theorem 2–36. The pair (hom G, ∘), where ∘ denotes functional composition, forms a semigroup with identity.

Proof. For the proof, which is quite elementary, it must first be shown that the composition $f \circ g$ of two functions f, $g \in$ hom G again preserves the group operation. This is easily accomplished by noting that whenever a, $b \in G$,

$$(f \circ g)(a * b) = f(g(a * b))$$
$$= f(g(a) * g(b))$$
$$= f(g(a)) * f(g(b)) = (f \circ g)(a) * (f \circ g)(b).$$

As we have seen in an earlier section, composition of functions is associative. Finally, Example 2–40 indicates that the identity mapping i_G (the identity element for composition) is itself operation-preserving.

A reasonable subject of curiosity would be the question of whether or not there exists a subset $S \subseteq$ hom G such that $(S, \circ)$ is a group. For inverses to exist, one must plainly single out the one-to-one functions. Moreover, in order that the domain of f^{-1} be the set G, consideration should be further restricted to those functions which map onto G. Thus a natural undertaking is to investigate the collection of all one-to-one homomorphisms from the group $(G, *)$ onto itself; as a matter of notation, we shall designate this set of mappings by the symbol $A(G)$, for *automorphism.*

The elements of $A(G)$ are now restricted to the extent that $(A(G), \circ)$ does indeed have the agreeable property of being a group. Let us give some details.

Theorem 2–37. The system $(A(G), \circ)$ is a subgroup of the symmetric group (sym G, ∘).

Proof. For functions f, $g \in A(G)$, we already know the composition of $f \circ g$ is in sym G. In conjunction with the last result, this shows $f \circ g$ belongs to $A(G)$, as does the identity map i_G. It remains only to verify here that whenever a function $f \in A(G)$, its inverse f^{-1} (which clearly is a member of sym G) is a homomorphism. If $\bar{a}$, $\bar{b} \in G$, the onto character of f implies $\bar{a} = f(a)$, $\bar{b} = f(b)$ for some choice of a, b in G. Therefore,

$$f^{-1}(\bar{a} * \bar{b}) = f^{-1}(f(a) * f(b))$$
$$= f^{-1}(f(a * b))$$
$$= a * b = f^{-1}(\bar{a}) * f^{-1}(\bar{b}),$$

and the proof is complete.

There are many important and interesting facts concerning homomorphic mappings. In the succeeding theorems, we shall examine some of these results in detail.

Theorem 2–38. If f is a homomorphism from the group $(G, *)$ into the group $(G', \circ)$, then

1) f maps the identity element e of $(G, *)$ onto the identity element e' of $(G', \circ)$: $f(e) = e'$,

2) f maps the inverse of an element $a \in G$ onto the inverse of $f(a)$ in $(G', \circ)$: $f(a^{-1}) = f(a)^{-1}$ for each $a \in G$.

Proof. To prove the first assertion, it is enough to observe that under the hypothesis of the theorem,

$$f(a) \circ e' = f(a) = f(a * e) = f(a) \circ f(e),$$

whenever $a \in G$. By the cancellation law in $(G', \circ)$, we then have

$$f(e) = e'.$$

In the second part of the theorem, it is first necessary to show that

$$f(a) \circ f(a^{-1}) = e' = f(a^{-1}) \circ f(a).$$

We can then conclude from the uniqueness of the inverse of $f(a)$ in $(G', \circ)$ that $f(a)^{-1} = f(a^{-1})$. To obtain this result, we make use of part (1) to get

$$f(a) \circ f(a^{-1}) = f(a * a^{-1}) = f(e) = e'.$$

Similarly,

$$f(a^{-1}) \circ f(a) = e'.$$

Example 2–44. As an immediate application of these ideas, we propose to establish that for each real number $r \neq 0$ there is exactly one homomorphism f from the group $(Z, +)$ into the group $(R^{\#} - \{0\}, \cdot)$ for which $f(1) = r$. The existence of such a function is trivial, for we need only consider the mapping $f(n) = r^n$, $n \in Z$.

To prove there can be at most one function satisfying the indicated conditions provides a more challenging problem. The basic idea is simple enough: assume there are two functions, f and g, having the required properties, and show that they are actually the same. Now, each positive integer n may be written as

$$n = 1 + 1 + \cdots + 1 \qquad (n \text{ summands}).$$

The operation-preserving character of f and g thus implies

$$f(n) = f(1)^n = r^n = g(1)^n = g(n), \qquad n \in Z_+.$$

On the other hand, if n is a nonzero negative integer, $-n \in Z_+$. Hence,

$$f(n) = f(-(-n)) = f(-n)^{-1} = g(-n)^{-1} = g(-(-n)) = g(n).$$

The crucial step, $f(-n) = g(-n)$, is justified by the fact f and g are already known to agree on the positive integers. By the first part of Theorem 2–38, $f(0) = 1 = g(0)$, so that $f(n) = g(n)$ for every integer n; therefore, $f = g$.

The next result indicates the algebraic nature of direct and inverse images of subgroups under homomorphisms. Among other things, we shall see that if f is a homomorphism from the group $(G, *)$ into the group $(G', \circ)$, then $(f(G), \circ)$ forms a subgroup of $(G', \circ)$. The complete story is told below:

Theorem 2–39. Let f be a homomorphism from the group $(G, *)$ into the group $(G', \circ)$. Then

1) for each subgroup $(H, *)$ of $(G, *)$, the pair $(f(H), \circ)$ is a subgroup of $(G', \circ)$,

2) for each subgroup $(H', \circ)$ of $(G', \circ)$, the pair $(f^{-1}(H'), *)$ is a subgroup of $(G, *)$.

Proof. To obtain the first part of the theorem, recall the definition of the image set $f(H)$:

$$f(H) = \{f(h) \mid h \in H\}.$$

Now, suppose $f(h)$ and $f(k)$ are arbitrary elements of $f(H)$. Then both h and k belong to the set H, as does the product $h * k^{-1}$. Hence,

$$f(h) \circ f(k)^{-1} = f(h) \circ f(k^{-1}) = f(h * k^{-1}) \in f(H).$$

Our argument shows that whenever $f(h), f(k) \in f(H)$, then $f(h) \circ f(k)^{-1}$ lies in $f(H)$; this is a sufficient condition for $(f(H), \circ)$ to be a subgroup of $(G', \circ)$.

The proof of the second statement proceeds in a similar manner. First, remember that

$$f^{-1}(H') = \{a \in G \mid f(a) \in H'\}.$$

Thus, if $a, b \in f^{-1}(H')$, the images $f(a)$ and $f(b)$ must be elements of H'. It follows at once that

$$f(a * b^{-1}) = f(a) \circ f(b^{-1}) = f(a) \circ f(b)^{-1} \in H'.$$

This means $a * b^{-1} \in f^{-1}(H')$, from which we conclude $(f^{-1}(H'), *)$ is a subgroup of $(G, *)$.

Left unresolved, as yet, is the matter of replacing the term "subgroup" in Theorem 2–39 by "normal subgroup." It is not particularly difficult to show that part (2) of the theorem remains true under such a substitution. Precisely speaking, if $(H', \circ)$ is a normal subgroup of $(G', \circ)$, the subgroup $(f^{-1}(H'), *)$ is normal in $(G, *)$. In establishing this fact, we will utilize both implications of Theorem 2–32. Suppose now $h \in f^{-1}(H')$, so that $f(h) \in H'$, and let a be an arbitrary element of G. Then,

$$f(a * h * a^{-1}) = f(a) \circ f(h) \circ f(a)^{-1} \in H'.$$

In other words, $a * h * a^{-1} \in f^{-1}(H')$, or in terms of sets,

$$a * f^{-1}(H') * a^{-1} \subseteq f^{-1}(H').$$

According to Theorem 2–32, this inclusion is enough to make $(f^{-1}(H'), *)$ a normal subgroup of $(G, *)$.

Without further restriction, it cannot be inferred that the image subgroup $(f(H), \circ)$ will be normal in $(G', \circ)$ whenever $(H, *)$ is itself a normal subgroup of $(G, *)$. One would need to know that

$$a' \circ f(h) \circ (a')^{-1} \in f(H)$$

for all $a' \in G'$ and $h \in H$. In general, there is no way of replacing the element a' by some $f(a)$ in order to exploit the normality of $(H, *)$. A slight strengthening of the hypothesis overcomes this difficulty; simply take f to be an onto mapping. (Recall that the word "onto" requires every member of G' to be the image of at least one element of G.)

Summarizing these remarks, we may now state:

Corollary. 1) For each normal subgroup $(H', \circ)$ of $(G', \circ)$, the subgroup $(f^{-1}(H'), *)$ is normal in $(G, *)$.

2) If $f(G) = G'$, then for each normal subgroup $(H, *)$ of $(G, *)$, the subgroup $(f(H), \circ)$ is normal in $(G', \circ)$.

In much of our subsequent work, the object of interest will be the kernel of a homomorphism.

Definition 2–28. Let f be a homomorphism from the group $(G, *)$ into the group $(G', \circ)$ and let e' be the identity element of $(G', \circ)$. The *kernel* of f, denoted by ker (f), is the set

$$\text{ker } (f) = \{a \in G \mid f(a) = e'\}.$$

Thus ker (f) consists of those elements in G which are mapped by f onto the identity eiement of the group $(G', \circ)$. Theorem 2–38 indicates that ker (f) ls a nonempty subset of G, since $e \in$ ker (f). It may well happen, as Example 2–41 shows, that ker $(f) = G$. Except for the trivial function indicated there, the kernel is always a proper subset of G.

Our definition of a homomorphism did not require that it be a one-to-one function, and indeed, we have presented several examples where it failed to be so. There is, however, a simple characterization of a one-to-one homomorphic mapping in terms of the kernel.

Theorem 2–40. Let f be a homomorphism from the group $(G, *)$ into the group $(G', \circ)$. Then f is one-to-one if and only if ker $(f) = \{e\}$.

Proof. Suppose the function f is one-to-one. We already know that $e \in$ ker (f). Our aim is to show that this is the only element in the kernel. If there existed another element $a \in$ ker (f), $a \neq e$, then we would have $f(a) = e' = f(e)$. That is, $f(a) = f(e)$ but $a \neq e$. This would contradict the hypothesis that f is one-to-one.

On the other hand, suppose that ker $(f) = \{e\}$. Let $a, b \in G$ and $f(a) = f(b)$. To prove f is one-to-one, we must show that $a = b$. But if $f(a) = f(b)$, then

$$f(a * b^{-1}) = f(a) \circ f(b^{-1}) = f(a) \circ f(b)^{-1}$$
$$= f(a) \circ f(a)^{-1} = e',$$

which implies $a * b^{-1} \in$ ker (f). But, ker $(f) = \{e\}$. Therefore $a * b^{-1} = e$ or $a = b$.

The next theorem will establish the algebraic character of the pair $(\text{ker } (f), *)$.

Theorem 2–41. If f is a homomorphism from the group $(G, *)$ into the group $(G', \circ)$, then the pair $(\text{ker } (f), *)$ is a normal subgroup of $(G, *)$.

Proof. We have already indicated that the trivial subgroup $(\{e'\}, \circ)$ is a normal subgroup of $(G', \circ)$. Since ker $(f) = f^{-1}(e')$, the conclusion follows from the general result stated in part (1) of the last corollary.

Example 2–45. As a simple illustration of the above theorems, consider the two groups $(Z, +)$ and $(R^{\#} - \{0\}, \cdot)$. The mapping $f: Z \to R^{\#} - \{0\}$ defined by

$$f(n) = \begin{cases} 1 & \text{if } n \in Z_e, \\ -1 & \text{if } n \in Z_o \end{cases}$$

is a homomorphism, as the reader may verify by checking the various cases that could arise. In the situation considered,

$$\text{ker } (f) = \{n \in Z \mid f(n) = 1\} = Z_e,$$

while the direct image

$$f(Z) = \{1, -1\}.$$

It is not particularly difficult to show that $(Z_e, +)$ is a normal subgroup of $(Z, +)$ and that $(\{1, -1\}, \cdot)$ is a subgroup of $(R^{\#} - \{0\}, \cdot)$.

We have just seen that every homomorphism determines a normal subgroup by means of its kernel. On the other hand, the following theorem will show that every normal subgroup gives rise to a homomorphic mapping, the so-called natural mapping. Simply put, the problems of finding homomorphisms and normal subgroups are inseparable.

Theorem 2–42. Let $(H, *)$ be a normal subgroup of the group $(G, *)$. Then the mapping $\mathrm{nat}_H \colon G \to G/H$ defined by

$$\mathrm{nat}_H(a) = a * H$$

is a homomorphism from $(G, *)$ onto the quotient group $(G/H, \otimes)$; the kernel of nat_H is precisely the set H.

Proof. The fact that the mapping nat_H is homomorphic follows directly from the manner in which multiplication is defined in the quotient group:

$$\mathrm{nat}_H(a * b) = (a * b) * H$$
$$= (a * H) \otimes (b * H) = \mathrm{nat}_H(a) \otimes \mathrm{nat}_H(b).$$

To show that nat_H is an onto function is almost trivial, since every element of G/H is a coset $a * H$ where $a \in G$ and $\mathrm{nat}_H(a) = a * H$.

Inasmuch as the coset H serves as the identity element for $(G/H, \otimes)$, we must have

$$\mathrm{ker}\,(\mathrm{nat}_H) = \{a \in G \mid \mathrm{nat}_H(a) = H\}$$
$$= \{a \in G \mid a * H = H\} = H.$$

The last equality was achieved by the use of Theorem 2–26.

It is possible, and sometimes convenient, to phrase Theorem 2–42 so that no reference is made to the notion of quotient group:

Theorem 2–43. Let $(H, *)$ be a normal subgroup of the group $(G, *)$. Then there exists a group $(G', \circ)$, and a homomorphism f from $(G, *)$ onto $(G', \circ)$ such that $\mathrm{ker}\,(f) = H$.

Of course, we take $(G', \circ)$ to be the quotient group $(G/H, \otimes)$ and $f = \mathrm{nat}_H$.

The usual custom is to refer to the function nat_H as the *natural or canonical mapping* of G onto G/H. Provided there is no danger of confusion, we shall frequently omit the subscript H in writing this function.

As a related remark, it might be emphasized that the natural mapping is not generally one-to-one. For if $a,\ b \in G$ are elements such that the product $a^{-1} * b$ is in H, then by Theorem 2–27, $a * H = b * H$, and consequently $\mathrm{nat}_H(a) = \mathrm{nat}_H(b)$.

Let us pause for a moment to interpret Theorem 2–42 in the case of the additive group of integers $(Z, +)$. We already know that its normal subgroups are the cyclic groups $((n), +)$, where n is a nonnegative integer. Moreover, the quotient group corresponding to any fixed $n \in Z_+$ is simply $(Z_n, +_n)$, the group of integers modulo n; that is, $Z/(n) = Z_n$. It is fairly evident from this that the natural mapping $\mathrm{nat}\colon Z \to Z_n$ does nothing more than send each integer into its congruence class modulo n: $\mathrm{nat}\,(a) = [a]$.

Definition 2–29. Two groups $(G, *)$ and $(G', \circ)$ are said to be *isomorphic*, denoted $(G, *) \simeq (G', \circ)$, if there exists a one-to-one homomorphism f of $(G, *)$ onto $(G', \circ)$, that is, $f(G) = G'$. Such a homomorphism f is called an *isomorphism*, or isomorphic mapping, of $(G, *)$ onto $(G', \circ)$.

Any property of $(G, *)$ which can be expressed in terms of the operation $*$ is preserved under f and consequently becomes a property of $(G', \circ)$ as well. The upshot is that the mapping f has the effect of transferring the algebraic structure of the group $(G, *)$ to the group $(G', \circ)$. Isomorphic groups are thus indistinguishable from the abstract point of view, even though they may differ in the notation for and nature of their elements and operations. Two such groups, while not in general formally identical, are the same for all practical purposes.

Actually, the concept of isomorphism is applicable to all types of mathematical systems, for it seems reasonable to treat two systems as essentially equal when they have exactly the same properties. The essence of the notion is that we can always find a one-to-one mapping between the elements of the two systems which preserves whatever structure we are interested in studying.

The observant reader probably noticed that Definition 2–29 is unsymmetric in that it makes mention of a function from one particular group to another. However, if $f: G \to G'$ is a one-to-one, onto, operation-preserving mapping, the function $f^{-1}: G' \to G$ also has these properties. We may therefore ignore this initial lack of symmetry and merely speak of two groups $(G, *)$ and $(G', \circ)$ as being isomorphic to each other; to indicate this, it suffices to write either $(G, *) \simeq (G', \circ)$ or $(G', \circ) \simeq (G, *)$.

Before proceeding further, a knowledge of several specific examples will provide some basis for an understanding of the general idea of isomorphism.

Example 2–46. Consider the two groups $(Z_4, +_4)$ and $(G, \cdot)$, where

$$G = \{1, -1, i, -i\}$$

and $i^2 = -1$. The operation tables for these two systems are

$+_4$	0	1	2	3		$\cdot$	1	-1	i	$-i$
0	0	1	2	3		1	1	-1	i	$-i$
1	1	2	3	0		-1	-1	1	$-i$	i
2	2	3	0	1		i	i	$-i$	-1	1
3	3	0	1	2		$-i$	$-i$	i	1	-1

We wish to prove that the groups $(Z_4, +_4)$ and $(G, \cdot)$ are abstractly "equal." To do so, we must produce a one-to-one homomorphism f from Z_4 onto G.

Since the preservation of identity elements is a general feature of any homomorphism, f must be such that $f(0) = 1$. Let us suppose for the moment that we were to define $f(1) = -1$. The image of an inverse element must equal the inverse of the image. We would then have

$$f(3) = f(1^{-1}) = f(1)^{-1} = (-1)^{-1} = -1,$$

or $f(3) = f(1)$. This, however, would prevent f from being one-to-one.

A more appropriate choice, in the sense that it avoids the above difficulty, is to take $f(1) = i$. The condition on inverses then implies $f(3) = -i$. Since f is further required to preserve modular addition,

$$f(2) = f(1 +_4 1) = f(1) \cdot f(1) = i \cdot i = -1.$$

We are thus led in a natural way to consider the function defined by

$$f(0) = 1, \qquad f(1) = i, \qquad f(2) = 1, \qquad f(3) = -i.$$

Clearly this function is a one-to-one mapping of the set Z_4 onto the set G. Furthermore, f actually preserves the operations of the groups. Merely to verify one instance, we observe that

$$f(1 +_4 2) = f(3) = -i = i \cdot -1 = f(1) \cdot f(2).$$

Consequently, we have $(Z_4, +_4) \simeq (G, \cdot)$.

Loosely speaking, two finite groups are isomorphic if it is possible to obtain each multiplication table from the other by merely renaming the elements. The nature of the function f suggests the appropriate rearrangement of the table for $(G, \cdot)$ is

$\cdot$	1	i	-1	$-i$
1	1	i	-1	$-i$
i	i	-1	$-i$	1
-1	-1	$-i$	1	i
$-i$	$-i$	1	i	-1

Apart from the particular symbols used, this group table is identical to that of $(Z_4, +_4)$, for corresponding elements appear at the same place in each table. Both groups are simply disguises for the same abstract system.

In passing, we might note that $(Z_4, +_4)$ is also isomorphic to $(G, \cdot)$ under the function g, whereby $g(0) = 1$, $g(1) = -i$, $g(2) = -1$, $g(3) = i$.

Example 2–47. Let $G = \{e, a, b, c\}$ and the operation $*$ be defined by the table at the right. The reader may verify that the pair $(G, *)$ is a group, known as Klein's four-group. The two groups $(Z_4, +_4)$ and $(G, *)$ are not abstractly equal, however, for every one-to-one function f from the set Z_4 onto G fails to be operation-preserving.

$*$	e	a	b	c
e	e	a	b	c
a	a	e	c	b
b	b	c	e	a
c	c	b	a	e

From this we conclude that there are at least two distinct algebraic structures for groups with four elements.

To illustrate this point, we shall check several possibilities for the function f. Consider the mapping defined on the set Z_4 by

$$f(0) = e, \qquad f(1) = a, \qquad f(2) = b, \qquad f(3) = c.$$

Then

$$f(1 +_4 3) = f(0) = e \neq b = a * c = f(1) * f(3),$$

which shows that the proposed f is not a homomorphism. Another possibility for f might be

$$f(0) = e, \qquad f(1) = b, \qquad f(2) = c, \qquad f(3) = a.$$

Note that we must always map identity elements to identify elements. This choice of f also fails to preserve the operations, since

$$f(1 +_4 1) = f(2) = c \neq e = b * b = f(1) * f(1).$$

We shall leave the test of the remaining possibilities as an exercise.

A standard procedure for showing that two groups are not isomorphic is to find some property of one, not possessed by the other, which by its nature would necessarily be shared if these groups were actually isomorphic. In the present case, the group $(Z_4, +_4)$ and the four-group are differentiated by the fact the former is a cyclic group whereas the latter is not.

Example 2–48. The two groups $(Z, +)$ and $(Q - \{0\}, \cdot)$ are not isomorphic. To see this, suppose that there exists a one-to-one onto function $f: Z \to Q - \{0\}$ with the property

$$f(a + b) = f(a) \cdot f(b)$$

for all a, $b \in Z$. If x denotes the element of Z such that $f(x) = -1$, then

$$f(2x) = f(x + x) = f(x) \cdot f(x) = (-1) \cdot (-1) = 1.$$

According to Theorem 2–40, the identity element of $(Z, +)$ is the unique element of Z corresponding to the identity of $(Q - \{0\}, \cdot)$, so that $2x = 0$ or $x = 0$. Consequently, both $f(0) = 1$, and $f(0) = -1$, contradicting the fact that the function f is one-to-one. This argument shows that $(Z, +)$ cannot be isomorphic to $(Q - \{0\}, \cdot)$, for no function satisfying Definition 2–29 can exist.

Example 2–49. For an instructive example in connection with the additive group of integers consider the following assertion: the only functions under which $(Z, +)$ is isomorphic to itself are the identity mapping and its negative. A fairly succinct description of all this is that $A(Z) = \{i_Z, -i_Z\}$.

Perhaps the quickest proof of the above assertion consists of showing that if $f \in A(Z)$, then the cyclic subgroup $((f(1)), +)$ generated by $f(1)$ is the group $(Z, +)$ itself. Since the inclusion $(f(1)) \subseteq Z$ trivially holds, our aim would be achieved by establishing $Z \subseteq (f(1))$. But this is a straightforward matter. If n is an arbitrary integer, $n = f(m)$ for some $m \in Z$—recall f is a mapping onto Z—so that

$$\begin{aligned} n &= f(1 + 1 + \cdots + 1) \qquad (m \text{ summands}) \\ &= f(1) + f(1) + \cdots + f(1) \\ &= m\,f(1), \end{aligned}$$

whence $n \in (f(1))$.

Since 1 and -1 are the only generators of $(Z, +)$, either $f(1) = 1$ or $f(1) = -1$. However, the preceding computation indicates $f(n) = nf(1)$ for each $n \in Z$; from this, it is clear that $f = i_Z$ or $f = -i_Z$ according as $f(1) = 1$ or $f(1) = -1$.

Let us return to general considerations by showing that the groups $(Z_n, +_n)$ and $(Z, +)$ are the prototypes of all finite and infinite cyclic groups, respectively.

Theorem 2–44. Every finite cyclic group of order n is isomorphic to $(Z_n, +_n)$ and every infinite cyclic group is isomorphic to $(Z, +)$.

Proof. First, suppose the cyclic group $((a), *)$ is of finite order n. In this case, we know from Theorem 2–23 that

$$(a) = \{e, a, a^2, \ldots, a^{n-1}\}.$$

It seems natural then to investigate the mapping $f \colon (a) \to Z_n$ given by the rule $f(a^k) = [k]$, $0 \le k < n$. This function plainly carries (a) onto the set Z_n. Next observe that f is one-to-one: if $f(a^k) = f(a^j)$, then $k \equiv j \pmod{n}$ so that $a^k = a^j$. Finally, for any elements a^k, a^j in (a), we have

$$f(a^k * a^j) = f(a^{k+j}) = [k + j] = [k] +_n [j] = f(a^k) +_n f(a^j).$$

This shows the function f preserves the respective group operations and completes the proof of the isomorphism $((a), *) \simeq (Z_n, +_n)$.

For the second part of the theorem, the cyclic group $((a), *)$ is assumed to be of infinite order. Here, the choice of a mapping f between (a) and Z is obvious: simply take $f(a^k) = k$. It is immediate that f, so defined, is an onto mapping. Further, this function is one-to-one, for all the powers of the generator must be distinct; if two different powers of a were equal, the argument of Theorem 2–23 could be employed to obtain the contradiction that (a) is a finite set. The rest is routine:

$$f(a^k * a^j) = f(a^{k+j}) = k + j = f(a^k) + f(a^j).$$

Hence, as we wished to establish, $((a), *)$ is isomorphic to the group $(Z, +)$.

Corollary. Any two cyclic groups of the same order are isomorphic.

Trivially, any group $(G, *)$ is isomorphic to itself under the identity mapping i_G. A reasonable query is whether $(G, *)$ is isomorphic to any group other than itself. The concluding theorem in this section, a classical result due to Cayley, answers the question in the affirmative.

We begin, however, by recalling some definitions and notation. For an arbitrary element a in G, the left-multiplication function $f_a: G \to G$ was defined by taking $f_a(x) = a * x$ for every $x \in G$. The collection of all functions obtained in this way is labeled by $F_G: F_G = \{f_a \mid a \in G\}$. Example 2–25 established the structural nature of the pair $(F_G, \circ)$—in the present context $\circ$ indicates the operation of functional composition—when this system was shown to be a group. Our task now is to prove the isomorphism of $(G, *)$ and $(F_G, \circ)$.

Theorem 2–45. *(Cayley).* If $(G, *)$ is an arbitrary group, then

$$(G, *) \simeq (F_G, \circ).$$

Proof. Define the mapping $f: G \to F_G$ by the rule $f(a) = f_a$ for each $a \in G$. That the function f is onto F_G is obvious. If $f(a) = f(b)$, so $f_a = f_b$, then $a * x = b * x$ for all elements x of G. In particular,

$$a = a * e = b * e = b,$$

which shows that f is one-to-one. We complete the proof by establishing that f is a homomorphism:

$$f(a * b) = f_{a*b} = f_a \circ f_b = f(a) \circ f(b).$$

As an illustration of this theorem, consider the group $(R^\#, +)$. Corresponding to an element $a \in R^\#$ is the left-multiplication function f_a, defined by

$$f_a(x) = a + x, \qquad x \in R^\#.$$

That is, the function f_a merely has the effect of translating or shifting elements by an amount a. Cayley's Theorem asserts that the group $(R^\#, +)$ and the group $(F_G, \circ)$ of translations of the real line are indistinguishable as far as their algebraic properties are concerned.

PROBLEMS

1. In the following situations, determine whether the indicated function f is a homomorphism from the first group into the second group.

a) $f(a) = -a$, $(R^\#, +)$, $(R^\#, +)$

b) $f(a) = |a|$, $(R^\# - \{0\}, \cdot)$, $(R^\#_+, \cdot)$

c) $f(a) = a + 1$, $(Z, +)$, $(Z, +)$

d) $f(a) = a^2$, $(R^{\#} - \{0\}, \cdot)$, $(R^{\#}_{+}, \cdot)$

e) $f(a) = a/q$ (q a fixed nonzero integer), $(Z, +)$, $(Q, +)$

f) $f(a) = na$ (n a fixed integer), $(Z, +)$, $(Z, +)$

2. Suppose f is a homomorphism from the group $(G, *)$ into the group $(G', \circ)$:

   a) If e designates the identity element of $(G, *)$, show that the kernel of f may be described by ker $(f) = f^{-1}(f(e))$.

   b) Provided the group $(G', \circ)$ is commutative, establish the inclusion $[G, G] \subseteq$ ker (f).

3. Let $(Z_8, +_8)$ be the group of integers modulo 8 and $((a), *)$ be any finite cyclic group of order 12. Assume further that the mapping $f: Z_8 \to (a)$ is defined as follows:

$$f(0) = f(4) = e, \qquad f(1) = f(5) = a^3,$$

$$f(2) = f(6) = a^6, \qquad f(3) = f(7) = a^9.$$

   a) Prove that the function f, so defined, is a homomorphism.

   b) Describe the subgroups $(\ker (f), +_8)$ and $(f(Z_8), *)$.

   c) If $H = \{e, a^6\}$, show the pair $(f^{-1}(H), +_8)$ is a subgroup of $(Z_8, +_8)$.

4. Consider the two groups $(Z, +)$ and $(\{1, -1, i, -i\}, \cdot)$, where $i^2 = -1$. Show that the mapping defined by $f(n) = i^n$ for $n \in Z$ is a homomorphism from $(Z, +)$ onto $(\{1, -1, i, -i\}, \cdot)$, and determine its kernel.

5. Let f be a homomorphism from the group $(G, *)$ into itself and let H denote the set of elements of G which are left fixed by f:

$$H = \{a \in G \mid f(a) = a\}.$$

Prove that $(H, *)$ is a subgroup of $(G, *)$.

6. Let $(G, *)$ be a group and the element $a \in G$ be fixed. Prove that $(G, *)$ is isomorphic to itself—that is, $(G, *) \simeq (G, *)$— under the mapping f defined by

$$f(x) = a * x * a^{-1}, \qquad x \in G.$$

What is the kernel of this function?

7. Prove that if the group $(G, *)$ is commutative (cyclic) and $(G, *) \simeq (G', \circ)$ then the group $(G', \circ)$ is also commutative (cyclic).

8. Let the set $G = Z \times Z$ and the binary operation $*$ on G be given by the rule $(a, b) * (c, d) = (a + c, b + d)$. It is easily verified that the pair $(G, *)$ is a commutative group.

   a) Show that the mapping $f: G \to Z$ defined by $f[(a, b)] = a$ is a homomorphism from $(G, *)$ onto the group $(Z, +)$.

   b) Determine the kernel of this mapping.

   c) If $H = \{(a, a) \mid a \in Z\}$, prove that $(H, *)$ is a subgroup of $(G, *)$, which is isomorphic to $(Z, +)$ under the function f.

9. Show that the two groups $(R^{\#}, +)$ and $(R^{\#} - \{0\}, \cdot)$ are not isomorphic.

10. Prove that all finite groups of order two are isomorphic.

11. If

$$G = \left\{ 1, \frac{-1 + i\sqrt{3}}{2}, \frac{-1 - i\sqrt{3}}{2} \right\},$$

where $i^2 = -1$, then the pair $(G, \cdot)$ forms a group. Determine whether $(G, \cdot) \simeq (Z_3, +_3)$.

12. Let f and g be two homomorphisms from the group $(G, *)$ into the group $(G', \circ)$. Define the function $h \colon G \to G'$ by

$$h(a) = f(a) \circ g(a).$$

Show that if the group $(G', \circ)$ is commutative, then h is also a homomorphism.

13. Consider the following two groups: $(G_1, *)$, where

$$G_1 = \{ R_{180}, R_{360}, H, V \},$$

and the operation $*$ consists of following one symmetry of the square by another; $(G_2, \circ)$, where G_2 consists of the four functions on $R^{\#} - \{0\}$,

$$f_1(x) = x, \qquad f_2(x) = -x, \qquad f_3(x) = 1/x, \qquad f_4(x) = -1/x,$$

and $\circ$ denotes functional composition. Verify that $(G_1, *) \simeq (G_2, \circ)$.

14. Given f is a homomorphism from a simple group $(G, *)$ onto a group $(G', \circ)$, show that either $(G, *) \simeq (G', \circ)$ or else that f must be the trivial homomorphism.

15. Let $(G, *)$ be an arbitrary group and j be the mapping of the set G onto itself defined by $j(a) = a^{-1}$, for all $a \in G$.

   a) Prove that the function j is a homomorphism if and only if $(G, *)$ is commutative.

   b) Generalize the result of Example 2–49 to the following: if $(G, *)$ is an infinite cyclic group, then $A(G) = \{i_G, j\}$.

16. Prove that any group $(G, *)$ is isomorphic to some subgroup of its symmetric group (sym $G, \circ$). [*Hint:* Use Theorem 2–45.]

17. Obtain the group of left-multiplication functions corresponding to the group $(Z_5, +_5)$; set up the homomorphism which results in the isomorphism of these groups.

2–7 THE FUNDAMENTAL THEOREMS

In this section, we shall discuss a number of significant results having to do with the relationship between homomorphisms and quotient groups. Of these, Theorem 2–47, generally known as the Fundamental Homomorphism Theorem for Groups, is perhaps the most crucial. The importance of this result would be difficult to overemphasize; in a sense, all which follows thereafter may be viewed as an enumeration of its special cases and implications.

Throughout this section, f denotes a homomorphism from the group $(G, *)$ onto the group $(G', \circ)$, that is, $f(G) = G'$. In order to simplify the statements of

various theorems, we shall frequently not trouble to specify this familiar open-
ing phrase. Accordingly, unless there is clear indication to the contrary, any
reference to the function f is understood implicitly to involve the aforementioned
hypothesis.

We begin with a proof of the Factor Theorem, stated here in a form best
suited to our immediate needs.

Theorem 2–46. (*Factor Theorem*). Let $(H, *)$ be a normal subgroup of
the group $(G, *)$ such that $H \subseteq \ker (f)$. Then there exists a unique homomorphism $\bar{f}: G/H \to G'$ with the property

$$f = \bar{f} \circ \mathrm{nat}_H.$$

Proof. Before becoming explicit in the details of the proof, let us remind the
reader that the symbol nat_H designates the natural mapping of G onto G/H;
that is, $\mathrm{nat}_H: G \to G/H$ with $\mathrm{nat}_H(a) = a * H$.

To start with, we define a function $\bar{f}: G/H \to G'$, called the *induced mapping*,
by taking

$$\bar{f}(a * H) = f(a), \qquad a \in G.$$

The first question to be raised concerns whether or not $\bar{f}$ is actually well-defined.
In other words, it must be established that this function depends only on the
cosets of H and in no way on the particular representative used. To see that
this is so, suppose $a * H = b * H$. As the elements a and b belong to the same
coset, the product $a^{-1} * b \in H \subseteq \ker (f)$. This means that

$$f(b) = f(a * a^{-1} * b) = f(a) \circ f(a^{-1} * b) = f(a) \circ e' = f(a),$$

and, by the manner in which $\bar{f}$ is defined, that

$$\bar{f}(a * H) = \bar{f}(b * H).$$

Hence, the function $\bar{f}$ is constant on the cosets of H, as we wished to demonstrate.

A routine computation, involving the definition of multiplication in $(G/H, \otimes)$,
shows $\bar{f}$ to be a homomorphism:

$$
\begin{aligned}
\bar{f}((a * H) \otimes (b * H)) &= \bar{f}((a * b) * H) \\
&= f(a * b) \\
&= f(a) \circ f(b) = \bar{f}(a * H) \circ \bar{f}(b * H).
\end{aligned}
$$

Next, we observe that for each element $a \in G$,

$$f(a) = \bar{f}(a * H) = \bar{f}(\mathrm{nat}_H(a)) = (\bar{f} \circ \mathrm{nat}_H)(a),$$

whence the equality $f = \bar{f} \circ \mathrm{nat}_H$. The proof is completed upon showing that
this factorization is unique. Thus, suppose also that $f = g \circ \mathrm{nat}_H$ for some other

function $g: G/H \to G'$. But then,

$$\bar{f}(a * H) = f(a) = (g \circ \mathrm{nat}_H)(a) = g(a * H)$$

for all a in G, so $\bar{f} = g$. The induced mapping $\bar{f}$ is therefore seen to be the only function from G/H to G' satisfying the equation $f = \bar{f} \circ \mathrm{nat}_H$.

   Corollary. The function $\bar{f}$ is one-to-one if and only if $\ker(f) \subseteq H$.

Proof. What is required here is an explicit description of the kernel of $\bar{f}$:

$$\begin{aligned}
\ker(\bar{f}) &= \{a * H \mid \bar{f}(a * H) = e'\} \\
&= \{a * H \mid f(a) = e'\},
\end{aligned}$$

where, of course, e' denotes the identity of the group $(G', \circ)$. Another way of saying the same thing is

$$\ker(\bar{f}) = \{a * H \mid a \in \ker(f)\} = \mathrm{nat}_H(\ker(f)).$$

Now, from Theorem 2–40, a necessary and sufficient condition for $\bar{f}$ to be a one-to-one mapping is that $\ker(\bar{f}) = e * H = H$. In the present situation, this condition reduces to requiring that

$$\mathrm{nat}_H(\ker(f)) = H,$$

which is equivalent to the inclusion $\ker(f) \subseteq H$.

   In view of the equality $f = \bar{f} \circ \mathrm{nat}_H$, the conclusion of Theorem 2–46 is often described by saying that the function f can be factored through the quotient group $(G/H, \otimes)$ or, alternatively, that f can be factored by nat_H. The following diagram may help to clarify the relations among the various functions:

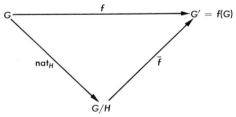

What we have just proved, in effect, is that there exists one and only one function $\bar{f}$ which makes this triangle of maps commutative.

Example 2–50. Let us cite a specific instance of the Factor Theorem. Our contention is that whenever the group $(G', \circ)$ is commutative, the function f can always be factored through the commutator quotient group $(G/[G, G], \otimes)$; otherwise stated,

$$f = \bar{f} \circ \mathrm{nat}_{[G,G]}.$$

For this, consider any commutator $[a, b] = a * b * a^{-1} * b^{-1}$, with a, $b \in G$. As a consequence of the commutativity of $(G', \circ)$,

$$f([a, b]) = [f(a), f(b)] = e',$$

so that $[a, b] \in \ker (f)$. Now, the commutator subgroup $([G, G], *)$ is, so to speak, the smallest subgroup of $(G, *)$ to contain all the commutators. Thus we must conclude that $[G, G] \subseteq \ker (f)$. Having this inclusion, it is only necessary to apply Theorem 2–46 to obtain the desired factorization.

Although we did not expressly require the information in the proof of Theorem 2–46, it might be pointed out that the induced mapping $\bar{f}$ carries G/H onto the set G'. This is readily obtainable from the definition of $\bar{f}$ and the fact f itself is an onto function. To be more specific, if $a' \in G'$, then $a' = f(a)$ for some element a in G; hence,

$$a' = f(a) = \bar{f}(a * H).$$

A rather simple observation, with far-reaching implications, is that whenever $H = \ker (f)$, so that both the Factor Theorem and its corollary are applicable, f induces a mapping $\bar{f}$ under which $(G/H, \otimes)$ and $(G', \circ)$ are isomorphic groups.

The discussion of the foregoing paragraph may be conveniently summarized in the following theorem, a result which will be invoked repeatedly.

Theorem 2–47. (*Fundamental Theorem*). If f is a homomorphism from the group $(G, *)$ onto the group $(G', \circ)$, then

$$(G/\ker (f), \otimes) \simeq (G', \circ).$$

Remark. If in the statement of the theorem, the word "onto" is replaced by "into," the conclusion takes the form $(G/\ker (f), \otimes) \simeq (f(G), \circ)$.

Theorem 2–47 is admittedly rather technical in nature and therefore perhaps a brief explanation of its significance is in order. Suppose that $(G, *)$ is an unfamiliar group whose algebraic properties we wish to determine. Clearly, if $(G, *)$ could be shown to be isomorphic to some well-known group $(G', \circ)$, then our problem is solved; for $(G, *)$, being a replica of $(G', \circ)$, would possess the same algebraic structure.

Another approach, which usually gives a less complete picture of $(G, *)$ is to examine its images under homomorphisms. The difficulty here, of course, is that when these functions fail to be one-to-one, not all the algebraic properties of the images are reflected in the original group. For instance, it is quite possible for the commutative law to hold in an image group without $(G, *)$ itself being commutative. Theorem 2–47 asserts that the images of $(G, *)$ under homomorphisms can be duplicated up to isomorphism by quotient groups of $(G, *)$. In a sense, it is not necessary to go beyond $(G, *)$ to obtain all its images under homomorphic mappings.

Example 2–51. A simple, but illuminating, example of the Fundamental Theorem is furnished by the groups $(Z, +)$, $(\{1, -1\}, \cdot)$, and the homomorphism $f: Z \to \{1, -1\}$, where

$$f(n) = \begin{cases} 1 & \text{if} \quad n \in Z_e, \\ -1 & \text{if} \quad n \in Z_o. \end{cases}$$

Here, the kernel of f is the set Z_e, so that

$$Z/\ker (f) = Z/Z_e = \{Z_e, Z_o\}.$$

The Fundamental Theorem then guarantees that $(\{Z_e, Z_o\}, \otimes)$ and $(\{1, -1\}, \cdot)$ are isomorphic groups—indeed, this is fairly evident from an inspection of their multiplication tables:

$\otimes$	Z_e	Z_o
Z_e	Z_e	Z_o
Z_o	Z_o	Z_e

$\cdot$	1	-1
1	1	-1
-1	-1	1

Further, the proof of the theorem indicates that the function $\bar{f}$ which actually establishes this isomorphism (the induced mapping) is given by

$$\bar{f}(Z_e) = \bar{f}(0 + Z_e) = f(0) = 1,$$
$$\bar{f}(Z_o) = \bar{f}(1 + Z_e) = f(1) = -1.$$

Example 2–52. For a more penetrating example, consider an arbitrary group $(G, *)$ and a fixed element $a \in G$. Define the mapping $f: Z \to G$ by the rule $f(n) = a^n$, $n \in Z$. It is not difficult to check that f, so defined, is a homomorphic mapping from the additive group of integers $(Z, +)$ onto the cyclic subgroup $((a), *)$. Hence, by virtue of Theorem 2–47,

$$(Z/\ker (f), \otimes) \simeq ((a), *),$$

where, in the situation at hand,

$$\ker (f) = \{n \in Z \mid a^n = e\}.$$

Now, two possibilities arise according to the magnitude of the kernel, the first being that $\ker (f) = \{0\}$; in other words, $a^n = e$ implies $n = 0$. Under the circumstances, $(Z/\ker (f), \otimes)$ is just the group $(Z, +)$ itself. On the other hand, if $\ker (f) \neq \{0\}$, there exists some least positive integer n for which $a^n = e$. One can easily deduce from this that $\ker (f) = (n)$, so we must have $(Z/\ker (f), \otimes) = (Z_n, +_n)$.

In summary, the preceding discussion reveals that (1) if the generator a is of infinite order, then $((a), *) \simeq (Z, +)$, and (2) if a is of finite order n, then

$((a), *) \simeq (Z_n, +_n)$.   These facts are already familiar, of course, but the argument involved furnishes an alternative approach to Theorem 2–44.

The next theorem not only provides further evidence of the power of the Fundamental Theorem, but is of independent interest since it gives additional insight into the structure of the quotient group $(G/\text{cent } G, \otimes)$.   To prepare the way, it is necessary to digress for a moment.

Given a fixed element a of the group $(G, *)$, define the mapping $\sigma_a \colon G \to G$ by taking

$$\sigma_a(x) = a * x * a^{-1}$$

for every x in G.   Let us obtain a few of the special properties of this function. First, σ_a turns out to be a homomorphism: if $x_1, x_2 \in G$, then

$$\sigma_a(x_1 * x_2) = a * (x_1 * x_2) * a^{-1}$$
$$= (a * x_1 * a^{-1}) * (a * x_1 * a^{-1}) = \sigma_a(x_1) * \sigma_a(x_2).$$

The next thing to notice is that σ_a maps the set G onto itself; specifically, for any element $x \in G$, $\sigma_a(a^{-1} * x * a) = x$.   Finally, it can be proved that σ_a is actually a one-to-one function.   For this purpose, assume $\sigma_a(x_1) = \sigma_a(x_2)$, so that $a * x_1 * a^{-1} = a * x_2 * a^{-1}$.   The superfluous elements may be removed through the cancellation law, allowing us then to conclude that $x_1 = x_2$.   All of these observations may be conveniently summarized by saying that

$$\sigma_a \in A(G).$$

Functions of the form σ_a, with $a \in G$, are usually called *inner automorphisms* of the group $(G, *)$; to be more precise, σ_a is the inner automorphism induced by the element a.   For brevity, we label the set of functions arising in this way by $I(G)$:

$$I(G) = \{\sigma_a \mid a \in G\}.$$

In the case of a commutative group, $I(G)$ reduces to just the identity mapping $i_G = \sigma_e$.   Thus, it is only when $(G, *)$ is noncommutative that the notion becomes meaningful.

Lemma. The pair $(I(G), \circ)$ constitutes a group, known as the *group of inner automorphisms* of $(G, *)$; in fact, $(I(G), \circ)$ is a normal subgroup of $(A(G), \circ)$.

Proof. The proof that $(I(G), \circ)$ is a group presents no difficulties; it consists of nothing more than noticing that whenever $\sigma_a, \sigma_b \in I(G)$,

$$\sigma_a \circ \sigma_b = \sigma_{a*b}.$$

In addition to disposing of the closure condition, this relation also indicates σ_e is the identity element for the system and $\sigma_a^{-1} = \sigma_{a^{-1}}$.

Regarding the second assertion, it suffices to show that if $f \in A(G)$, the product $f \circ \sigma_a \circ f^{-1}$ is an inner automorphism. The argument proceeds as follows: for each element x in G,

$$(f \circ \sigma_a \circ f^{-1})(x) = f\big(\sigma_a(f^{-1}(x))\big)$$
$$= f(a * f^{-1}(x) * a^{-1})$$
$$= f(a) * f\big(f^{-1}(x)\big) * f(a^{-1})$$
$$= f(a) * x * f(a)^{-1} = \sigma_{f(a)}(x).$$

The reasons for each of these steps are reasonably self-evident, and the reader should make sure he understands them. What is significant is that

$$f \circ \sigma_a \circ f^{-1} = \sigma_{f(a)} \in I(G),$$

as was to be proved.

We are now in a position to obtain the result which has been our goal. Namely, that the groups $(G/\text{cent } G, \otimes)$ and $(I(G), \circ)$ resemble each other in all essential aspects.

Theorem 2–48. For each group $(G, *)$, $(G/\text{cent } G, \otimes) \simeq (I(G), \circ)$.

Proof. To begin, consider the mapping $g: G \to I(G)$ whereby $g(a) = \sigma_a$. That this function maps G onto the set $I(G)$ is quite plain. It is equally easy to see that g is a homomorphism, since

$$g(a * b) = \sigma_{a*b} = \sigma_a \circ \sigma_b = g(a) \circ g(b), \qquad a, b \in G.$$

The crucial aspect of the proof is now to show that $\ker (g) = \text{cent } G$; once this is done, the desired conclusion will follow immediately from the Fundamental Theorem.

In the case at hand, the inner automorphism σ_e serves as the identity element for the group $(I(G), \circ)$. Accordingly, the kernel of the function g is defined by

$$\ker (g) = \{a \in G \mid g(a) = \sigma_e\}$$
$$= \{a \in G \mid \sigma_a = i_G\}.$$

Referring to the definition of equality of functions, we conclude that $a \in \ker (g)$ if and only if

$$a * x * a^{-1} = x$$

for every x in G. But this is obviously equivalent to demanding the element a be such that $a * x = x * a$ for all $x \in G$, or what amounts to the same thing, that $a \in \text{cent } G$.

Returning to the general development, once again let f be a homomorphism from the group $(G, *)$ onto the group $(G', \circ)$. We have already noticed that every subgroup $(H, *)$ of the group $(G, *)$ determines a subgroup $(f(H), \circ)$ of the group $(G', \circ)$. It goes without saying that group theory would be considerably simplified if the subgroups of $(G, *)$ were in a one-to-one correspondence with those of $(G', \circ)$ in this manner. Unfortunately, this need not be the case.

The situation is reflected in the fact that if $(H, *)$ and $(K, *)$ are two subgroups of $(G, *)$ with $H \subseteq K \subseteq H * \ker (f)$, then $(f(H), *) = (f(K), *)$. The quickest way to see this is to note that

$$f(H) \subseteq f(K) \subseteq f(H * \ker (f)) = f(H) \circ f(\ker (f)) = f(H),$$

from which we infer that all the inclusions are actually equalities. In essence, we are observing that distinct subsets of G may have the same image set in G'.

The difficulty in the last paragraph could be remedied by either requiring that $\ker (f) = \{e\}$ or else by narrowing our view to consider only subgroups $(H, *)$ with $\ker (f) \subseteq H$. In either event, it follows that

$$H \subseteq K \subseteq H * \ker (f) \subseteq H,$$

yielding the subsequent equality $H = K$. The first of these aforementioned conditions has the effect of making the function f one-to-one, in which case $(G, *)$ and $(G', \circ)$ are isomorphic groups. The second possibility is the subject of the next theorem.

We pause to establish a preliminary lemma which will provide the key to later success.

Lemma. If H is any subset of G such that $\ker (f) \subseteq H$, then $H = f^{-1}(f(H))$.

Proof. Suppose the element a is in $f^{-1}(f(H))$, so that $f(a) \in f(H)$. Then $f(a) = f(h)$ for some choice of $h \in H$. As the equation $f(a) = f(h)$ is equivalent to $f(a * h^{-1}) = e'$, we have $a * h^{-1} \in \ker (f) \subseteq H$. This implies a also belongs to the set H and yields the inclusion $f^{-1}(f(H)) \subseteq H$. The opposite inclusion always holds (Theorem 1–7), whence $H = f^{-1}(f(H))$.

The relationship between the subgroups of $(G, *)$ and the subgroup of $(G', \circ)$ may be stated as follows:

Theorem 2–49. (*Correspondence Theorem*).   There is a one-to-one correspondence between those subgroups $(H, *)$ of the group $(G, *)$ such that $\ker (f) \subseteq H$ and the set of all subgroups $(H', \circ)$ of the group $(G', \circ)$; specifically, H' is given by $H' = f(H)$.

Proof. Let us first check that the indicated correspondence is onto. In other words, if $(H', \circ)$ is any subgroup of $(G', \circ)$, we must produce some subgroup $(H, *)$ of $(G, *)$ with $\ker (f) \subseteq H$ for which $f(H) \doteq H'$. To accomplish this, it is sufficient to take $H = f^{-1}(H')$. By Theorem 2–39, the pair $(f^{-1}(H'), *)$ is a subgroup of $(G, *)$ and, since $e' \in H'$,

$$\ker (f) = f^{-1}(e') \subseteq f^{-1}(H').$$

Moreover, the function f being an onto mapping, the corollary to Theorem 1–6 indicates that $f(f^{-1}(H')) = H'$.

Next, we verify that this correspondence is also one-to-one. To this end, suppose $(H_1, *)$ and $(H_2, *)$ are both subgroups of $(G, *)$ with $\ker (f) \subseteq H_1$, $\ker (f) \subseteq H_2$ and such that $f(H_1) = f(H_2)$. According to the preceding lemma, we then must have

$$H_1 = f^{-1}(f(H_1)) = f^{-1}(f(H_2)) = H_2.$$

It follows that the correspondence $(H, *) \leftrightarrow (f(H), \circ)$ is one-to-one, thereby completing the proof.

The theorem applies, in particular, to the case in which we start with a normal subgroup $(H, *)$ of $(G, *)$ and take f to be the natural mapping $\mathrm{nat}_H \colon G \to G/H$ of G onto G/H. Since $\ker (\mathrm{nat}_H) = H$, the conclusion is modified slightly.

> **Corollary.** Let $(H, *)$ be a normal subgroup of the group $(G, *)$. There is a one-to-one correspondence between those subgroups $(K, *)$ of $(G, *)$ such that $H \subseteq K$ and the set of all subgroups of the quotient group $(G/H, \otimes)$.

Before proceeding, it should be remarked that the Correspondence Theorem remains valid if we replace the term "subgroup" throughout by "normal subgroup." That is to say, there is also a one-to-one correspondence between those normal subgroups of $(G, *)$ which contain $\ker (f)$ and the set of all normal subgroups of $(G', \circ)$. The additional argument needed to establish this fact is left for the reader to supply.

Example 2–53. As an application of these ideas, consider the following statement: if $(G, *)$ is a finite cyclic group of order n, then $(G, *)$ has exactly one subgroup of order m for each positive divisor m of n and no other proper subgroups. Although there is nothing very surprising about this assertion, our aim is to demonstrate its validity by using the corollary to the Correspondence Theorem.

First observe that, since the groups $(G, *)$ and $(Z_n, +_n)$ are isomorphic, there is no loss in generality in working with $(Z_n, +_n)$. Furthermore, as we have pointed out on several occasions, $(Z_n, +_n) = (Z/(n), \otimes)$. By the corollary, we learn there is a one-to-one correspondence between those subgroups of the group $(Z, +)$ which contain the set (n) and the subgroups of $(Z_n, +_n)$.

But, the subgroups of $(Z, +)$ are just the cyclic subgroups $((m), +)$, where m is a nonnegative integer. Combining these results, we arrive at the conclusion there is a one-to-one correspondence between the subgroups of $(Z_n, +_n)$

and those subgroups $((m), +)$ of $(Z, +)$ such that $(m) \supseteq (n)$. This last inclusion occurs if and only if m divides n.

The two concluding theorems of this section are somewhat deeper results than usual and require the full force of our accumulated machinery; they comprise what are often called the First and Second Isomorphism Theorems for Groups and are of great importance in the study of group structure.

Theorem 2–50. If $(H, *)$ is any normal subgroup of the group $(G, *)$ such that $\ker (f) \subseteq H$, then $(G/H, \otimes) \simeq (G'/f(H), \otimes')$.

Proof. As a prefatory remark, we might point out that the corollary to Theorem 2–39 implies the pair $(f(H), \circ)$ is a normal subgroup of $(G', \circ)$, so that it is certainly permissible to form the quotient group $(G'/f(H), \otimes')$.

Let us now define the function $\bar{f} \colon G \to G'/f(H)$ by

$$\bar{f} = \mathrm{nat}_{f(H)} \circ f,$$

where $\mathrm{nat}_{f(H)} \colon G \to G'/f(H)$ designates the natural mapping. The following diagram helps to visualize the situation:

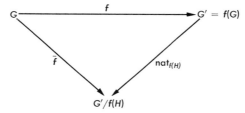

Observe that $\bar{f}$ merely assigns to each element $a \in G$ the coset $f(a) \circ f(H)$ of $G'/f(H)$. Since both the functions f and $\mathrm{nat}_{f(H)}$ are onto and operation-preserving, the composition of these gives us a homomorphic mapping from the group $(G, *)$ onto the group $(G'/f(H), \otimes')$.

The main line of the argument is to show that $\ker (\bar{f}) = H$, for then the desired result would be a simple consequence of the Fundamental Theorem. Now the identity element of $(G'/f(H), \otimes')$ is just the coset $f(H) = e' \circ f(H)$. This means the kernel of $\bar{f}$ consists of those members of G which are mapped by $\bar{f}$ onto $f(H)$; that is,

$$\begin{aligned}
\ker (\bar{f}) &= \{a \in G \mid \bar{f}(a) = f(H)\} \\
&= \{a \in G \mid f(a) \circ f(H) = f(H)\} \\
&= \{a \in G \mid f(a) \in f(H)\} = f^{-1}(f(H)).
\end{aligned}$$

As we are given that $\ker (f) \subseteq H$, the lemma preceding Theorem 2–49 may be invoked to conclude $H = f^{-1}(f(H))$. Hence, $\ker (\bar{f}) = H$, which completes the proof.

In applications of this theorem, we frequently start with an arbitrary normal subgroup of $(G', \circ)$ and utilize inverse images rather than direct images.

Corollary. If $(H', \circ)$ is any normal subgroup of the group $(G', \circ)$, then $(G/f^{-1}(H'), \otimes) \simeq (G'/H', \otimes')$.

Proof. By the corollary to Theorem 2–39, the pair $(f^{-1}(H'), *)$ is a normal subgroup of $(G, *)$. Moreover, ker $(f) \subseteq f^{-1}(H')$, so the hypothesis of the theorem is completely satisfied. This leads to the isomorphism

$$(G/f^{-1}(H'), \otimes) \simeq \big(G'/f(f^{-1}(H')), \otimes'\big).$$

Since f is a mapping onto G', $H' = f(f^{-1}(H'))$, and we are done.

Our final theorem, a rather technical result, will be crucial to the proof of the Jordan-Hölder Theorem.

Theorem 2–51. If $(H, *)$ and $(K, *)$ are subgroups of the group $(G, *)$ with $(K, *)$ normal, then $(H/H \cap K, \otimes) \simeq (H * K/K, \otimes')$.

Proof. Needless to say, it should be checked that the quotient groups appearing in the statement of the theorem are actually defined. We leave to the reader the routine task of verifying that $(H \cap K, *)$ is a normal subgroup of $(H, *)$, that $(H * K, *)$ is a group, and that $(K, *)$ is normal in $(H * K, *)$.

Our proof is patterned on that of Theorem 2–50. Here, the problem is to construct a homomorphism α from the group $(H, *)$ onto the quotient group $(H * K/K, \otimes')$ for which ker $(\alpha) = H \cap K$. To achieve this, consider the function $\alpha(h) = h * K$, $h \in H$. Note, $H = H * e \subseteq H * K$, so that α can be obtained by composing the inclusion map $i_H \colon H \to H * K$ with the natural mapping $\mathrm{nat}_K \colon H * K \to H * K/K$. In other words,

$$\alpha = \mathrm{nat}_K \circ i_H,$$

or, in diagrammatic language,

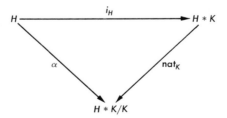

The foregoing factorization implies α is a homomorphism and $\alpha(H) = H * K/K$.

We next proceed to establish that the kernel of α is precisely the set $H \cap K$. First, observe that the coset $K = e * K$ serves as the identity element of the quotient group $(H * K/K, \otimes')$. This means

$$\mathrm{ker}\,(\alpha) = \{h \in H \mid \alpha(h) = K\} = \{h \in H \mid h * K = K\}$$
$$= \{h \in H \mid h \in K\} = H \cap K.$$

The required isomorphism is now evident from the Fundamental Theorem.

Example 2–54. As an illustration of this last result, let us return again to the group of integers $(Z, +)$ and consider the cyclic subgroups $((3), +)$ and $((4), +)$. Both these subgroups are normal, since $(Z, +)$ is a commutative group. Moreover, it is fairly obvious that

$$(3) \cap (4) = (12) \quad \text{and} \quad (3) + (4) = Z.$$

Theorem 2–51 then tells us that

$$((3)/(12), \otimes) \simeq (Z/(4), \otimes'),$$

where $\otimes$ and $\otimes'$ designate the respective quotient group operations.

The notation tends to obscure the simplicity of our conclusion. For the reader will doubtless recall that $(Z/(4), \otimes')$ is just the group of integers modulo 4. A closer examination of the cosets and operation in the system $((3)/(12), \otimes)$ reveals this to be nothing more than the group $(\{0, 3, 6, 9\}, +_{12})$. What we actually have is a disguised version of the isomorphism,

$$(\{0, 3, 6, 9\}, +_{12}) \simeq (Z_4, +_4).$$

PROBLEMS

1. Let $(G, *)$ be the group of symmetries of the square and $(G', \circ)$ be the Klein four-group (see Examples 2–24 and 2–47). The following mapping defines a homomorphism from $(G, *)$ onto $(G', \circ)$:

$$f(R_{180}) = f(R_{360}) = e, \quad f(R_{90}) = f(R_{270}) = a,$$

$$f(H) = f(V) = b, \quad f(D_1) = f(D_2) = c.$$

   a) Establish the isomorphism $(G/\text{cent } G, \otimes) \simeq (G', \circ)$.
   b) Write out the induced mapping $\bar{f}: G/\text{cent } G \to G'$ which leads to this isomorphism.

2. Prove the following generalization of the Factor Theorem: Let f_1 and f_2 be homomorphisms from the group $(G, *)$ onto the groups $(G_1, \circ_1)$ and $(G_2, \circ_2)$, respectively. If $\ker (f_1) \subseteq \ker (f_2)$, then there exists a unique homomorphism $\bar{f}: G_1 \to G_2$ satisfying $f_2 = \bar{f} \circ f_1$. Diagrammatically,

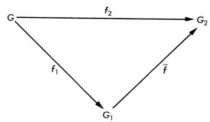

[*Hint:* Use nearly the same argument as for Theorem 2–46; that is, for any element $f_1(a) \in G_1$, define $\bar{f}$ by $\bar{f}(f_1(a)) = f_2(a)$.]

3. Deduce the Factor Theorem from the result of Problem 2.

4. Given a group $(G, *)$, establish the following facts regarding the inner automorphisms of G.

   a) Whenever $(G, *)$ is noncommutative, $I(G) \neq \{i_G\}$.

   b) If $(H, *)$ is a subgroup of $(G, *)$, then the pair $(\sigma_a(H), *)$ is also a subgroup for every $a \in G$.

   c) A subgroup $(H, *)$ is normal in $(G, *)$ if and only if the set H is mapped into itself by each inner automorphism of G.

   d) If the element $x \in G$ is such that $\sigma_a(x) = x$ for every $a \in G$, then the cyclic subgroup $((x), *)$ is normal in $(G, *)$.

5. Let $(G, *)$ be a group and the elements x, $y \in G$. We say x is *conjugate* to y, written $x \sim y$, if and only if $\sigma_a(x) = y$ for some $a \in G$. Prove that conjugation is an equivalence relation in G.

6. Obtain the isomorphism $(S_3, \circ) \simeq (I(S_3), \circ)$.

7. Assume f is a homomorphism from the group $(G, *)$ into itself having the property of commuting with every inner automorphism of G; that is, $\sigma_a \circ f = f \circ \sigma_a$ for every $a \in G$. If the set H is defined by

$$H = \{x \in G \mid f(x) = x\},$$

prove that

   a) the pair $(H, *)$ is a normal subgroup of $(G, *)$,

   b) the quotient group $(G/H, \otimes)$ is commutative. [*Hint:* $[G, G] \subseteq H$.]

8. Let $(H, *)$ be a normal subgroup of the group $(G, *)$. Further, let $(K_1, *)$ and $(K_2, *)$ be subgroups of $(G, *)$ such that $H \subseteq K_1$, $H \subseteq K_2$. Prove that $K_1 \subseteq K_2$ if and only if $\mathrm{nat}_H K_1 \subseteq \mathrm{nat}_H K_2$.

9. Given $(G, *)$ is the group of symmetries of the square. Exhibit the correspondence between those subgroups $(H, *)$ of $(G, *)$ with cent $G \subseteq H$ and the subgroups of $(G/\mathrm{cent}\ G, \otimes)$.

   In Problems 10 through 14, f denotes a homomorphism from the group $(G, *)$ onto the group $(G', \circ)$.

10. Show that the Factor Theorem implies the function f can be expressed (nontrivially) as the composition of an onto function and a one-to-one function.

11. If $(H, *)$ is a subgroup of $(G, *)$ for which $H = f^{-1}(f(H))$, verify that ker $(f) \subseteq H$. [*Hint:* $f^{-1}(f(H)) = H * \ker (f)$.]

12. For a proof of Theorem 2–50 that does not depend on the Fundamental Theorem, define the function $g: G/H \to G'/f(H)$ by taking

$$g(a * H) = f(a) \circ f(H).$$

   a) Show that g is well-defined, one-to-one, operation-preserving, and onto $G'/f(H)$; hence, $(G/H, \otimes) \simeq (G'/f(H), \otimes')$.

   b) Establish that g is the unique mapping which makes the diagram at the right commutative.

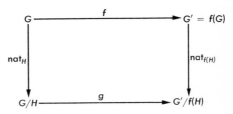

13. If ker $(f) \subseteq [G, G]$, prove that $(G/[G, G], \otimes) \simeq (G'/[G', G'], \otimes')$.

14. Suppose $(H, *)$ and $(K, *)$ are normal subgroups of the group $(G, *)$ with $H \subseteq K$. Prove that
    a) $(H, *)$ is a normal subgroup of $(K, *)$,
    b) $(K/H, \otimes)$ is a normal subgroup of the quotient group $(G/H, \otimes)$,
    c) $(G/H \ / \ K/H, \otimes') \simeq (G/K, \otimes)$.
    [*Hint:* Apply Theorem 2–50 with nat_H and $(G/H, \otimes)$ replacing f and $(G', \circ)$.]

15. Given $(H, *)$ and $(K, *)$ are subgroups of the group $(G, *)$ with $(K, *)$ normal. Assuming $H \cap K = \{e\}$, derive the isomorphism $(H, *) \simeq (H * K/K, \otimes)$.

16. In the symmetric group $(S_4, \circ)$, let the set K consist of the four permutations

$$\begin{pmatrix} 1 & 2 & 3 & 4 \\ 1 & 2 & 3 & 4 \end{pmatrix}, \quad \begin{pmatrix} 1 & 2 & 3 & 4 \\ 2 & 1 & 4 & 3 \end{pmatrix}, \quad \begin{pmatrix} 1 & 2 & 3 & 4 \\ 3 & 4 & 1 & 2 \end{pmatrix}, \quad \begin{pmatrix} 1 & 2 & 3 & 4 \\ 4 & 3 & 2 & 1 \end{pmatrix}.$$

    a) Show that the pair $(K, \circ)$ is a normal subgroup of $(S_4, \circ)$.
    b) Establish that $(S_4/K, \otimes)$ and $(S_3, \circ)$ are isomorphic groups. [*Hint:* Define $H = \{f \in S_4 \mid f(4) = 4\}$ and use Problem 15.]

17. Let $(G, *)$ and $(G', \circ)$ be two groups with identity elements e and e', respectively. Recall that their direct product is the group $(G \times G', \cdot)$, with the operation $\cdot$ defined on the Cartesian product $G \times G'$ in the natural way:

$$(a, a') \cdot (b, b') = (a * b, a' \circ b')$$

    for all $(a, a'), (b, b') \in G \times G'$. Prove the following statements:
    a) If $H = G \times e'$ and $H' = e \times G'$, then $(H, \cdot)$ and $(H', \cdot)$ are both normal subgroups of $(G \times G', \cdot)$.
    b) $(H, \cdot) \simeq (G, *)$ and $(H', \cdot) \simeq (G', \circ)$.
    c) Every element of H commutes with every element of H'.
    d) Each member of $G \times G'$ can be uniquely expressed as the product of an element of H by an element of H'.
    e) $(G \times G'/H, \otimes) \simeq (H', \cdot)$ and $(G \times G'/H', \otimes) \simeq (H, \cdot)$. Derive these isomorphisms in two ways: use the Fundamental Theorem, and then Theorem 2–51.

18. Illustrate the various parts of Problem 17 by considering the direct product of the groups $(Z_3, +_3)$ and $(Z_4, +_4)$. In addition, show that

$$(Z_3 \times Z_4, \cdot) \simeq (Z_{12}, +_{12}).$$

    [*Hint:* $(Z_3 \times Z_4, \cdot)$ is a cyclic group of order 12.]

19. Suppose $(H, *)$ and $(K, *)$ are subgroups of the group $(G, *)$ such that
    1) every element of H commutes with every element of K,
    2) every member of G can be uniquely expressed as the product of an element of H by an element of K.
    Prove that $(G, *) \simeq (H \times K, \cdot)$.

20. Illustrate the result of Problem 19 with $(Z_6, +_6)$, the group of integers modulo 6, and the two subgroups $(\{0, 3\}, +_6)$ and $(\{0, 2, 4\}, +_6)$.

21. Prove that the Klein four-group is isomorphic to $(Z_2 \times Z_2, \cdot)$.

22. Show that if m and n are relatively prime, then the direct product $(Z_m \times Z_n, \cdot)$ is a cyclic group of order mn.

2–8 THE JORDAN-HÖLDER THEOREM

As the title indicates, the main purpose of this brief section is to establish the significant and historic Jordan-Hölder Theorem. For the sake of simplicity, we shall limit ourselves to the case of finite groups; the interested reader is referred to a more general treatment in [19]. Because the theorem is rather involved, it will be convenient to begin by introducing some special terminology.

Definition 2–30. By a *chain* for a group $(G, *)$ is meant any finite sequence of subsets of G,

$$G = H_0 \supset H_1 \supset \cdots \supset H_{n-1} \supset H_n = \{e\} \qquad \text{(proper inclusions)},$$

descending from G to $\{e\}$ with the property that all the pairs $(H_i, *)$ are subgroups of $(G, *)$. The integer n is called the *length* of the chain.

What we are really interested in, and henceforth shall confine our attention to, are the so-called *normal chains*. These are chains in which each group $(H_i, *)$ is a normal subgroup of its immediate predecessor $(H_{i-1}, *)$. For groups $(G, *)$ with two or more elements there is always one normal chain, namely the trivial chain $G \supset \{e\}$; however, this may very well be the only such chain.

Example 2–55. In the group $(Z_{12}, +_{12})$ of integers modulo 12, the following chains are normal chains:

$$Z_{12} \supset (6) \supset \{0\}, \qquad\qquad Z_{12} \supset (2) \supset (4) \supset \{0\},$$
$$Z_{12} \supset (3) \supset (6) \supset \{0\}, \qquad Z_{12} \supset (2) \supset (6) \supset \{0\}.$$

All subgroups are automatically normal, since $(Z_{12}, +_{12})$ is a commutative group.

Among other things, this particular example indicates that a given chain may be lengthened or refined by the insertion of admissable subsets. In technical terms, a second chain

$$G = K_0 \supset K_1 \supset \cdots \supset K_{m-1} \supset K_m = \{e\}$$

is said to be a *refinement* of the chain

$$G = H_0 \supset H_1 \supset \cdots \supset H_{n-1} \supset H_n = \{e\}$$

provided there exists a one-to-one function f from $\{0, 1, \ldots, n\}$ into $\{0, 1, \ldots, m\}$

such that $H_i = K_{f(i)}$ for all i. What we are requiring, in effect, is that every H_i coincide with one of the K_j. The lengths of the foregoing chains must clearly satisfy the inequality $n \leq m$, equality being allowed since every chain is trivially a refinement of itself. A refinement of a chain is termed *proper* if the refinement contains a set not in the original chain. A normal chain which has no proper refinement is customarily called a composition chain. We summarize all this in the following definition.

Definition 2–31. In the group $(G, *)$, the descending sequence of sets

$$G = H_0 \supset H_1 \supset \cdots \supset H_{n-1} \supset H_n = \{e\}$$

forms a *composition chain* for $(G, *)$ provided

1) $(H_i, *)$ is a subgroup of $(G, *)$,
2) $(H_i, *)$ is a normal subgroup of $(H_{i-1}, *)$,
3) the inclusion $H_{i-1} \supseteq K \supseteq H_i$, where $(K, *)$ is a normal subgroup of $(H_{i-1}, *)$, implies either $K = H_{i-1}$ or $K = H_i$.

Before proceeding to develop some of the properties of composition chains, let us pause to consider several examples.

Example 2–56. In the group $(Z_{24}, +_{24})$, the normal chain

$$Z_{24} \supset (2) \supset (12) \supset \{0\}$$

is not a composition chain, since it may be further refined by inserting either of the sets (4) or (6). On the other hand,

$$Z_{24} \supset (2) \supset (4) \supset (8) \supset \{0\}$$

and

$$Z_{24} \supset (3) \supset (6) \supset (12) \supset \{0\}$$

are both composition chains for $(Z_{24}, +_{24})$. One way of verifying this is to check the orders of the subgroups concerned. For instance, to insert a subset between (2) and (4) there would have to exist a subgroup of $(Z_{24}, +_{24})$ of order n, $6 < n < 12$, such that n divides 12 and is itself divisible by 6; clearly no such subgroup exists.

Example 2–57. For a second illustration, let $(G, *)$ be the group of symmetries of the square. In this case, the following sequence of sets serves as a composition chain:

$$G \supset \{R_{180}, R_{360}, H, V\} \supset \{R_{360}, H\} \supset \{R_{360}\}.$$

It is worth noting that the subgroup $(\{R_{360}, H\}, *)$ is not normal in the parent group $(G, *)$, but only in its immediate predecessor.

A normal chain for $(G, *)$ which fails to be a composition chain is

$$G \supset \{R_{180}, R_{360}\} \supset \{R_{360}\}.$$

This chain admits any one of several refinements; among others, there is

$$G \supset \{R_{90}, R_{180}, R_{270}, R_{360}\} \supset \{R_{180}, R_{360}\} \supset \{R_{360}\}.$$

Example 2–58. To see that not every group possesses a composition chain, merely consider the additive group of integers $(Z, +)$. We have previously observed that the normal subgroups of $(Z, +)$ are the cyclic subgroups $((n), +)$, n a nonnegative integer. Since the inclusion $(kn) \subseteq (n)$ holds for all $k \in Z_+$, there always exists a proper subgroup of any given group. Accordingly, each chain for $(Z, +)$ may be refined indefinitely.

Condition (3) of Definition 2–31 merits closer attention. Loosely speaking, it prohibits us from squeezing a normal subgroup between $(H_{i-1}, *)$ and $(H_i, *)$. There is a special terminology for this situation.

Definition 2–32. A normal subgroup $(H, *)$ is called a *maximal normal subgroup* of the group $(G, *)$ if $H \neq G$ and there exists no normal subgroup $(K, *)$ of $(G, *)$ such that $H \subset K \subset G$.

In terms of this new notion, a chain

$$G = H_0 \supset H_1 \supset \cdots \supset H_{n-1} \supset H_n = \{e\}$$

is a composition chain for $(G, *)$ if each subgroup $(H_i, *)$ is a maximal normal subgroup of $(H_{i-1}, *)$.

We should point out that Definition 2–32 does not imply $(H, *)$ is maximal in the sense of being the subgroup of $(G, *)$ with largest order. A given group may well have many distinct maximal normal subgroups of various orders. Indeed, in the group $(Z_{24}, +_{24})$, the cyclic subgroups $((2), +_{24})$ and $((3), +_{24})$ are both maximal normal with orders 12 and 8, respectively.

The next theorem develops the connection between a maximal normal subgroup and its associated quotient group. For this, recall that a group is said to be simple if the only normal subgroups are the two trivial ones.

Theorem 2–52. A normal subgroup $(H, *)$ of the group $(G, *)$ is maximal if and only if the quotient $(G/H, \otimes)$ is simple.

Proof. This result follows immediately from the Correspondence Theorem. We saw that to each normal subgroup $(K, *)$ of $(G, *)$ with $H \subseteq K$ there corresponds a normal subgroup of the quotient group $(G/H, \otimes)$ and this correspondence is one-to-one. Hence, $(H, *)$ is maximal normal in $(G, *)$ if and only if there are exactly two normal subgroups in $(G/H, \otimes)$, the entire group and the identity subgroup.

Certainly all the quotient groups $(H_{i-1}/H_i, \otimes)$ of a composition chain are simple. Conversely, any normal chain whose quotient groups are all simple groups is not subject to further refinement and is therefore a composition chain.

Not every group contains a maximal normal subgroup, so we cannot always find a composition chain for a given group. However, in the case of finite groups, there is the following result.

Theorem 2–53. Every finite group $(G, *)$ with more than one element has a composition chain.

Proof. If $(G, *)$ is a simple group, then the trivial chain $G \supset \{e\}$ is a composition chain. Suppose $(G, *)$ is not simple, so that there exists a normal subgroup $(H, *)$—there may be several choices for $(H, *)$. If $(H, *)$ is maximal in $(G, *)$ and $(\{e\}, *)$ is maximal in $(H, *)$, then

$$G \supset H \supset \{e\}$$

is a composition chain, and we are through. When $(H, *)$ is not already maximal normal, a larger normal subgroup $(K, *)$ with $H \subset K \subset G$ exists. Now, if $(H, *)$ is maximal in $(K, *)$ and $(K, *)$ is maximal in $(G, *)$, $G \supset K \supset H \supset \{e\}$ is the desired composition chain. Continue to argue along these lines. Since $(G, *)$ is finite, there are only a finite number of subgroups and this process must ultimately terminate. The resulting chain of sets is obviously a composition chain for $(G, *)$.

Definition 2–33. Two composition chains for the group $(G, *)$,

$$G = H_0 \supset H_1 \supset \cdots \supset H_{n-1} \supset H_n = \{e\}$$

and

$$G = K_0 \supset K_1 \supset \cdots \supset K_{m-1} \supset K_m = \{e\},$$

are termed *equivalent* if they have the same length $(n = m)$ and there exists a permutation $f \in S_n$ such that

$$(H_{i-1}/H_i, \otimes) \simeq (K_{f(i)-1}/K_{f(i)}, \otimes), \qquad i = 1, 2, \ldots, n.$$

In other words, two chains are equivalent if their associated quotient groups are isomorphic in some order.

We are now in a position, having assembled the necessary machinery, to attack the Jordan-Hölder Theorem. To simplify our presentation, part of the proof is separated as a preliminary lemma.

Lemma. If $(H, *)$ and $(K, *)$ are distinct maximal normal subgroups of the group $(G, *)$, then

1) the pair $(H \cap K, *)$ is a maximal normal subgroup of both $(H, *)$ and $(K, *)$,

2) $(G/H, \otimes) \simeq (K/H \cap K, \otimes)$ and $(G/K, \otimes) \simeq (H/H \cap K, \otimes)$.

Proof. Since the subgroups $(H, *)$ and $(K, *)$ are both normal, the pair $(H * K, *)$ is itself a normal subgroup of $(G, *)$ [Problem 11, Section 2–5]. Plainly, we have the inclusion $H \subseteq H * K \subseteq G$. By hypothesis, the subgroup $(H, *)$ is maximal normal in $(G, *)$, which implies either $H * K = H$ or $H * K = G$. Our contention is that $H * K = G$. Were this not the case, the equality $H * K = H$ would mean $K \subseteq H$ (with $K \neq H$), contradicting the maximality of $(K, *)$; therefore, the only possibility left us is that $G = H * K$.

A straightforward application of Theorem 2–51 now establishes the isomorphism $(G/K, \otimes) \simeq (H/H \cap K, \otimes)$. But the quotient group $(G/K, \otimes)$ is a simple group (Theorem 2–52), so the same must also be true of $(H/H \cap K, \otimes)$. From this, we conclude the group $(H \cap K, *)$ is maximal normal in $(H, *)$, again utilizing Theorem 2–52.

If the letters H and K are interchanged, the symmetry of the hypothesis yields the remaining parts of the lemma.

Theorem 2–54. (*Jordan-Hölder*). In a finite group $(G, *)$ with more than one element, any two composition chains are equivalent.

Proof. The proof will proceed by induction on the order of the group. If $(G, *)$ is simple, the only possible composition chain is the trivial chain $G \supset \{e\}$, so the theorem is certainly true. This establishes the result for groups of order 2, the smallest admissible order. In general, let

$$G = H_0 \supset H_1 \supset \cdots \supset H_{n-1} \supset H_n = \{e\} \tag{1}$$

and

$$G = K_0 \supset K_1 \supset \cdots \supset K_{m-1} \supset K_m = \{e\} \tag{2}$$

be any two composition chains for the group $(G, *)$. Assume further that the theorem holds for all groups having order less than that of $(G, *)$. We distinguish two cases:

CASE 1. $H_1 = K_1$. In this case, if the set G is deleted from (1) and (2), the resulting chains

$$H_1 \supset H_2 \supset \cdots \supset H_{n-1} \supset H_n = \{e\}$$

and

$$H_1 \supset K_2 \supset \cdots \supset K_{m-1} \supset K_m = \{e\}$$

both represent composition chains for the subgroup $(H_1, *)$. As the theorem is assumed true for $(H_1, *)$, whose order is less than that of $(G, *)$, these two chains are necessarily equivalent. But $(G/H_1, \otimes) = (G/K_1, \otimes)$; hence, the given composition chains (1) and (2) must also be equivalent.

CASE 2. $H_1 \neq K_1$. Either $H_1 \cap K_1 = \{e\}$, or by Theorem 2–53, there exists a composition chain

$$H_1 \cap K_1 \supset L_1 \supset \cdots \supset L_{r-1} \supset L_r = \{e\}$$

for the subgroup $(H_1 \cap K_1, *)$. Now, according to the lemma just established, $(H_1 \cap K_1, *)$ is a maximal normal subgroup of both $(H_1, *)$ and $(K_1, *)$. It then follows that the two chains

$$G \supset H_1 \supset H_1 \cap K_1 \supset L_1 \supset \cdots \supset L_{r-1} \supset L_r = \{e\} \tag{3}$$

and

$$G \supset K_1 \supset H_1 \cap K_1 \supset L_1 \supset \cdots \supset L_{r-1} \supset L_r = \{e\} \tag{4}$$

are actually composition chains for $(G, *)$. Appealing to the lemma once more, we see that

$$(G/H_1, \otimes) \simeq (K_1/H_1 \cap K_1, \otimes)$$

and

$$(G/K_1, \otimes) \simeq (H_1/H_1 \cap K_1, \otimes).$$

Hence, the composition quotient groups obtained from (3) are isomorphic in pairs to those obtained from the chain (4); let us agree to abbreviate this situation by writing $(3) \simeq (4)$.

Next, consider the following two composition chains for the group $(G, *)$:

$$G \supset H_1 \supset H_2 \supset \cdots \supset H_{n-1} \supset H_n \supset \{e\}$$

and

$$G \supset H_1 \supset H_1 \cap K_1 \supset L_1 \supset \cdots \supset L_{r-1} \supset L_r = \{e\}.$$

Since these chains have their first two terms in common, we can conclude from case 1 that they must be equivalent. In a like manner,

$$G \supset K_1 \supset K_2 \supset \cdots \supset K_{m-1} \supset K_m = \{e\}$$

and

$$G \supset K_1 \supset H_1 \cap K_1 \supset L_1 \supset \cdots \supset L_{r-1} \supset L_r = \{e\}$$

are equivalent chains for $(G, *)$. Combining our results, we observe that

$$(1) \simeq (3) \simeq (4) \simeq (2),$$

from which it follows that the original chains (1) and (2) are equivalent.

Let us quickly review what has just been learned. First, the preceding theorem implies that the composition chains of a given finite group $(G, *)$ must all be of the same length. Moreover, by means of the quotient groups of any such chain, we are able to associate with $(G, *)$ a finite sequence of simple groups. Up to isomorphism, these simple groups depend solely on $(G, *)$ and are independent of the particular composition chain from which they were originally obtained. The important point is that the composition quotient groups will to some degree mirror the properties of the given group and provide a hint to its algebraic structure.

Example 2–59. To illustrate the Jordan-Hölder Theorem, consider the group $(Z_{60}, +_{60})$ of integers modulo 60 and the two composition chains:

$$Z_{60} \supset (3) \supset (6) \supset (12) \supset \{0\},$$

$$Z_{60} \supset (2) \supset (6) \supset (30) \supset \{0\}.$$

After suitable rearrangement, the isomorphic pairs of composition quotient groups are

$$(Z_{60}/(3), \otimes) \simeq ((2)/(6), \otimes),$$

$$((3)/(6), \otimes) \simeq (Z_{60}/(2), \otimes),$$

$$((6)/(12), \otimes) \simeq ((30)/\{0\}, \otimes),$$

$$((12)/\{0\}, \otimes) \simeq ((6)/(30), \otimes).$$

All these quotient groups are simple, being cyclic groups of prime order: the first pair of isomorphic groups is of order 3, the second pair of order 5, while the remaining groups are all of order 2. Note that the product of all these orders is 60.

We now take a brief look at a wide class of groups which contains, among others, all commutative groups.

Definition 2–34. A group $(G, *)$ is *solvable* if it has a normal chain (possibly of length 1)
$$G = H_0 \supset H_1 \supset \cdots \supset H_{n-1} \supset H_n = \{e\},$$

in which every quotient group $(H_{i-1}/H_i, \otimes)$ $[i = 1, 2, \ldots, n]$ is commutative. As a matter of language, we shall call such a chain a *solvable chain* for $(G, *)$.

It should be clear at once that all commutative groups $(G, *)$ with more than one element are solvable, since in this case, the trivial chain $G \supset \{e\}$ is a solvable chain. As an example of a noncommutative solvable group, one need only consider the symmetric group on three symbols, $(S_3, \circ)$; here, a solvable chain is

$$S_3 \supset \left\{ \begin{pmatrix} 1 & 2 & 3 \\ 1 & 2 & 3 \end{pmatrix}, \ \begin{pmatrix} 1 & 2 & 3 \\ 2 & 3 & 1 \end{pmatrix}, \ \begin{pmatrix} 1 & 2 & 3 \\ 3 & 1 & 2 \end{pmatrix} \right\} \supset \left\{ \begin{pmatrix} 1 & 2 & 3 \\ 1 & 2 & 3 \end{pmatrix} \right\}.$$

Recently, W. Feit and J. Thompson succeeded in proving the long-standing conjecture that all finite groups of odd order are solvable. Thus, if we are interested in nonsolvable groups, they will be found among the noncommutative groups of even order.

Some basic properties of solvable groups are given in our next theorem.

Theorem 2–55. If $(G, *)$ is a solvable group, then every subgroup of $(G, *)$ is solvable and every homomorphic image of $(G, *)$ is solvable.

Proof. Let

$$G = H_0 \supset H_1 \supset \cdots \supset H_{n-1} \supset H_n = \{e\}$$

be a fixed solvable chain for $(G, *)$. Given a subgroup $(K, *)$ of $(G, *)$, define $K_i = K \cap H_i$ $[i = 0, 1, \ldots, n]$. We intend to prove that the chain

$$K = K_0 \supset K_1 \supset \cdots \supset K_{n-1} \supset K_n = \{e\}$$

is a solvable chain for the subgroup $(K, *)$. First, observe that the pair $(K_i, *)$ is a normal subgroup of $(K_{i-1}, *)$; in fact, for each $a \in K_{i-1}$,

$$a * K_i * a^{-1} = (a * K_i * a^{-1}) \cap K$$
$$\subseteq (a * H_i * a^{-1}) \cap K \subseteq H_i \cap K = K_i.$$

Also,

$$K_i = K \cap H_i = K \cap H_{i-1} \cap H_i = K_{i-1} \cap H_i,$$

so that

$$(K_{i-1}/K_i, \otimes) = (K_{i-1}/K_{i-1} \cap H_i, \otimes).$$

According to Theorem 2–51, we have the isomorphism

$$(K_{i-1}/K_{i-1} \cap H_i, \otimes) \simeq (K_{i-1} * H_i/H_i, \otimes).$$

But the quotient group $(K_{i-1} * H_i/H_i, \otimes)$ is commutative, being a subgroup of the commutative group $(H_{i-1}/H_i, \otimes)$. This implies all the quotient groups $(K_{i-1}/K_i, \otimes)$ are commutative, as required.

As for the second part of the theorem, let f be a homomorphism from the group $(G, *)$ onto the group $(G', \circ)$. Setting $H_i' = f(H_i)$ $[i = 0, 1, \ldots, n]$, we obtain a chain for $(G', \circ)$:

$$G' = H_0' \supset H_1' \supset \cdots \supset H_{n-1}' \supset H_n' = \{e\}.$$

By the corollary to Theorem 2–39, the subgroup $(H_i', \circ)$ is certainly normal in $(H_{i-1}', \circ)$. What little difficulty there is arises in showing the corresponding quotient group $(H_{i-1}'/H_i', \otimes')$ to be commutative. For this, we define mappings $f_i : H_{i-1}/H_i \to H_{i-1}'/H_i'$ by taking

$$f_i(a * H_i) = f(a) \circ H_i', \qquad a \in H_{i-1} \qquad (i = 1, 2, \ldots, n).$$

It is easily seen that f_i is well-defined; indeed, if $a * H_i = b * H_i$, then $a^{-1} * b \in H_i$, hence

$$f(a)^{-1} \circ f(b) = f(a^{-1} * b) \in f(H_i) = H_i',$$

which, in turn, implies

$$f_i(a * H_i) = f(a) \circ H_i' = f(b) \circ H_i' = f_i(b * H_i).$$

Next, note that each f_i is itself a homomorphism; for if $a, b \in H_{i-1}$,

$$f_i((a * H_i) \otimes (b * H_i)) = f_i(a * b * H_i) = f(a * b) \circ H_i'$$
$$= f(a) \circ f(b) \circ H_i' = (f(a) \circ H_i') \otimes' (f(b) \circ H_i').$$

Finally, because $f(H_i) = H_i'$, the function f_i maps onto the set H_{i-1}'/H_i'. From these facts, we are able to conclude that

$$(H_{i-1}/H_i, \otimes) \simeq (H_{i-1}'/H_i', \otimes'),$$

and, since $(H_{i-1}/H_i, \otimes)$ is a commutative group, so also is the quotient group $(H_{i-1}'/H_i', \otimes')$.

Corollary. If $(G, *)$ is solvable and $(H, *)$ is a proper normal subgroup of $(G, *)$, then the quotient group $(G/H, \otimes)$ is solvable.

In the way of a converse to this theorem, we prove

Theorem 2–56. Let $(H, *)$ be a nontrivial normal subgroup of $(G, *)$. If both $(H, *)$ and $(G/H, \otimes)$ are solvable groups, then $(G, *)$ is itself solvable.

Proof. To begin, let

$$G/H = K_0' \supset K_1' \supset \cdots \supset K_{n-1}' \supset K_n' = \{e * H\}$$

be a solvable chain for the quotient group $(G/H, \otimes)$. Using the Correspondence Theorem, we obtain a sequence of sets

$$G = K_0 \supset K_1 \supset \cdots \supset K_{n-1} \supset K_n = H$$

descending from G to H with the property that $(K_i, *)$ is a normal subgroup of $(K_{i-1}, *)$; in fact, $K_i = \mathrm{nat}_H^{-1}(K_i')$. Furthermore, by Theorem 2–50,

$$(K_{i-1}/K_i, \otimes) \simeq (K_{i-1}'/K_i', \otimes'),$$

so that the quotient group $(K_{i-1}/K_i, \otimes)$ is commutative. Since $(H, *)$ is solvable, it has a solvable chain running from H to $\{e\}$, say

$$H = H_0 \supset H_1 \supset \cdots \supset H_{m-1} \supset H_m = \{e\}.$$

By stringing these sequences of sets together, we can construct a solvable chain for $(G, *)$:

$$G \supset K_1 \supset \cdots \supset K_{n-1} \supset H \supset H_1 \supset \cdots \supset H_{m-1} \supset \{e\}.$$

Therefore, $(G, *)$ is a solvable group.

In conjunction, Theorems 2–55 and 2–56 tell us that if $(H, *)$ is a nontrivial normal subgroup of $(G, *)$, then $(G, *)$ is a solvable group if and only if both $(H, *)$ and $(G/H, \otimes)$ are solvable groups. The decision regarding solvability is often facilitated by this criterion.

The following theorem gives further insight into the nature of the composition chains for a finite solvable group.

Theorem 2–57. Let $(G, *)$ be a finite solvable group. Then the quotient groups of any composition chain for $(G, *)$ are cyclic groups of prime order.

Proof. We proceed by induction on the order of $(G, *)$. If order G is a prime, there is nothing to prove, since $G \supset \{e\}$ is the only composition chain. (This remark takes care of the basis for the induction when order $G = 2$.) In the contrary case, $(G, *)$ has a nontrivial, normal subgroup $(H, *)$. [Why?] By the induction assumption, $(H, *)$ and $(G/H, \otimes)$, being solvable, have composition chains whose quotient groups are of prime order: say, the chains

$$H = H_0 \supset H_1 \supset \cdots \supset H_{n-1} \supset H_n = \{e\}$$

and

$$G/H = K_0' \supset K_1' \supset \cdots \supset K_{m-1}' \supset K_m' = \{e * H\}.$$

Taking $K_i = \mathrm{nat}_H^{-1}(K_i')$ $[i = 0, 1, \ldots, m]$, it follows from Theorem 2–49 that

$$G = K_0 \supset K_1 \supset \cdots \supset K_{m-1} \supset K_m = H,$$

where $(K_i, *)$ is a normal subgroup of $(K_{i-1}, *)$. As before, Theorem 2–50 implies

$$(K_{i-1}/K_i, \otimes) \simeq (K_{i-1}'/K_i', \otimes'),$$

whence $(K_{i-1}/K_i, \otimes)$ is (cyclic) of prime order. Hooking these sequences together, we obtain (after removing the second occurrence of H), a composition chain for $(G, *)$, all of whose quotient groups are cyclic groups of prime order. By the Jordan-Hölder Theorem the same is true of every composition chain.

Before concluding the present section, let us state a few results, omitting their proofs. We have seen that every permutation in S_n $(n \geq 2)$ can be written as a product of transpositions. While this expression is not unique, the number of transpositions occurring in the various representations for a given permutation is always even or always odd. Accordingly, we define an *even (odd) permutation* as one which can be expressed as the product of an even (odd) number of transpositions.

If A_n denotes the subset of S_n consisting of all even permutations, then it may be shown that $(A_n, \circ)$ is a normal subgroup of index 2 in the symmetric group $(S_n, \circ)$; this subgroup is the so-called *alternating group* on n symbols. More important still is the celebrated fact that for $n \geq 5$ $(A_n, \circ)$ is a simple group. As such, its only normal chain is the trivial chain $A_n \supset \{e\}$. We are thus led to conclude that for $n \geq 5$ $(A_n, \circ)$ is a solvable group if and only if $(A_n, \circ)$ is commutative. Since

$$(1, 2, 3) \circ (1, 2, 4) \neq (1, 2, 4) \circ (1, 2, 3),$$

the alternating group $(A_n, \circ)$ fails to be commutative for $n \geq 4$ and hence is insolvable for $n \geq 5$. The significance of this observation lies in the fact that, by Theorem 2–55, the symmetric group $(S_n, \circ)$ cannot be solvable when $n \geq 5$.

The foregoing remarks may be stated as a theorem.

Theorem 2–58. If $n \geq 5$, then $(S_n, \circ)$ and $(A_n, \circ)$ are not solvable groups.

PROBLEMS

1. Check that the following chains represent composition chains for the indicated group.

   a) For $(Z_{36}, +_{36})$, the group of integers modulo 36:

   $$Z_{36} \supset (3) \supset (9) \supset (18) \supset \{0\}.$$

   b) For $(G, *)$, the group of symmetries of the square:

   $$G \supset \{R_{180}, R_{360}, D_1, D_2\} \supset \{R_{360}, D_1\} \supset \{R_{360}\}.$$

   c) For $((a), *)$, a cyclic group of order 30:

   $$(a) \supset (a^5) \supset (a^{10}) \supset \{e\}.$$

   d) For $(S_3, \circ)$, the symmetric group on 3 symbols:

   $$S_3 \supset \left\{ \begin{pmatrix} 1 & 2 & 3 \\ 1 & 2 & 3 \end{pmatrix}, \begin{pmatrix} 1 & 2 & 3 \\ 2 & 3 & 1 \end{pmatrix}, \begin{pmatrix} 1 & 2 & 3 \\ 3 & 1 & 2 \end{pmatrix} \right\} \supset \left\{ \begin{pmatrix} 1 & 2 & 3 \\ 1 & 2 & 3 \end{pmatrix} \right\}.$$

2. Find a composition chain for the symmetric group $(S_4, \circ)$. [*Hint:* Consider the set of permutations on p. 80.]

3. Show that no infinite cyclic group possesses a composition chain.

4. Prove that if $(G, *)$ is a finite cyclic group of order 2^n, then there is exactly one composition chain for $(G, *)$.

5. Derive the result: if the quotient group $(G/H, \otimes)$ is of prime order, then $(H, *)$ is a maximal normal subgroup of $(G, *)$. [*Hint:* Use the Correspondence Theorem.]

6. Prove that the cyclic subgroup $((n), +)$ is a maximal normal subgroup of $(Z, +)$ if and only if n is a prime number.

7. Establish that the following two composition chains for $(Z_{24}, +_{24})$ are equivalent:

   $$Z_{24} \supset (3) \supset (6) \supset (12) \supset \{0\},$$
   $$Z_{24} \supset (2) \supset (4) \supset (12) \supset \{0\}.$$

8. Find all composition chains for (a) the group $(Z_{30}, +_{30})$ of integers modulo 30, (b) the group of symmetries of the square, and verify the Jordan-Hölder Theorem in both cases. [*Hint:* There are four composition chains for each group.]

9. Apply the Jordan-Hölder Theorem to the group of integers modulo n to prove that a positive integer n may be factored uniquely (apart from the order of the factors) into positive primes.

10. Let $(G, \cdot)$ be the direct product of three nontrivial groups $(G_k, *_k)$ [$k = 1, 2, 3$]; that is to say, $G = G_1 \times G_2 \times G_3$ with the binary operation $\cdot$ defined by

$$(a, b, c) \cdot (a', b', c') = (a *_1 a', b *_2 b', c *_3 c').$$

a) Verify that

$$G \supset e_1 \times G_2 \times G_3 \supset e_1 \times e_2 \times G_3 \supset e_1 \times e_2 \times e_3$$

is a normal chain for $(G, \cdot)$.

b) If the original groups $(G_k, *_k)$ are simple, prove that the foregoing chain must be a composition chain for $(G, \cdot)$.

c) State and prove an analogous result for n groups.

11. Suppose $(H, *)$ is a proper normal subgroup of the group $(G, *)$ and

$$G \supset K_1 \supset \cdots \supset K_r \supset H \supset L_1 \supset \cdots \supset L_n \supset \{e\}$$

is a composition chain for $(G, *)$. Prove that

$$G/H \supset K_1/H \supset \cdots \supset K_r/H \supset \{H\}$$

represents a composition chain for the quotient group $(G/H, \otimes)$.

12. Show that the symmetric group $(S_4, \circ)$ is solvable.

13. Prove that if $(G, *)$ and $(G', \circ)$ are solvable groups, then their direct product $(G \times G', \cdot)$ is also a solvable group. [*Hint:* Problem 17, Section 2–7 and Theorem 2–56.]

14. Let $(H, *)$ and $(K, *)$ be solvable subgroups of the group $(G, *)$, with $(H, *)$ normal in $(G, *)$. Verify that the subgroup $(H * K, *)$ is also solvable.

15. Prove that a simple group with more than one element is solvable if and only if it is of prime order.

16. Establish the following facts concerning the alternating group $(A_n, \circ)$, $n \geq 3$:

a) $(A_n, \circ)$ is generated by the set of all 3-cycles.

b) Order $A_n = n!/2$.

c) $(A_n, \circ)$ is the commutator subgroup of the symmetric group $(S_n, \circ)$.

2–9 SYLOW THEOREMS

As noted earlier, if m divides n, we cannot be certain that a group of order n will possess at least one subgroup of order m. To be sure, under special circumstances (for example, given a finite cyclic group) it is true that such subgroups always do exist. In general, the problem of finding subgroups of a prescribed order in an arbitrary finite group is one of considerable difficulty and constitutes the subject matter of this, our final section on group theory. We begin with a quick survey of a number of results, some previously encountered in the exercises, which will play a prominant role in the sequel.

If $(H, *)$ is a subgroup of the finite group $(G, *)$, the index of H in G was defined to be the number of distinct left cosets of H (in light of Problem 3(c), Section 2–5, the number of right cosets of H in G is the same as the number of left cosets, so there is no need to distinguish between a right and left index). To simplify the writing later on, we shall hereafter represent the index of H in G by $[G : H]$. Since the order of the group $(G, *)$ may be interpreted as the index of the trivial subgroup $(\{e\}, *)$, one might, in keeping with the foregoing notation, write order $G = [G : e]$. We shall not employ this convention, however, but instead conform to the practice of denoting the order of $(G, *)$ by the symbol $o(G)$.

For any subgroup $(H, *)$ of the group $(G, *)$ and any element $a \in G$, consider the following subset of G:

$$a * H * a^{-1} = \{a * h * a^{-1} \mid h \in H\}.$$

If x and y are members of $a * H * a^{-1}$, there exist h_1, $h_2 \in H$ for which, $x = a * h_1 * a^{-1}$, $y = a * h_2 * a^{-1}$. Then,

$$x * y^{-1} = (a * h_1 * a^{-1}) * (a * h_2 * a^{-1})^{-1} = a * (h_1 * h_2^{-1}) * a^{-1},$$

where, since $(H, *)$ is a subgroup, the product $h_1 * h_2^{-1} \in H$. But this means $x * y^{-1} \in a * H * a^{-1}$, so that $(a * H * a^{-1}, *)$ is itself a subgroup of $(G, *)$. We are thus led to the next theorem.

Theorem 2–59. If $(H, *)$ is a subgroup of the group $(G, *)$ and if $a \in G$, then the pair $(a * H * a^{-1}, *)$ is also a subgroup of $(G, *)$ called the *conjugate subgroup of* $(H, *)$ *induced by the element a.*

If $a * H * a^{-1} = H$ for some $a \in G$, we say that the subgroup $(H, *)$ is *invariant,* or *self-conjugate, under a.* Any subgroup is, of course, invariant under each of its own elements. From this definition, it is immediate that the concept of a normal subgroup can be arrived at in an alternative way: a subgroup $(H, *)$ is normal in $(G, *)$ if and only if $(H, *)$ is invariant under each element of G.

Observe also that conjugate subgroups are isomorphic. If $(a * H * a^{-1}, *)$ is a conjugate subgroup of $(H, *)$, define $f : H \rightarrow a * H * a^{-1}$ by taking $f(h) = a * h * a^{-1}$; then f is an isomorphism.

Now, if $(K, *)$ is any other subgroup of $(G, *)$, we may certainly consider those elements of K under which $(H, *)$ is invariant; in other words, the set

$$N_K(H) = \{k \in K \mid k * H * k^{-1} = H\}.$$

The reader should prove the theorem below.

Theorem 2–60. If $(H, *)$ and $(K, *)$ are two subgroups of the group $(G, *)$, then the pair $(N_K(H), *)$ is also a subgroup, known as the *normalizer of H in K.*

When $K = G$, one customarily writes $N(H)$ for $N_G(H)$ and refers to the subgroup $(N(H), *)$ simply as the *normalizer* of H. Although the subgroup $(H, *)$ is not necessarily normal in $(G, *)$, a simple argument shows it to be normal in its normalizer; in fact, $(N(H), *)$ is the largest subgroup of $(G, *)$ in which $(H, *)$ is normal.

With this notation in mind, we can now "count" the conjugate subgroups $(a * H * a^{-1}, *)$ of $(H, *)$.

Theorem 2–61. The number of distinct conjugates of a subgroup $(H, *)$ of $(G, *)$ induced by the elements of a subgroup $(K, *)$ is equal to $[K : N_K(H)]$, the index of $N_K(H)$ in K.

Proof. For $k_1, k_2 \in K$, we have $k_1 * H * k_1^{-1} = k_2 * H * k_2^{-1}$ if and only if $H = (k_1^{-1} * k_2) * H * (k_1^{-1} * k_2)^{-1}$, which holds if and only if $k_1^{-1} * k_2 \in N_K(H)$; this is true, in turn, if and only if $k_1 * N_K(H) = k_2 * N_K(H)$. Hence, the number of distinct conjugate subgroups of $(H, *)$ by elements of K is equal to the number of distinct cosets of $N_K(H)$ in K, namely, $[K : N_K(H)]$.

Corollary. Let $(H, *)$ and $(K, *)$ be two subgroups of the group $(G, *)$. If $(H, *)$ is invariant under n elements of K, then $(H, *)$ has $o(K)/n$ conjugate subgroups by elements of K.

Proof. The hypothesis asserts $o(N_K(H)) = n$. But, by Lagrange's Theorem

$$o(K) = [K : N_K(H)] \, o(N_K(H)),$$

from which the corollary follows.

Let us continue our discussion by introducing a new class of groups.

Definition 2–35. A group $(G, *)$ is said to be a *p-group* if the order of each element of G is a power of a fixed prime p.

Example 2–60. Any group of order p^n (p a prime) is a p-group, since the order of each element must divide the order of the group. In particular, the group of symmetries of a square is a p-group, where $p = 2$.

Example 2–61. Let $(G, *)$ be a commutative group and the set H consist of those elements whose orders are powers of a fixed prime p (quite possibly, $H = \{e\}$). Then $(H, *)$ forms a subgroup of $(G, *)$ which, by its definition, is automatically a p-group.

One might ask whether the converse of Example 2–60 holds. More precisely, if $(G, *)$ is a p-group, is $o(G)$ some power of p? The following lemma will serve as a starting point in obtaining the answer.

Lemma. If $(G, *)$ is a finite commutative group whose order is divisible by a prime p, then G contains an element of order p.

Proof. We proceed by induction on the order of $(G, *)$. First, observe that if $o(G)$ is itself a prime, this prime must be p and every element other than the identity has order p; this takes care of the basis for the induction when $o(G) = 2$. Now, let $a \in G$, with $a \neq e$. Since $(G, *)$ is a finite group, the element a has a finite order n. Either $p \mid n$ or $p \nmid n$. In case $p \mid n$, say $n = kp$, then $(a^k)^p = a^n = e$. The order of a^k therefore divides p, which, because p is prime, implies $o(a^k) = p$. (Recall that $x^m = e$ if and only if $o(x) \mid m$.)

Next, let us suppose $p \nmid n$. Because $(G, *)$ is commutative, the cyclic subgroup $((a), *)$ is surely normal, and we can form the (commutative) quotient group $(G/(a), \otimes)$. Also, since $(a) \neq \{e\}$, $o(G/(a)) < o(G)$. From

$$o(G) = [G : (a)] o((a)) = o(G/(a))n$$

and the fact $p \nmid n$, it follows that $o(G/(a))$ is divisible by p. Using our induction hypothesis, $G/(a)$ must therefore contain some element $b * (a)$ of order p. But the equation

$$b^p * (a) = (b * (a))^p = e * (a)$$

implies $b^p \in (a)$, so that $(b^n)^p = (b^p)^n = e$. Were $b^n = e$, then $(b * (a))^n = e * (a)$ and we would conclude $p \mid n$, a contradiction. Thus the element b^n has order p.

Corollary. Let $(G, *)$ be a finite commutative group and p a prime dividing $o(G)$. Then $(G, *)$ has a subgroup of order p.

Our next objective is to establish the preceding lemma without the hypothesis of commutativity. We pause, however, to develop the necessary mathematical tools.

Definition 2–36. The *centralizer of an element* a of the group $(G, *)$, denoted by $C(a)$, is the set of all elements in G which commute with a:

$$C(a) = \{x \in G \mid x * a = a * x\}.$$

Note, incidentally, that $C(a) = G$ if and only if $a \in \text{cent } G$. For any cyclic subgroup $((a), *)$, we always have $C(a) \subseteq N((a))$. The proof of the result below is routine and is left as an exercise.

Theorem 2–62. For any element $a \in G$, the pair $(C(a), *)$ constitutes a subgroup of $(G, *)$.

Before entering into a further discussion of the centralizer, an additional concept must be introduced.

Definition 2–37. Let $(G, *)$ be a group and $a, b \in G$. The element b is said to be a *conjugate* of a (in G) if there exists some $x \in G$ for which $b = x * a * x^{-1}$.

The reader should now prove the following analog of Theorem 2–61 which clarifies the relationship between the last two definitions.

Theorem 2–63. If $a \in G$, the number of conjugate elements of a is equal to $[G:C(a)]$, the index of the centralizer of a in G.

Given $a, b \in G$, we may define an equivalence relation $\sim$ in G by requiring that $a \sim b$ if and only if b is a conjugate of a. The relation $\sim$ induces a partition of the set G into equivalence classes, usually referred to as the *conjugacy classes* of $(G, *)$. Elements in the same conjugacy class are called *conjugates* of one another. By the preceding theorem, there are $[G:C(a)]$ elements in the conjugacy class containing a.

Certain of these classes will consist of exactly one member; for example, if $a \in \text{cent } G$, then $x * a * x^{-1} = a$ for every $x \in G$, so that the conjugacy class containing a reduces to $\{a\}$. It should be clear, on the other hand, that $a \in \text{cent } G$ when the conjugacy class of a is $\{a\}$. From this, we infer that a group is commutative if and only if each of its conjugacy classes is a singleton.

Example 2–62. There are three conjugacy classes of $(S_3, \circ)$, the symmetric group on 3 symbols. We leave to the reader the task of verifying that these classes are given by

$$\left\{ \begin{pmatrix} 1 & 2 & 3 \\ 1 & 2 & 3 \end{pmatrix} \right\},$$

$$\left\{ \begin{pmatrix} 1 & 2 & 3 \\ 2 & 3 & 1 \end{pmatrix}, \begin{pmatrix} 1 & 2 & 3 \\ 3 & 1 & 2 \end{pmatrix} \right\},$$

$$\left\{ \begin{pmatrix} 1 & 2 & 3 \\ 2 & 1 & 3 \end{pmatrix}, \begin{pmatrix} 1 & 2 & 3 \\ 1 & 3 & 2 \end{pmatrix}, \begin{pmatrix} 1 & 2 & 3 \\ 3 & 2 & 1 \end{pmatrix} \right\}.$$

As each element of G lies in one and only one conjugacy class, we may determine the number of elements in G by counting them class by class. To do so, first observe that there are exactly $o(\text{cent } G)$ classes which contain one element. If we add to $o(\text{cent } G)$ the number of elements in the nonsingleton conjugacy classes, the elements of G will have all been counted. This leads to the important (conjugacy) *class equation*:

$$o(G) = o(\text{cent } G) + \Sigma \, [G:C(a)],$$

where the summation runs over a set of representatives for the distinct conjugacy classes having more than one member; that is to say, we sum over a set of nonconjugate elements not in cent G.

In the group of symmetries of the square, for instance, the conjugacy classes are

$$\{R_{180}\}, \qquad \{R_{360}\}, \qquad \{R_{90}, R_{270}\}, \qquad \{D_1, D_2\}, \qquad \{H, V\},$$

so that the class equation would read

$$o(G) = o(\text{cent } G) + [G:C(R_{90})] + [G:C(D_1)] + [G:C(H)].$$

Using the class equation of a group, we are able to extend the last lemma on commutative groups to a more general setting.

Theorem 2–64. (*Cauchy*). If $(G, *)$ is a finite group whose order is divisible by a prime p, then G contains an element of order p.

Proof. Use induction on the order of $(G, *)$. If $o(G) = 2$, then $(G, *)$ is a commutative group and the theorem reduces to the lemma. Suppose, inductively, that the theorem holds true for all groups of order less than $o(G)$. Now consider the class equation for $(G, *)$,

$$o(G) = o(\text{cent } G) + \Sigma\, [G : C(a)],$$

where the summation, as noted previously, is made by choosing one representative from each conjugacy class with more than one element.

If $G = \text{cent } G$, the $(G, *)$ is commutative and we need only appeal to the lemma to complete the proof; in the contrary case, there is some element $a \in G$ with $a \notin \text{cent } G$. For such an a, $[G : C(a)] > 1$, so that by Lagrange's Theorem,

$$o(G) = [G : C(a)]\, o(C(a)) > o(C(a)).$$

Since the theorem is assumed to hold for the subgroup $(C(a), *)$, if $p \mid o(C(a))$, then $C(a)$ has an element of order p, and we are done. On the other hand, if $p \nmid o(C(a))$ for every $a \notin \text{cent } G$, p must divide $[G : C(a)]$; for p is prime and divides $o(G) = [G : C(a)]\, o(C(a))$. But then, in the class equation, p divides each term of the summation and also divides $o(G)$, so that $p \mid o(\text{cent } G)$. As $(\text{cent } G, *)$ is a commutative subgroup of $(G, *)$, it follows (again, from the lemma) that cent G contains an element of order p.

Corollary. $(G, *)$ is a finite p-group if and only if $o(G) = p^k$, for some $k > 0$.

Proof. Suppose $(G, *)$ is a p-group, but $q \mid o(G)$ for some prime $q \neq p$. Then by Cauchy's Theorem, G has an element of order q, contradicting the fact that $(G, *)$ is a p-group. Thus, p is the only prime divisor of $o(G)$, which implies $o(G) = p^k$ $(k > 0)$. Conversely, if $o(G) = p^k$, then from Lagrange's Theorem each element of G has a power of p as its order.

As an application of Cauchy's Theorem, it might be of interest to mention the result below.

Theorem 2–65. If $(G, *)$ is a finite p-group with more than one element, then cent $G \neq \{e\}$.

Proof. As a starting point, consider the class equation for $(G, *)$,

$$o(G) = o(\text{cent } G) + \Sigma\, [G : C(a)],$$

the summation being over certain elements a for which $[G : C(a)] \neq 1$. For $a \notin \text{cent } G$, $(C(a), *)$ is a nontrivial subgroup of $(G, *)$; in fact, $(C(a), *)$ is itself a p-group (any subgroup of a p-group is a p-group!). By the preceding corollary, it follows that $o(C(a)) = p^k$ for some $k > 0$. Then

$$[G:C(a)] = o(G)/o(C(a))$$

must be divisible by p. Now, p divides each term of the summation, as well as divides $o(G)$, so that $p \mid o(\text{cent } G)$. This implies $o(\text{cent } G) > 1$.

We now shift our emphasis from arbitrary p-groups to Sylow p-subgroups.

Definition 2–38. Let $(G, *)$ be a finite group and p a prime. A subgroup $(P, *)$ of $(G, *)$ is said to be a *Sylow p-subgroup* if $(P, *)$ is a p-group and is not properly contained in any other p-subgroup of $(G, *)$ for the same prime p.

Example 2–63. The symmetric group $(S_3, \circ)$ has three (conjugate) Sylow 2-subgroups, specifically, the subgroups whose sets of elements are

$$\left\{ \begin{pmatrix} 1 & 2 & 3 \\ 1 & 2 & 3 \end{pmatrix}, \begin{pmatrix} 1 & 2 & 3 \\ 2 & 1 & 3 \end{pmatrix} \right\},$$

$$\left\{ \begin{pmatrix} 1 & 2 & 3 \\ 1 & 2 & 3 \end{pmatrix}, \begin{pmatrix} 1 & 2 & 3 \\ 1 & 3 & 2 \end{pmatrix} \right\},$$

$$\left\{ \begin{pmatrix} 1 & 2 & 3 \\ 1 & 2 & 3 \end{pmatrix}, \begin{pmatrix} 1 & 2 & 3 \\ 3 & 2 & 1 \end{pmatrix} \right\}.$$

Thus a Sylow p-subgroup of a given group need not be unique.

Theorem 2–66. For each prime p, the finite group $(G, *)$ has a Sylow p-subgroup.

Proof. If $o(G) = 1$ or $p \nmid o(G)$, $(\{e\}, *)$ is, in a trivial sense, the required Sylow p-subgroup. On the other hand, whenever $p \mid o(G)$, Cauchy's Theorem guarantees the existence of at least one subgroup $(H, *)$ of order p. If $(H, *)$ is not already a Sylow p-subgroup, then since G is finite, we are led (after a finite number of inspections) to a Sylow p-subgroup containing H.

Since the order of an element is preserved under conjugation, it is clear that any conjugate of a p-group is again a p-group. Even more is true. The conjugates of a Sylow p-subgroup $(P, *)$ are themselves Sylow p-subgroups (as an exercise, the reader should verify this fact); of course, some or all of these conjugate subgroups may be identical with $(P, *)$.

In the coming theorems, our goal is to show that if $(P, *)$ is a fixed Sylow p-subgroup of the finite group $(G, *)$, then any other Sylow p-subgroup of $(G, *)$ must in fact be a conjugate of $(P, *)$. We will also want to determine, so far as possible, the number of distinct Sylow p-subgroups of $(G, *)$. If, for example, there is a unique Sylow p-subgroup corresponding to a particular prime p, then this subgroup must be normal, since it is conjugate to itself.

Utilizing the Sylow Theorems, we can obtain some rather general results concerning the existence of subgroups of finite groups; for this, one need only know something about the order of the group.

The next theorems are major ones and require two preparatory lemmas.

Lemma. Let $(H, *)$ be a normal subgroup of $(G, *)$. If $(H, *)$ and $(G/H, \otimes)$ are both p-groups, then $(G, *)$ itself is a p-group.

Proof. For each a in G, the coset $a * H \in G/H$ has order some power of p, say order p^k. Then, $a^{p^k} * H = (a * H)^{p^k} = e * H$, so that $a^{p^k} \in H$. Thus, the element a^{p^k} also has p-power order, for instance, order p^j. This implies $(a^{p^k})^{p^j} = a^{p^{k+j}} = e$, whence $o(a) \mid p^{k+j}$. But, since p is a prime, it follows that $o(a)$ is a power of p.

We shall also need to know the following:

Lemma. Let $(P, *)$ be a Sylow p-subgroup of $(G, *)$ and $a \in G$ be any element whose order is a power of p. If $a * P * a^{-1} = P$, then $a \in P$.

Proof. Since the condition $a * P * a^{-1} = P$ means $a \in N(P)$, the problem is one of showing there can be no element in $N(P) - P$ of p-power order. Suppose such an element a actually did exist. Now, $(P, *)$ is normal in its normalizer, so we may consider the quotient group $(N(P)/P, \otimes)$ and the coset $a * P$. The order of a coset as an element in the quotient group divides the order of any of its representatives, whence $o(a * P)$ is a power of p. This implies the cyclic subgroup $((a * P), \otimes)$ of $(N(P)/P, \otimes)$ has p-power order and consequently is a p-group (corollary to Cauchy's Theorem). By the Correspondence Theorem, $(N(P), *)$ thus has a subgroup $(K, *)$ with $K \supseteq P$ and $K/P = (a * P)$. As $a \notin P$, K properly contains P. Furthermore, from the previous lemma, $(K, *)$ must be a p-group, since both $(P, *)$ and $((a * P), \otimes)$ are such. But this clearly contradicts the fact $(P, *)$ is a maximal p-subgroup. Accordingly, there can be no element of $N(P) - P$ whose order is a power of p.

We are now ready to state the first of the so-called Sylow Theorems.

Theorem 2–67. (*Sylow*). Let $(G, *)$ be a finite group and p a prime. Then the number of distinct Sylow p-subgroups of $(G, *)$ is congruent to 1 modulo p and is a divisor of $o(G)$.

Proof. Let $(P, *)$ be a fixed Sylow p-subgroup of $(G, *)$. We have already observed that any conjugate subgroup $(a * P * a^{-1}, *)$ of $(P, *)$ is also a Sylow p-subgroup. Thus, a natural starting point is to count the number of distinct conjugates of $(P, *)$. If $(P, *)$ is a normal subgroup (that is, self-conjugate), this number is 1. Otherwise, $(P, *)$ has a conjugate subgroup $(P_1, *)$, with $P_1 \neq P$.

Since any conjugate of $(P_1, *)$ is, at the same time, a conjugate of $(P, *)$, we first consider conjugates of $(P_1, *)$ induced by elements from P. According to the last lemma, the elements of P under which $(P_1, *)$ is invariant are precisely those of $P_1 \cap P$:

$$N_P(P_1) = \{a \in P \mid a * P_1 * a^{-1} = P_1\} = P_1 \cap P.$$

Since $(P_1 \cap P, *)$ is a p-subgroup of $(G, *)$, it follows that $o(P_1 \cap P)$ is a power of p. Now, from Theorem 2–61, the number of distinct conjugates of $(P_1, *)$ by elements of P is equal to

$$[P : N_P(P_1)] = o(P)/o(P_1 \cap P).$$

This shows that $[P : N_P(P_1)]$ must be some power of p, say p^{k_1}. Furthermore, $k_1 > 0$, for if $k_1 = 0$, then $o(P) = o(P_1 \cap P)$, so $P = P_1 \cap P$, or rather $P \subseteq P_1$. But the fact that $(P, *)$ is a maximal p-subgroup would imply $P = P_1$, which is impossible. Note also that $(P, *)$ will not be found among the conjugate subgroups of $(P_1, *)$ by elements of P; were $P = a * P_1 * a^{-1}$ for some $a \in P$, then $P_1 = a^{-1} * P * a \subseteq P$, again leading to a contradiction.

Now, if the conjugate subgroups of $(P, *)$ are not exhausted by $(P, *)$ and the p^{k_1} conjugates of $(P_1, *)$ induced by members of P, choose another conjugate $(P_2, *)$ distinct from any yet enumerated. As above, we can obtain the p^{k_2}, $k_2 > 0$, distinct conjugates of $(P_2, *)$ induced by P. No conjugate of $(P_2, *)$ by an element of P will also be an conjugate of $(P_1, *)$ by an element of P, for if

$$a * P_1 * a^{-1} = b * P_2 * b^{-1}, \qquad a, b \in P,$$

then $(b^{-1} * a) * P_1 * (b^{-1} * a)^{-1} = P_2$, with $b^{-1} * a \in P$, contrary to the choice of P_2. If necessary, repeat this argument once more. Since $(G, *)$ is a finite group, all the conjugates of $(P, *)$ are found after a finite number of steps, say n steps. The conjugate subgroups of $(P, *)$ are these: $(P, *)$ itself, the p^{k_1} conjugates of $(P_1, *)$ by elements of P, the p^{k_2} conjugates of $(P_2, *)$ by elements of P, etc. The total number of distinct conjugates is therefore

$$1 + p^{k_1} + p^{k_2} + \cdots + p^{k_n} = 1 + mp \equiv 1 \pmod{p}, \qquad k_i > 0.$$

At this stage, an obvious question arises: are there any Sylow p-subgroups which are not conjugate subgroups of $(P, *)$? The answer will be seen to be no. Let us assume such a subgroup $(R, *)$ does exist and arrive at a contradiction. As before, we count the conjugates of $(R, *)$. This is done by first finding the conjugates of $(R, *)$ induced by elements of P; there are

$$o(P)/o(R \cap P) = p^{j_1}$$

of them, where $j_1 > 0$ (if $j_1 = 0$, then $R = P$, a contradiction). Note that $(R, *)$ is itself included in this count, since $R = e * R * e^{-1}$, $e \in P$. Following the procedure above, the total number of conjugate subgroups of $(R, *)$ is found to be

$$p^{j_1} + p^{j_2} + \cdots + p^{j_n} \equiv 0 \pmod{p}, \qquad j_i > 0.$$

The important point here is that no term of this sum reduces to 1; if some $j_i = 0$, then $(R, *)$ would be a conjugate of $(P, *)$, which is impossible. But we have previously determined that the number of conjugates of any Sylow p-subgroup is congruent to 1 modulo p. Since no integer can at once be $\equiv 0 \pmod{p}$ and $\equiv 1 \pmod{p}$, we have the desired contradiction.

Finally, the number of distinct conjugates of the Sylow p-subgroup $(P, *)$ is, by Theorem 2–61, $[G : N_G(P)]$; since $(N_G(P), *)$ is a subgroup of $(G, *)$, $[G : N_G(P)]$ divides $o(G)$. This proves the theorem in its entirety.

The following facts were proved in the course of the argument.

Corollary. Any two Sylow p-subgroups of $(G, *)$ corresponding to the same prime p are conjugate, hence isomorphic.

Corollary. The number of distinct Sylow p-subgroups is $[G : N(P)]$, where $(P, *)$ is any particular Sylow p-subgroup of $(G, *)$.

This leads directly to the second major result of the section.

Theorem 2–68. (*Sylow*). Let $(G, *)$ be a finite group of order $p^k q$, where p is a prime not dividing q. Then $(G, *)$ has a Sylow p-subgroup of order p^k.

Proof. Suppose $(P, *)$ is any Sylow p-subgroup of $(G, *)$. Our contention is that $o(P) = p^k$. For this, it is enough to show $[G : P]$ has no p-power divisor. Since $(P, *)$ is a p-subgroup of $(G, *)$, $o(P) = p^j$, with $j \leq k$; hence,

$$p^k q = o(G) = [G : P]\, o(P) = (p^{k-j} q) p^j,$$

and, if one knows that $[G : P]$ is divisible by no power of p, then $j = k$.

The strategy we employ is to prove that both factors on the right of the equation

$$[G : P] = [G : N(P)][N(P) : P] = [G : N(P)]\, o(N(P)/P)$$

are prime to p. Now, $[G : N(P)]$ is equal to the number of conjugate subgroups of $(P, *)$ and, by our last result, this value must be congruent to 1 modulo p; therefore, the possibility $p \mid [G : N(P)]$ cannot occur.

To see that $o(N(P)/P)$ has no p-power divisor, let us assume the coset $a * P \in N(P)/P$ is of order p. Then, as before, $a^p * P = (a * P)^p = e * P$, which means $a^p \in P$. As $(P, *)$ is a p-group, the element a^p has order a power of p, so that a itself has p-power order. Because $a \in N(P)$, the last lemma implies $a \in P$; hence, $a * P = e * P$, or $o(a * P) = 1$. From this contradiction and Cauchy's Theorem, we infer that $p \nmid o(N(P)/P)$. Since p is a prime and divides neither of the factors of $[G : P]$, it cannot divide $[G : P]$ either, thereby completing the argument.

Example 2–64. There can be no simple group $(G, *)$ with $o(G) = 42$. Since $42 = 2 \cdot 3 \cdot 7$, the preceding theorem implies the group contains a subgroup $(H, *)$ of order 7. By Theorem 2–67, the number of conjugate subgroups of

$(H, *)$ is of the form $1 + 7k$, $k \in Z$, and divides 42; $k = 0$ is the only possibility. Hence $(H, *)$ is cyclic and a normal subgroup (i.e., self-conjugate), so that $(G, *)$ cannot be simple.

From Theorem 2–68, we can obtain a partial converse to Lagrange's Theorem: If $(G, *)$ is a finite group whose order is a product of powers of distinct primes,

$$o(G) = p_1^{k_1} p_2^{k_2} \cdots p_n^{k_n},$$

then $(G, *)$ has subgroups of orders $p_i^{k_i}$ $(i = 1, 2, \ldots, n)$. As a matter of fact, it can be shown that for each prime p_i, $(G, *)$ contains subgroups of orders $p_i, p_i^2, p_i^3, \ldots, p_i^{k_i}$. Thus, for instance, any group of order $12 = 2^2 \cdot 3$ will have subgroups of orders 2, 2^2 and 3; nothing, however, can be concluded in regard to a subgroup of order 6.

Example 2–65. Our work up to now has given us sufficient tools to show that any group $(G, *)$ of order 15 is cyclic. Since $15 = 3 \cdot 5$, we first note that $(G, *)$ has at least one Sylow 3-subgroup and at least one Sylow 5-subgroup. The number of Sylow 3-subgroups must, by Theorem 2–67, divide 15 and yet be $\equiv 1 \pmod 3$. As the only such integer is 1, there is a unique Sylow 3-subgroup, call it $(\mathrm{Sy}_3, *)$; in other words, $(\mathrm{Sy}_3, *)$ is cyclic (being of prime order) and normal in $(G, *)$. By the same reasoning, there is precisely one Sylow 5-subgroup, label it $(\mathrm{Sy}_5, *)$, which is also cyclic and normal. We propose to show that $(G, *) \simeq (\mathrm{Sy}_3 \times \mathrm{Sy}_5, \cdot)$.

Detouring slightly, let us record several preliminary observations: Because $(\mathrm{Sy}_3 \cap \mathrm{Sy}_5, *)$ is a subgroup of both $(\mathrm{Sy}_3, *)$ and $(\mathrm{Sy}_5, *)$, it follows that $o(\mathrm{Sy}_3 \cap \mathrm{Sy}_5)$ divides both 3 and 5. The only possibility is for $o(\mathrm{Sy}_3 \cap \mathrm{Sy}_5) = 1$, whence $\mathrm{Sy}_3 \cap \mathrm{Sy}_5 = \{e\}$. In particular, this means each element of $(\mathrm{Sy}_3, *)$ commutes with each element of $(\mathrm{Sy}_5, *)$ [Problem 10, Section 2–5].

Next, we consider cosets $a * \mathrm{Sy}_5$, where the element $a \in \mathrm{Sy}_3$. These cosets are evidently all distinct; for, if $a * \mathrm{Sy}_5 = b * \mathrm{Sy}_5$ $(a, b \in \mathrm{Sy}_3)$, then

$$a^{-1} * b \in \mathrm{Sy}_3 \cap \mathrm{Sy}_5 = \{e\},$$

so that $a = b$. However, $[G : \mathrm{Sy}_5] = 3$ and Sy_3 contains just 3 elements, which implies the cosets of Sy_5 in G must be of the form $a * \mathrm{Sy}_5$, $a \in \mathrm{Sy}_3$. Since each element of G lies in one and only one such coset, we infer at once that each element of G is uniquely expressible as a product $a * b$, with $a \in \mathrm{Sy}_3$, $b \in \mathrm{Sy}_5$.

The results of these last two paragraphs permit us to use Problem 19, Section 2–7, and thereby conclude $(G, *) \simeq (\mathrm{Sy}_3 \times \mathrm{Sy}_5, \cdot)$; but, on closer scrutiny, we note that

$$(\mathrm{Sy}_3 \times \mathrm{Sy}_5, \cdot) \simeq (Z_3 \times Z_5, \cdot) \simeq (Z_{15}, +_{15}),$$

a cyclic group of order 15 (the equipment needed is Problem 22, Section 2–7).

This finishes our study of group theory. We have not attempted to range over the whole theory nor to examine in depth any particular aspect of it. Instead, we have merely scratched the surface, introducing the reader to a few of the high points. Needless to say, current research in this branch of mathematics is both vigorous and extensive. A variety of classical problems still remain unsettled, while in some directions the research has only recently begun.

PROBLEMS

In the following set of problems, p always denotes a prime number.

1. Let $(H, *)$ and $(K, *)$ be two subgroups of the group $(G, *)$. Show that $(H, *)$ is normal in $(K, *)$ if and only if $H \subseteq K \subseteq N_G(H)$.

2. For a finite group $(G, *)$, prove that
   a) if $(G, *)$ has exactly two conjugacy classes, then $o(G) = 2$;
   b) if there exists an element $a \in G$ with exactly two conjugates, then $(G, *)$ contains a nontrivial normal subgroup.

3. Prove that a subgroup $(H, *)$ of $(G, *)$ is a normal subgroup if and only if the set H is the union of conjugacy classes of $(G, *)$.

4. Suppose $(H, *)$ is a proper subgroup of the finite group $(G, *)$. Verify that G contains an element which belongs to no conjugate subgroup of $(H, *)$.

5. Let $(G, *)$ be any group, a a fixed element in G. Define the function f by $f(x * C(a)) = x * a * x^{-1}$, $x \in G$. Prove that f is a one-to-one mapping from the left cosets of $C(a)$ onto the set of distinct conjugates of a, thereby deducing Theorem 2–63.

6. a) Describe the class equation of the symmetric group $(S_3, \circ)$.
   b) Show that, in a p-group, the number of self-conjugate elements (that is, elements whose conjugacy classes are singletons) must be a multiple of p.

7. For a finite p-group $(G, *)$, prove the following:
   a) Any homomorphic image of $(G, *)$ is again a p-group.
   b) $(G, *)$ has a normal subgroup of order p. [*Hint:* cent G contains an element of order p.]
   c) $(G, *)$ is a solvable group. [*Hint:* Induct on $o(G)$; show that (cent $G, *$) and $(G/\text{cent } G, \otimes)$ are both solvable.]

8. Prove that if $o(G) = p^n$, then the group $(G, *)$ has at least one normal subgroup of order p^k for all $0 \leq k \leq n$. [*Hint:* Proceed by induction on n and utilize part (b) of the last problem.]

9. Let $(H, *)$ be a normal subgroup of a finite p-group $(G, *)$ and suppose that $o(H) = p$. Establish the inclusion $H \subseteq \text{cent } G$.

10. Prove that if $o(G) = p^2$, then $(G, *)$ is a commutative group. [*Hint:* Recall Problem 21, Section 2–5.]

11. Let $(G, *)$ be a group such that $o(G) = p^n$. Verify the following assertions:

   a) $o(\text{cent } G) \neq p^{n-1}$.
   b) cent G contains at least p elements.
   c) Every subgroup of order p^{n-1} is normal in $(G, *)$.

12. Determine all Sylow p-subgroups of the group $(Z_{24}, +_{24})$.

13. Let $(P, *)$ be a Sylow p-subgroup of the finite group $(G, *)$. Prove that if $(H, *)$ is any subgroup of $(G, *)$ with $P \subseteq N(P) \subseteq H$, then $N(H) = H$; in particular, deduce that $N(N(P)) = N(P)$.

14. Prove that if $(H, *)$ is a p-subgroup of $(G, *)$ which is contained in exactly one Sylow p-subgroup $(P, *)$ of $(G, *)$, then $N(H) \subseteq N(P)$.

15. Suppose $(H, *)$ is a normal p-subgroup of the finite group $(G, *)$. Show that $(H, *)$ is a subgroup of each Sylow p-subgroup (for the same prime p) of $(G, *)$.

16. Prove that

   a) any group of order $2p$ has a normal subgroup of order p,
   b) there are no simple groups of orders 20, 30, or 56.

17. Let $(G, *)$ be a group of order pq, where $p < q$ are both primes.

   a) Show that $(G, *)$ has precisely one normal subgroup of order q.
   b) If $q \not\equiv 1 \pmod{p}$, prove that $(G, *)$ is a cyclic group.

18. Assume $(G, *)$ is a group of order $p^n q$, with p and q relatively prime. Prove that a subgroup $(H, *)$ of $(G, *)$ is a Sylow p-subgroup if and only if $o(H) = p^n$.

CHAPTER 3

RING THEORY

3–1 DEFINITION AND ELEMENTARY PROPERTIES OF RINGS

In this chapter, we shall investigate algebraic systems having two suitably restricted binary operations. Obvious examples are the familiar number systems of elementary mathematics (the integers, the rational numbers, etc.) and the algebra of sets.

Using these systems as models, we shall presently define an algebraic structure known as a ring. Inasmuch as a ring is basically a combination of a commutative group and a semigroup, our previous experience with groups will prove to be of considerable help. As the reader will see, many of the important notions in group theory have natural extensions to systems with two operations.

When there are two binary operations present, it is reasonable to expect them to be related in some way. The usual requirement is that one of the operations be distributive over the other.

Definition 3–1. Let $(S, *, \circ)$ be a mathematical system with binary operations $*$ and $\circ$. The operation $\circ$ is said to be *distributive* over the operation $*$ if

$$a \circ (b * c) = (a \circ b) * (a \circ c) \qquad \text{(left distributive law)}$$

and

$$(b * c) \circ a = (b \circ a) * (c \circ a) \qquad \text{(right distributive law)}$$

for every triple of elements $a, b, c \in S$.

If the operation $\circ$ happens to be commutative, then whenever $\circ$ is left distributive over the operation $*$, it is also right distributive (and conversely), since

$$(b * c) \circ a = a \circ (b * c) = (a \circ b) * (a \circ c) = (b \circ a) * (c \circ a).$$

Certainly, ordinary multiplication is distributive over ordinary addition, and we use this fact in the next example.

Example 3–1. Consider two binary operations $*$ and $\circ$ defined on the set Z of integers by $a * b = a + 2b$, $a \circ b = 2ab$. A simple calculation shows the operation $\circ$ to be left distributive over $*$, for

$$a \circ (b * c) = a \circ (b + 2c) = 2a(b + 2c) = 2ab + 4ac,$$

while

$$(a \circ b) * (a \circ c) = (2ab) * (2ac) = 2ab + 2(2ac)$$
$$= 2ab + 4ac.$$

Because ∘ is a commutative operation, we conclude that it is also right distributive over *.

Definition 3–2. A *ring* is a mathematical system $(R, *, \circ)$ consisting of a nonempty set R and two binary operations * and ∘ defined on R such that

1) $(R, *)$ is a commutative group,
2) $(R, \circ)$ is a semigroup,
3) the semigroup operation ∘ is distributive over the group operation *.

It is convenient and customary to use $+$ for the group operation and $\cdot$ for the semigroup operation, rather than the symbols * and ∘. This convention is long-standing and is particularly helpful in emphasizing the analogy between results obtained for rings and those of the familiar number systems. The above definition then takes the following form.

Definition 3–3. A ring is an ordered triple $(R, +, \cdot)$ consisting of a nonempty set R and two binary operations $+$ and $\cdot$ on R such that

1) $(R, +)$ is a commutative group,
2) $(R, \cdot)$ is a semigroup,
3) the two operations are related by the distributive laws

$$a \cdot (b + c) = (a \cdot b) + (a \cdot c),$$
$$(b + c) \cdot a = (b \cdot a) + (c \cdot a)$$

for all $a, b, c \in R$.

The reader should clearly understand that $+$ and $\cdot$ represent abstract unspecified operations and not ordinary addition and multiplication. For convenience, however, we shall refer to the operation $+$ as *addition* and the operation $\cdot$ as *multiplication*. In the light of this terminology, it is natural then to speak of the commutative group $(R, +)$ as being the *additive group* of the ring and $(R, \cdot)$ the *multiplicative semigroup* of the ring.

The unique identity element for addition is called the *zero element* of the ring and is denoted by the usual symbol for zero, 0. The unique additive inverse of an element $a \in R$ shall be written as $-a$.

In order to minimize the use of parentheses in expressions involving both operations, we make the stipulation that multiplication is to be performed before addition. Thus the expression $a \cdot b + c$ stands for $(a \cdot b) + c$ and not for $a \cdot (b + c)$.

With this notation in mind, we can now amplify our current definition of a ring. A ring $(R, +, \cdot)$ consists of a nonempty set R and two operations, called addition and multiplication and denoted by $+$ and $\cdot$, respectively, satisfying the requirements:

1) R is closed under addition,
2) $a + b = b + a$,
3) $(a + b) + c = a + (b + c)$,
4) there exists an element 0 in R such that $a + 0 = a$ for every $a \in R$,
5) for each $a \in R$, there exists an element $-a \in R$ such that $a + (-a) = 0$,
6) R is closed under multiplication,
7) $(a \cdot b) \cdot c = a \cdot (b \cdot c)$,
8) $a \cdot (b + c) = a \cdot b + a \cdot c$ and $(b + c) \cdot a = b \cdot a + c \cdot a$,

where it is understood that a, b, c represent arbitrary elements of R.

By placing further restrictions on the operation of multiplication, several special types of rings are obtained.

Definition 3–4. 1) A *commutative ring* is a ring in which $(R, \cdot)$ is a commutative semigroup; that is, the operation of multiplication is commutative.

2) A *ring with identity* is a ring in which $(R, \cdot)$ is a semigroup with identity; that is, there exists an identity element for the operation of multiplication, customarily denoted by the symbol 1.

In a ring $(R, +, \cdot)$ with identity, we say an element $a \in R$ is *invertible* if it possesses an inverse relative to multiplication. Multiplicative inverses are unique, when they exist, and shall be denoted as before by a^{-1}. The symbol R^* will be used subsequently to represent the set of all invertible elements of the ring.

Theorem 3–1. Let $(R, +, \cdot)$ be a ring with identity. Then the pair $(R^*, \cdot)$ forms a group, known as the *group of invertible elements*.

Proof. The set R^* is nonempty, for at the very least the multiplicative identity $1 \in R^*$; moreover, 1 serves as the identity element for the system $(R^*, \cdot)$. If $a, b \in R^*$, the equations

$$(a \cdot b) \cdot (b^{-1} \cdot a^{-1}) = a \cdot 1 \cdot a^{-1} = 1,$$
$$(b^{-1} \cdot a^{-1}) \cdot (a \cdot b) = b^{-1} \cdot 1 \cdot b = 1$$

show the product $a \cdot b$ is also a member of R^*. Whenever a is invertible, then we have $a \cdot a^{-1} = a^{-1} \cdot a = 1$, indicating that a^{-1} is in R^*. The associative law for multiplication is obviously inherited since $R^* \subseteq R$, so $(R^*, \cdot)$ is a group.

Before proceeding to the proofs of the basic results of ring theory, we shall consider several examples.

Example 3–2. Each of the following familiar systems, where $+$ and $\cdot$ indicate ordinary addition and multiplication, is a commutative ring:

$$(R^{\#}, +, \cdot), \quad (Q, +, \cdot), \quad (Z, +, \cdot), \quad (Z_e, +, \cdot).$$

The first three of these rings have an identity element, the integer 1, for multiplication.

Example 3–3. Another example of a ring is provided by the set

$$R = \{a + b\sqrt{3} \mid a,\, b \in Z\},$$

and the operations of ordinary addition and multiplication. The set R is obviously closed under these operations, for

$$(a + b\sqrt{3}) + (c + d\sqrt{3}) = (a + c) + (b + d)\sqrt{3} \in R,$$

$$(a + b\sqrt{3}) \cdot (c + d\sqrt{3}) = (ac + 3bd) + (ad + bc)\sqrt{3} \in R,$$

whenever $a,\, b,\, c,\, d \in Z$. We omit the details of showing that $(R, +, \cdot)$ is a commutative ring with identity element $1 = 1 + 0\sqrt{3} \in R$.

Example 3–4. If $P(X)$ is the power set of some nonempty set X, then both the triples $(P(X), \cup, \cap)$ and $(P(X), \cap, \cup)$ fail to be rings, since neither $(P(X), \cup)$ nor $(P(X), \cap)$ forms a group. However, the reader may recall that in Example 2–20 we showed the pair $(P(X), \Delta)$ to be a commutative group; here, the symbol Δ indicates the symmetric difference operation

$$A \,\Delta\, B = (A - B) \cup (B - A).$$

Since $(P(X), \cap)$ is clearly a commutative semigroup, in order to establish that the triple $(P(X), \Delta, \cap)$ constitutes a ring it is only necessary to verify the left distributivity of $\cap$ over Δ. For this, we require the set identity (Problem 6, Section 1–1)

$$A \cap (B - C) = (A \cap B) - (A \cap C).$$

The argument now proceeds as follows: for all subsets $A,\, B,\, C \subseteq X$,

$$\begin{aligned}
A \cap (B \,\Delta\, C) &= A \cap [(B - C) \cup (C - B)] \\
&= [A \cap (B - C)] \cup [A \cap (C - B)] \\
&= [(A \cap B) - (A \cap C)] \cup [(A \cap C) - (A \cap B)] \\
&= (A \cap B) \,\Delta\, (A \cap C).
\end{aligned}$$

Example 3–5. Let R denote the set of all functions $f \colon R^{\#} \to R^{\#}$. The sum $f + g$ and product $f \cdot g$ of two functions $f,\, g \in R$ are defined as usual, by the equations

$$(f + g)(a) = f(a) + g(a),$$

$$(f \cdot g)(a) = f(a) \cdot g(a), \qquad a \in R^{\#}.$$

In other words, we specify the functional value of these combinations at each point in their domain. That $(R, +, \cdot)$ is a commutative ring with identity follows from the fact that the real numbers with ordinary addition and multiplication comprise such a system. In particular, the multiplicative identity element is the constant function whose value at each real number is 1.

It is interesting to note that the triple $(R, +, \circ)$, where $\circ$ indicates the operation of functional composition, fails to be a ring. The left distributive law

$$f \circ (g + h) = (f \circ g) + (f \circ h)$$

does not hold in this case.

Example 3–6. For a more interesting example, let $(G, *)$ be an arbitrary commutative group and hom G be the set of all homomorphisms from $(G, *)$ into itself. From Theorem 2–36, it is already known that (hom G, $\circ$) is a semigroup with identity. We propose to introduce a notion of addition in hom G such that the triple (hom G, $+$, $\circ$) forms a ring with identity. To achieve this, simply define the sum $f + g$ of two functions f, $g \in$ hom G by the rule

$$(f + g)(a) = f(a) * g(a), \qquad a \in G.$$

With the possible exception of the closure condition, it is fairly evident that the pair (hom G, $+$) is a commutative group; the trivial homomorphism acts as the zero element, while the negative of each function $f \in$ hom G is obtained by taking $(-f)(a) = f(a)^{-1}$ for all $a \in G$. To establish closure, choose arbitrary elements a, $b \in G$ and functions f, g in hom G. Then

$$\begin{aligned}
(f + g)(a * b) &= f(a * b) * g(a * b) \\
&= f(a) * f(b) * g(a) * g(b) \\
&= \big(f(a) * g(a)\big) * \big(f(b) * g(b)\big) \\
&= (f + g)(a) * (f + g)(b),
\end{aligned}$$

so that the sum $f + g$ is also a homomorphism of $(G, *)$ into itself.

In regard to the left distributive law, we have, for any a in G,

$$\begin{aligned}
[f \circ (g + h)](a) &= f\big((g + h)(a)\big) \\
&= f\big(g(a) * h(a)\big) \\
&= f\big(g(a)\big) * f\big(h(a)\big) \\
&= (f \circ g)(a) * (f \circ h)(a) \\
&= (f \circ g + f \circ h)(a).
\end{aligned}$$

Therefore, $f \circ (g + h) = f \circ g + f \circ h$. The right distributive law follows in a similar manner, showing $(R, +, \circ)$ indeed to be a ring.

Needless to say, commutativity of the underlying group $(G, *)$ is essential to our discussion; in its absence, we could not even prove addition to be a binary operation in hom G.

Example 3–7. In Section 2–3, we considered the group $(Z_n, +_n)$ of integers modulo n. This group was obtained upon defining in the set Z_n the notion of addition of congruence classes:

$$[a] +_n [b] = [a + b].$$

A binary operation $\cdot_n$ of multiplication of classes may equally well be introduced in Z_n by specifying that for each pair of elements $[a], [b] \in Z_n$,

$$[a] \cdot_n [b] = [a \cdot b].$$

This latter definition presents a problem similar to that of addition in that we must show that the resulting product $[a \cdot b]$ is independent of the particular representatives chosen from the congruence classes $[a]$ and $[b]$. In other words, it must be established that whenever $[a'] = [a]$ and $[b'] = [b]$, then

$$[a' \cdot b'] = [a \cdot b].$$

We first observe that $a' \in [a'] = [a]$ and $b' \in [b'] = [b]$ imply that

$$a' \equiv a \pmod{n}, \qquad b' \equiv b \pmod{n}.$$

From Theorem 2–10 we are then able to conclude that

$$a' \cdot b' \equiv a \cdot b \pmod{n},$$

and consequently $a' \cdot b' \in [a \cdot b]$. This means, in view of Theorem 2–12, that $[a' \cdot b'] = [a \cdot b]$, as desired.

For each positive integer n, the system $(Z_n, +_n, \cdot_n)$ is a commutative ring with identity, known as the *ring of integers modulo n*. The verification that the ring axioms are satisfied is very straightforward, depending only on the definitions of the operations $+_n$ and $\cdot_n$ and the fact that $(Z, +, \cdot)$ itself is a ring.

For instance, to show the left distributivity of $\cdot_n$ over $+_n$, we choose $[a]$, $[b], [c] \in Z_n$ and obtain

$$
\begin{aligned}
[a] \cdot_n ([b] +_n [c]) &= [a] \cdot_n [b + c] \\
&= [a \cdot (b + c)] \\
&= [a \cdot b + a \cdot c] \\
&= [a \cdot b] +_n [a \cdot c] \\
&= [a] \cdot_n [b] +_n [a] \cdot_n [c].
\end{aligned}
$$

Clearly [1] is the multiplicative identity element. We shall leave the confirmation of the remaining ring axioms and of commutativity to the reader.

As mentioned earlier, it is convenient to remove the brackets in the designation of the congruence classes of Z_n, and this shall be our practice subsequently.

Given a ring $(R, +, \cdot)$, all the results of the previous chapter on groups apply to the system $(R, +)$. For instance, we know that the zero element and additive inverses are unique, that the cancellation law holds for addition, and so on. In the theorems to follow, we shall establish some of the fundamental properties which depend on both ring operations. As usual, we may assume nothing about the specific nature of the system $(R, +, \cdot)$ except that it satisfies the postulates presented in Definition 3–3.

Theorem 3–2. In any ring $(R, +, \cdot)$, if $a \in R$, then $a \cdot 0 = 0 \cdot a = 0$.

Proof. First note that an application of the left distributive law (and the fact that zero is the identity element for addition) yields

$$a \cdot 0 + a \cdot 0 = a \cdot (0 + 0) = a \cdot 0 = a \cdot 0 + 0.$$

By the cancellation law for addition, $a \cdot 0 = 0$. In similar fashion, one can show that $0 \cdot a = 0$.

The reader may have speculated as to whether, in a ring with multiplicative identity, the identity and zero elements of the ring are ever equal. It follows at once from Theorem 3–2 that this situation can only occur in the one-element ring $(\{0\}, +, \cdot)$, the so-called *zero ring;* the proof is given below:

Theorem 3–3. Let $(R, +, \cdot)$ be a ring with identity such that $R \neq \{0\}$. Then the elements 0 and 1 are distinct.

Proof. Since $R \neq \{0\}$, there exists some nonzero element $a \in R$. Now, if $1 = 0$, it would follow that

$$a = a \cdot 1 = a \cdot 0 = 0,$$

which is an obvious contradiction.

Unless stated to the contrary, we shall tacitly assume that *any ring with identity contains more than one element;* this will exclude the possibility that $1 = 0$.

Theorem 3–2 indicates that the product of two elements in a ring is zero whenever either factor is zero. The converse is not true. As the following examples will show, it may perfectly well happen that the product of two non-zero ring elements will be zero.

Example 3–8(a). Consider the set $R = R^{\#} \times R^{\#}$ of ordered pairs of real numbers. We define addition and multiplication in R by the formulas

$$(a, b) + (c, d) = (a + c, b + d), \qquad (a, b) \cdot (c, d) = (ac, bd).$$

Then straightforward calculations will show that $(R, +, \cdot)$ is a commutative ring with identity element $(1, 1)$. Here the zero element is the pair $(0, 0)$.

Observe that while

$$(1, 0) \cdot (0, 1) = (0, 0),$$

neither $(1, 0)$ nor $(0, 1)$ is the zero of the ring.

Example 3–8(b). Another example in which this situation occurs is the ring $(Z_4, +_4, \cdot_4)$ of integers modulo 4. The addition and multiplication tables are shown below:

$+_4$	0	1	2	3
0	0	1	2	3
1	1	2	3	0
2	2	3	0	1
3	3	0	1	2

$\cdot_4$	0	1	2	3
0	0	0	0	0
1	0	1	2	3
2	0	2	0	2
3	0	3	2	1

Here, we have $2 \cdot_4 2 = 0$, the product of nonzero elements being zero. Note also that $2 \cdot_4 1 = 2 \cdot_4 3$, yet it is clearly not true that $1 = 3$. The multiplicative semigroup $(Z_4, \cdot_4)$ does not satisfy the cancellation law.

Definition 3–5. A ring $(R, +, \cdot)$ is said to have *divisors of zero* if there exist nonzero elements $a, b \in R$ such that the product $a \cdot b = 0$.

We exhibited two rings in the above example which possess divisors of zero. The second ring, in particular, suggests a relationship between the existence of divisors of zero and the failure of the cancellation law for multiplication. We shall see shortly that this is indeed the case.

First, several preliminary results concerning additive inverses are required. We shall adopt the usual convention of writing $a + (-b)$ as $a - b$ and refer to this expression as the *difference* between a and b.

Theorem 3–4. Let $(R, +, \cdot)$ be a ring and $a, b \in R$. Then

$$-(a \cdot b) = a \cdot (-b) = (-a) \cdot b.$$

Proof. From the definition of additive inverse, we know that $b + (-b) = 0$. Using the left distributive law,

$$a \cdot b + a \cdot (-b) = a(b + (-b)) = a \cdot 0 = 0.$$

Inasmuch as the inverse of an element under addition is unique, this last equation implies that

$$-(a \cdot b) = a \cdot (-b).$$

A similar argument shows that $-(a \cdot b) = (-a) \cdot b$.

Corollary. For any elements $a, b \in R$,

$$(-a) \cdot (-b) = a \cdot b.$$

Proof. It follows from the above theorem that

$$(-a) \cdot (-b) = -((-a) \cdot b) = -(-(a \cdot b)) = a \cdot b.$$

The last equality stems from the fact that $(x^{-1})^{-1} = x$ in any group.

Corollary. If a, b, $c \in R$, then

$$a \cdot (b - c) = a \cdot b - a \cdot c, \qquad (b - c) \cdot a = b \cdot a - c \cdot a.$$

That is, multiplication is distributive over differences.

Proof. Since multiplication is left distributive over addition,

$$\begin{aligned} a \cdot (b - c) &= a \cdot (b + (-c)) = a \cdot b + a \cdot (-c) \\ &= a \cdot b + (-(a \cdot c)) \\ &= a \cdot b - a \cdot c. \end{aligned}$$

In a like manner, a ring distributive law for differences is obtained.

Having thus laid the groundwork, we are now able to establish the following result.

Theorem 3–5. A ring $(R, +, \cdot)$ is without divisors of zero if and only if the cancellation law holds for multiplication.

Proof. First, we assume the ring $(R, +, \cdot)$ contains no divisors of zero. Let a, b, c be elements of R such that $a \neq 0$ and $a \cdot b = a \cdot c$. Then,

$$a \cdot (b - c) = a \cdot b - a \cdot c = 0.$$

Since $a \neq 0$ and $(R, +, \cdot)$ has no zero divisors, this last equation implies $b - c = 0$ or $b = c$. In a similar manner, we can prove that $b \cdot a = c \cdot a$, with $a \neq 0$, yields $b = c$.

Conversely, suppose that the cancellation law holds in the semigroup $(R, \cdot)$ and the product $a \cdot b = 0$. If the element a is nonzero, then it may be canceled from the equation $a \cdot b = a \cdot 0$ to conclude $b = 0$. On the other hand, $b \neq 0$ implies $a = 0$ by the same argument. This shows $(R, +, \cdot)$ is free of divisors of zero.

Corollary. Let $(R, +, \cdot)$ be a ring with identity which has no zero divisors. Then the only solutions of the equation $a^2 = a$ are $a = 0$ and $a = 1$.

Proof. The proof is easy. If $a^2 = a = a \cdot 1$, with $a \neq 0$, then by virtue of the cancellation law $a = 1$.

Definition 3–6. An *integral domain* is a commutative ring with identity which does not have divisors of zero.

We have just shown that the cancellation law for multiplication is satisfied in any integral domain.

A word of caution: Some authors omit the requirement of an identity and use the term integral domain to indicate any commutative ring without zero divisors. For our purposes, the preceding definition is more appropriate.

In Section 2–4, we discussed the concept of a subgroup of a group. It is natural that there should be a corresponding notion of subsystems for rings.

Definition 3–7. Let $(R, +, \cdot)$ be a ring and $S \subseteq R$ be a nonempty subset of R. If the triple $(S, +, \cdot)$ is itself a ring, then $(S, +, \cdot)$ is said to be a *subring* of $(R, +, \cdot)$.

An examination of the definition of ring as given in Definition 3–2 shows that $(S, +, \cdot)$ is a subring of $(R, +, \cdot)$ provided $(S, +)$ is a subgroup of $(R, +)$, $(S, \cdot)$ is a subsemigroup of $(R, \cdot)$, and the two distributive laws hold for elements of S. But both the distributive and associative laws hold automatically in S as a consequence of their validity in R. Since these laws are inherited from R, there is no particular necessity of requiring them in the definition of a subring.

In view of this observation, a subring could alternatively be defined as follows: the triple $(S, +, \cdot)$ is a subring of the ring $(R, +, \cdot)$ whenever

1) S is a nonempty subset of R,
2) $(S, +)$ is a subgroup of $(R, +)$,
3) S is closed under multiplication.

Even this definition may be improved upon, for the reader may recall that if $\emptyset \neq H \subseteq G$, then the pair $(H, *)$ is a subgroup of the group $(G, *)$ provided that $a, b \in H$ implies $a * b^{-1} \in H$. Adjusting the notation to our present situation, we obtain a minimal set of conditions for determining subrings.

Definition 3–8. Let $(R, +, \cdot)$ be a ring and $\emptyset \neq S \subseteq R$. Then the triple $(S, +, \cdot)$ is a subring of $(R, +, \cdot)$ if and only if

1) $a - b \in S$ whenever $a, b \in S$ (closed under differences),
2) $a \cdot b \in S$ whenever $a, b \in S$ (closed under multiplication).

Example 3–9. Every ring $(R, +, \cdot)$ has two *trivial* subrings; for, if 0 denotes the zero element of the ring $(R, +, \cdot)$, then both $(\{0\}, +, \cdot)$ and $(R, +, \cdot)$ are subrings of $(R, +, \cdot)$.

Example 3–10. In the ring of integers $(Z, +, \cdot)$, the triple $(Z_e, +, \cdot)$ is a subring, while $(Z_o, +, \cdot)$ is not. In particular, we infer that in a ring with identity, a subring does not need to contain the identity element.

Example 3–11. Consider $(Z_6, +_6, \cdot_6)$, the ring of integers modulo 6. If $S = \{0, 2, 4\}$, then $(S, +_6, \cdot_6)$, whose operation tables are given at the right, is a subring of $(Z_6, +_6, \cdot_6)$.

$+_6$	0	2	4
0	0	2	4
2	2	4	0
4	4	0	2

$\cdot_6$	0	2	4
0	0	0	0
2	0	4	2
4	0	2	4

Example 3–12. Let $S = \{a + b\sqrt{3} \mid a, b \in Z\}$. Then $(S, +, \cdot)$ is a subring of $(R, +, \cdot)$, since for $a, b, c, d \in Z$,

$$(a + b\sqrt{3}) - (c + d\sqrt{3}) = (a - c) + (b - d)\sqrt{3} \in S,$$

$$(a + b\sqrt{3}) \cdot (c + d\sqrt{3}) = (ac + 3bd) + (bc + ad)\sqrt{3} \in S.$$

This shows that S is closed under both differences and products.

It has already been pointed out that, when a ring has an identity, this need not be true of its subrings. Other interesting situations may arise:

1) Some subring has multiplicative identity, but the entire ring does not.
2) Both the ring and one of its subrings possess identity elements which are distinct.

In each of these cases, the identity for the subring must be a divisor of zero in the parent ring.

To justify this last assertion, let $1'$ denote the identity element of the subring $(S, +, \cdot)$; we assume $1'$ is not an identity for the entire ring $(R, +, \cdot)$. Accordingly, there exists an element $a \in R$ for which $a \cdot 1' \neq a$. It is clear that

$$(a \cdot 1') \cdot 1' = a \cdot (1' \cdot 1') = a \cdot 1'$$

or

$$(a \cdot 1' - a) \cdot 1' = 0.$$

Since neither $a \cdot 1' - a$ nor $1'$ is zero, the ring $(R, +, \cdot)$ has zero divisors; in particular, $1'$ is a zero divisor of $(R, +, \cdot)$.

To give a simple illustration of a ring in which possibility (2) occurs, we may refer to Example 3–8. There, the system $(R^\# \times R^\#, +, \cdot)$ was shown to be a ring provided addition and multiplication are defined by

$$(a, b) + (c, d) = (a + c, b + d), \qquad (a, b) \cdot (c, d) = (ac, bd).$$

It is a routine matter to verify that the triple $(R^\# \times 0, +, \cdot)$ forms a subring with identity element $(1, 0)$; in this case, $(1, 0)$ differs from the identity for the parent ring which is the ordered pair $(1, 1)$.

Regarding each element of the ring $(R, +, \cdot)$ as simply a member of the additive group $(R, +)$, the familiar laws pertaining to integral exponents (Theorem 2–8) may be translated directly into properties of integral multiples. Thus, for $a, b \in R$ and arbitrary integers n and m, the following hold:

$$(n + m)a = na + ma,$$

$$(nm)a = n(ma),$$

$$n(a + b) = na + nb.$$

In addition to these rules, there are two further properties resulting from the distributive law, namely

$$n(a \cdot b) = (na) \cdot b = a \cdot (nb),$$

$$(na) \cdot (mb) = (nm)(a \cdot b).$$

We should emphasize that the symbol na does not necessarily represent a ring product; indeed, the integer n may not even be a member of R. For $n > 0$, the notation na is merely an abbreviation for the finite sum $a + a + \cdots + a$, n summands. However, when there is an identity element present, it is possible to express na as the product of two ring elements: $na = (n1) \cdot a$.

Definition 3–9. Let $(R, +, \cdot)$ be an arbitrary ring. If there exists a positive integer n such that $na = 0$ for all $a \in R$, then the least positive integer with this property is called the *characteristic* of the ring. If no such positive integer exists (that is, $na = 0$ for all $a \in R$ implies $n = 0$), then we say $(R, +, \cdot)$ has *characteristic zero*.

The rings of integers, rational numbers and real numbers are standard examples of systems having characteristic zero. On the other hand, the ring $(P(X), \Delta, \cap)$ is of characteristic two, since

$$2A = A \; \Delta \; A = (A - A) \cup (A - A) = \emptyset$$

from every subset A of X.

Theorem 3–6. Let $(R, +, \cdot)$ be a ring with identity. Then $(R, +, \cdot)$ has characteristic $n > 0$ if and only if n is the least positive integer for which $n1 = 0$.

Proof. If the ring $(R, +, \cdot)$ is of characteristic $n > 0$, it follows trivially that $n1 = 0$. Were $m1 = 0$, where $0 < m < n$, then

$$ma = m(1 \cdot a) = (m1) \cdot a = 0 \cdot a = 0$$

for every element $a \in R$. This would mean the characteristic of $(R, +, \cdot)$ is less than n, an obvious contradiction. The converse is established in much the same way.

Corollary. In an integral domain, all the nonzero elements have the same additive order, which is the characteristic of the domain.

Proof. To verify this assertion, suppose the integral domain $(R, +, \cdot)$ has positive characteristic n. According to the definition of characteristic, any $a \in R$ $(a \neq 0)$ will then possess a finite additive order m, with $m \leq n$. But the equation

$$0 = ma = (m1) \cdot a$$

implies $m1 = 0$, since $(R, +, \cdot)$ is free of zero divisors. We may therefore conclude from the theorem that $n \leq m$. Hence $m = n$ and every nonzero element of R has additive order n.

A somewhat similar argument can be employed when $(R, +, \cdot)$ is of characteristic zero. The equation $ma = 0$ would lead, as before, to $m1 = 0$ and consequently $m = 0$. In this case, each nonzero element of R must be of infinite order.

The last theorem serves to bring out another point.

Corollary. The characteristic of an integral domain $(R, +, \cdot)$ is either zero or a prime number.

Proof. Let $(R, +, \cdot)$ be of positive characteristic n and assume that n is not a prime. Then n can be written as $n = n_1 n_2$ with $1 < n_i < n$ $(i = 1, 2)$. We therefore have

$$0 = n1 = (n_1 n_2)1 = (n_1 n_2)1^2 = (n_1 1) \cdot (n_2 1).$$

Since by hypothesis $(R, +, \cdot)$ is without zero divisors, either $n_1 1 = 0$ or $n_2 1 = 0$. But this is plainly absurd, for it contradicts the choice of n as the least positive integer such that $n1 = 0$. Hence, we are led to conclude that the characteristic must be prime.

Now, suppose $(R, +, \cdot)$ is an arbitrary ring with identity and consider the set $Z1$ of integral multiples of the identity

$$Z1 = \{n1 \mid n \in Z\}.$$

From the relations

$$n1 - m1 = (n - m)1 \qquad \text{and} \qquad (n1) \cdot (m1) = (nm)1$$

one can easily see that the triple $(Z1, +, \cdot)$ itself forms a commutative subring with identity. The order of the additive cyclic group $(Z1, +)$ is simply the characteristic of the original ring $(R, +, \cdot)$.

In case $(R, +, \cdot)$ is an integral domain of characteristic $p > 0$, p a prime number, we are able to show considerably more: each nonzero element of $(Z1, +, \cdot)$ is invertible. Before proving this, first observe that by Theorem 2–23, the set $Z1$ consists of p distinct elements; namely, the p sums $n1$, where $n = 0$, $1, \ldots, p - 1$. Now, let $n1$ be any nonzero element of $Z1$, $0 < n < p$. Since p and n are relatively prime, there exist integers r, s for which $rp + sn = 1$. Therefore,

$$1 = (rp + sn)1 = (r1) \cdot (p1) + (s1) \cdot (n1).$$

As $p1 = 0$, we obtain $1 = (s1) \cdot (n1)$, so that $s1$ constitutes the multiplicative inverse of $n1$ in $(Z1, +, \cdot)$.

We shall return to a further discussion of the characteristic of a ring at the appropriate place in the sequel; in particular, the value of this last result will have to await future developments.

PROBLEMS

1. Define two binary operations $*$ and $\circ$ on the set Z of integers by

$$a * b = a + b + 2,$$
$$a \circ b = ab + 2a + 2b + 2.$$

   Show that $\circ$ is distributive over $*$.

2. Let $(R, +)$ be any commutative group. Determine whether $(R, +, \cdot)$ forms a ring if multiplication is defined by
   a) $a \cdot b = a$,
   b) $a \cdot b = 0$, where 0 is the identity element of the group $(R, +)$.

3. Let $(R, +, \cdot)$ be an arbitrary ring. In R define a new binary operation $\circ$ by the rule

$$a \circ b = a \cdot b + b \cdot a$$

   for all $a, b \in R$. Establish that $(R, +, \circ)$ is a commutative ring.

4. Obtain the group of invertible elements $(Z_{12}^*, \cdot_{12})$ for the ring $(Z_{12}, +_{12}, \cdot_{12})$. In addition, show that $(Z_{12}^*, \cdot_{12})$ is isomorphic to Klein's four-group.

5. Given that a, b, c, d are elements of a ring $(R, +, \cdot)$, prove that
   a) $(a + b) \cdot (c + d) = a \cdot c + b \cdot c + a \cdot d + b \cdot d$,
   b) $-(a \cdot b \cdot c) = (-a) \cdot (-b) \cdot (-c)$,
   c) if $a \cdot b = b \cdot a = 0$, then $(a + b)^n = a^n + b^n$ for $n \in Z_+$.
   (As usual, $a^n = a \cdot a \cdots a$, n times.)

6. Define two binary operations $*$ and $\circ$ on the set Z of integers as follows:

$$a * b = a + b - 1,$$
$$a \circ b = a + b - ab.$$

   Prove that the system $(Z, *, \circ)$ is a commutative ring with identity.

7. Let R be the set of all ordered pairs of nonzero real numbers. In the following cases, determine whether $(R, +, \cdot)$ is a commutative ring with identity. For those systems failing to be so, indicate which axioms are not satisfied:
   a) $(a, b) + (c, d) = (ac, bc + d)$, $(a, b) \cdot (c, d) = (ac, bd)$,
   b) $(a, b) + (c, d) = (a + c, b + d)$, $(a, b) \cdot (c, d) = (ac + bd, ad + bd)$,
   c) $(a, b) + (c, d) = (ad + bd, bd)$, $(a, b) \cdot (c, d) = (ac, bd)$,
   d) $(a, b) + (c, d) = (a + c, b + d)$, $(a, b) \cdot (c, d) = (ac, ad + bc)$.

8. In a ring $(R, +, \cdot)$ with identity, prove that
   a) the multiplicative identity element is unique,
   b) if $a \in R$ has a multiplicative inverse, then a^{-1} is unique,
   c) if the element a is invertible, so also is $-a$ and $(-a)^{-1} = -a^{-1}$,
   d) no divisor of zero can possess a multiplicative inverse.

9. Let $(R, +, \cdot)$ be a ring which has the property that $a^2 = a$ for every $a \in R$. Prove that $(R, +, \cdot)$ is a commutative ring. [*Hint:* First show $a + a = 0$ for any $a \in R$.]

10. Prove that a ring $(R, +, \cdot)$ is commutative if and only if

$$(a + b)^2 = a^2 + 2(a \cdot b) + b^2$$

for every pair of elements $a, b \in R$.

11. Discover divisors of zero to show that $(Z_6, +_6, \cdot_6)$ is not an integral domain. More generally, show that $(Z_n, +_n, \cdot_n)$ contains divisors of zero if n is not prime.

12. a) In an integral domain, show that the only solutions of the equation $a^2 = 1$ are either $a = 1$ or $a = -1$.

    b) If the set X contains more than one element, prove that every nonempty proper subset of X is a divisor of zero in the ring $(P(X), \triangle, \cap)$.

13. An element a of a ring $(R, +, \cdot)$ is said to be *nilpotent* if $a^n = 0$ for some $n \in Z_+$. Prove that in an integral domain the zero element is the only nilpotent element.

14. Prove that the system $(\{0, 3, 6, 9\}, +_{12}, \cdot_{12})$ is a subring of $(Z_{12}, +_{12}, \cdot_{12})$, the ring of integers modulo 12.

15. Derive the result: if $(S, +, \cdot)$ and $(T, +, \cdot)$ are both subrings of the ring $(R, +, \cdot)$, then so also is the triple $(S \cap T, +, \cdot)$.

16. Prove that in an integral domain any subring which contains the identity element is again an integral domain.

17. The *center* of a ring $(R, +, \cdot)$, denoted by cent R, is the set

$$\text{cent } R = \{c \in R \mid c \cdot x = x \cdot c \text{ for all } x \in R\}.$$

Prove that (cent $R, +, \cdot$) is a subring of $(R, +, \cdot)$.

18. For every $n > 1$, show that there exists at least one ring of characteristic n. [*Hint:* Consider the ring $(Z_n, +_n, \cdot_n)$.]

19. a) If a and b are elements of a commutative ring with identity and $n \in Z_+$, obtain the analog of the familiar binomial expansion for $(a + b)^n$:

$$(a + b)^n = \sum_{k=0}^{n} \binom{n}{k} a^{n-k} b^k.$$

As usual, the binomial coefficient $\binom{n}{k} = \dfrac{n!}{(n-k)!k!}$.

    b) From this, deduce that in an integral domain of characteristic $p > 0$,

$$(a + b)^p = a^p + b^p$$

for all a and b.

20. Suppose $(R, *, \circ)$ and $(R', *', \circ')$ are two rings. Define binary operations $+$ and $\cdot$ on the Cartesian product $R \times R'$ as follows:

$$(a, b) + (c, d) = (a * c, b *' d), \qquad (a, b) \cdot (c, d) = (a \circ c, b \circ' d).$$

    a) Prove that the system $(R \times R', +, \cdot)$ forms a ring, called the *direct product* of the rings $(R, *, \circ)$ and $(R', *', \circ')$.

    b) If the original rings are commutative with identity, show that the same must be true of $(R \times R', +, \cdot)$.

3–2 IDEALS AND QUOTIENT RINGS

In this section we introduce an important class of subrings, known as ideals, whose role in ring theory is similar to that of the normal subgroups in the study of groups. As shall be seen, ideals lead to the construction of quotient rings which are the appropriate analogs of quotient groups.

Definition 3–10. A subring $(I, +, \cdot)$ of the ring $(R, +, \cdot)$ is an *ideal* of $(R, +, \cdot)$ if and only if $r \in R$ and $a \in I$ imply both $r \cdot a \in I$ and $a \cdot r \in I$.

Thus we require that whenever one of the factors in a product belongs to I, the product itself must be a member of I. In a sense, the set I "captures" products.

If $(I, +, \cdot)$ is a subring of $(R, +, \cdot)$, I is already closed under multiplication. For $(I, +, \cdot)$ to be an ideal, a stronger closure condition is imposed: I is closed under multiplication by an arbitrary element of R.

In view of Definition 3–8, which gives a minimum set of conditions on I for $(I, +, \cdot)$ to be a subring, our present definition of ideal may be rephrased as follows:

Definition 3–11. Let $(R, +, \cdot)$ be a ring and I a nonempty subset of R. Then $(I, +, \cdot)$ is an ideal of $(R, +, \cdot)$ if and only if

1) $a, b \in I$ imply $a - b \in I$,

2) $r \in R$ and $a \in I$ imply both $r \cdot a \in I$ and $a \cdot r \in I$.

In the case of a commutative ring, of course, we need only require $r \cdot a \in I$.

Before proceeding further, we shall examine this concept by means of several specific examples.

Example 3–13. In any ring $(R, +, \cdot)$, the trivial subrings $(R, +, \cdot)$ and $(\{0\}, +, \cdot)$ are both ideals. A ring which contains no ideals except these two is said to be *simple*. Any ideal different from $(R, +, \cdot)$ is termed *proper*.

Example 3–14. The subring $(\{0, 3, 6, 9\}, +_{12})$ is an ideal of $(Z_{12}, +_{12}, \cdot_{12})$, the ring of integers modulo 12.

Example 3–15. For a fixed integer $a \in Z$, let (a) denote the set of all integral multiples of a, that is,

$$(a) = \{na \mid n \in Z\}.$$

The following relations show the triple $((a), +, \cdot)$ to be an ideal of the ring of integers $(Z, +, \cdot)$:

$$na - ma = (n - m)a,$$

$$m(na) = (mn)a, \qquad n, m \in Z.$$

In particular, since $(2) = Z_e$, the ring of even integers $(Z_e, +, \cdot)$ is an ideal of $(Z, +, \cdot)$.

Example 3–16. Suppose $(R, +, \cdot)$ is the commutative ring of functions of Example 3–5. Define

$$I = \{f \in R \mid f(1) = 0\}.$$

For functions $f, g \in I$ and $h \in R$, we have

$$(f - g)(1) = f(1) - g(1) = 0 - 0 = 0$$

and also

$$(h \cdot f)(1) = h(1) \cdot f(1) = h(1) \cdot 0 = 0.$$

Since both $f - g$ and $h \cdot g$ belong to I, $(I, +, \cdot)$ is an ideal of $(R, +, \cdot)$.

If condition (2) of the definition of ideal is weakened so as to only require that the product $r \cdot a$ belongs to I for every $a \in I$ and $r \in R$, then we arrive at the notion of a *left ideal* (*right ideals* are defined in a similar way). For commutative rings, it is plain that every left (right) ideal is an ideal or, as it is sometimes called, a *two-sided ideal*.

We next derive several interesting and useful results concerning ideals of arbitrary rings.

Theorem 3–7. If $(I, +, \cdot)$ is a proper ideal of a ring $(R, +, \cdot)$ with identity, then no element of I has a multiplicative inverse; that is, $I \cap R^* = \emptyset$.

Proof. Suppose to the contrary that there is some member $a \neq 0$ of I such that a^{-1} exists. Since I is closed under multiplication by arbitrary elements of R, $a^{-1} \cdot a = 1 \in I$. It then follows by the same reasoning that I contains $r \cdot 1 = r$ for every $r \in R$. That is, $R \subseteq I$. Inasmuch as the opposite inclusion always holds, $I = R$, contradicting the hypothesis that I is a proper subset of R.

Theorem 3–8. If $(I_i, +, \cdot)$ is an arbitrary indexed collection of ideals of the ring $(R, +, \cdot)$, then so also is $(\cap I_i, +, \cdot)$.

Proof. First, observe that the intersection $\cap I_i$ is nonempty, for each of the sets I_i must contain the zero element of the ring. Suppose the elements a, $b \in \cap I_i$ and $r \in R$. Then a and b are members of I_i, where i ranges over the index set. As the triple $(I_i, +, \cdot)$ is an ideal of $(R, +, \cdot)$, it follows from Definition 3–11 that $a - b$, $r \cdot a$ and $a \cdot r$ all lie in the set I_i. But this is true for every value of i, so the elements $a - b$, $r \cdot a$ and $a \cdot r$ belong to $\cap I_i$, which implies that $(\cap I_i, +, \cdot)$ is an ideal of $(R, +, \cdot)$.

Consider, for the moment, an arbitrary ring $(R, +, \cdot)$ and a nonempty subset S of R. By the symbol (S) we shall mean the set

$$(S) = \cap \{I \mid S \subseteq I; (I, +, \cdot) \text{ is an ideal of } (R, +, \cdot)\}.$$

The collection of all ideals which contain S is not empty, since the improper ideal $(R, +, \cdot)$ clearly belongs to it; thus, the set (S) exists and is such that $S \subseteq (S)$. Theorem 3–8 leads directly to the following result.

Theorem 3–9. The triple $((S), +, \cdot)$ is an ideal of the ring $(R, +, \cdot)$, known as *the ideal generated by the set S.*

It is noteworthy that whenever $(I, +, \cdot)$ is any ideal of $(R, +, \cdot)$ for which $S \subseteq I$, then $(S) \subseteq I$. In view of this, one frequently speaks of $((S), +, \cdot)$ as being the *smallest* ideal to contain the set S. An ideal generated by a single ring element, say a, is called a *principal ideal* and is designated by $((a), +, \cdot)$.

A natural undertaking is to determine the precise form of the members of (S). If we impose the requirement that $(R, +, \cdot)$ be a commutative ring, it is a fairly simple matter to check that (S) is given by

$$(S) = \{ \textstyle\sum r_i \cdot s_i + \sum n_j s_j \mid r_i \in R;\, s_i,\, s_j \in S;\, n_j \in Z \},$$

where the symbol $\sum$ indicates a finite sum with one or more terms. The proof is left to the reader as an exercise.

In the case of the principal ideal $((a), +, \cdot)$, this description of (S) reduces to

$$(a) = \{ r \cdot a + na \mid r \in R,\, n \in Z \}.$$

Observe, incidentally, that the element a is contained in (a), since $a = 0 \cdot a + 1a$. When there is an identity element present, the term na becomes superfluous. For, in this situation, we may write the expression $r \cdot a + na$ as

$$r \cdot a + na = r \cdot a + n(1 \cdot a)$$
$$= r \cdot a + (n1) \cdot a = (r + n1) \cdot a,$$

with $r + n1$ a ring element. Thus, the set (a) merely consists of all ring multiples of a:

$$(a) = \{ r \cdot a \mid r \in R \}.$$

In actual fact, the elements $r \cdot a$ $(r \in R)$ comprise the set of elements of an ideal of $(R, +, \cdot)$ even when the ring does not possess an identity; the difficulty, however, is that this ideal need not contain a itself. The next theorem formalizes these ideas.

Theorem 3–10. If $(R, +, \cdot)$ is a commutative ring with identity and $a \in R$, then the principal ideal $((a), +, \cdot)$ generated by a is such that

$$(a) = \{ r \cdot a \mid r \in R \}.$$

The principal ideals are the only ideals of the ring of integers, as the following theorem will show.

Theorem 3–11. If $(I, +, \cdot)$ is an ideal of the ring $(Z, +, \cdot)$, then $I = (n)$ for some nonnegative integer n.

Proof. If $I = \{0\}$, the theorem is trivially true, for the zero ideal $(\{0\}, +, \cdot)$ is the principal ideal generated by 0. Suppose then that I does not consist of the zero element alone. Now, if $m \in I$, $-m$ also belongs to I, so that I contains positive integers. Let n designate the least positive integer in I. As $(I, +, \cdot)$ is an ideal, each integral multiple of n must be in I, that is, $(n) \subseteq I$.

On the other hand, any integer $k \in I$ may be expressed as $k = qn + r$, where $q, r \in Z$ and $0 \leq r < n$. Since k and qn are members of I, it follows that $k - qn = r \in I$. Our definition of the integer n implies $r = 0$, and consequently $k = qn$. Thus every member of I is a multiple of n implying that $I \subseteq (n)$. The two inclusions show $I = (n)$, completing the argument.

Actually, a much shorter proof of the foregoing result could be obtained using Theorem 2–24; the proof, as given, has the advantage of being self contained.

By a *principal ideal ring* is meant a commutative ring with identity in which every ideal is principal. It is apparent from Theorem 3–11 that the ring of integers constitutes a principal ideal ring.

Now, suppose that $a_1, a_2, \ldots, a_n$ are nonzero elements of $(R, +, \cdot)$, a commutative ring with identity. An element $a \in R$ is said to be a *common multiple* of $a_1, a_2, \ldots, a_n$ provided a is a ring multiple of each of these. For instance, the products $a_1 \cdot a_2 \cdots a_n$ and $-(a_1 \cdot a_2 \cdots a_n)$ are both common multiples of $a_1, a_2, \ldots, a_n$. We shall call the element a a *least common multiple* of $a_1, a_2, \ldots, a_n$ if (1) a is a common multiple of these elements and (2) any other common multiple of $a_1, a_2, \ldots, a_n$ is a multiple of a as well.

We make immediate use of this terminology to prove the next theorem.

Theorem 3–12. Let $a_1, a_2, \ldots, a_n$ be nonzero elements of a principal ideal ring $(R, +, \cdot)$. Then

$$(\cap(a_i), +, \cdot) = ((a), +, \cdot),$$

where a is a least common multiple of $a_1, a_2, \ldots, a_n$.

Proof. According to Theorem 3–9, the triple $(\cap(a_i), +, \cdot)$ is an ideal of $(R, +, \cdot)$. But every ideal of $(R, +, \cdot)$ is a principal ideal; hence, there exists an element $a \in R$ for which $(a) = \cap(a_i)$. Since $(a) \subseteq (a_i)$ $[i = 1, 2, \ldots, n]$, $a = r_i \cdot a_i$ for some $r_i \in R$. We thus conclude that a is a common multiple of $a_1, a_2, \ldots, a_n$.

Next, assume b is any common multiple of $a_1, a_2, \ldots, a_n$, say $b = s_i \cdot a_i$, where $s_i \in R$ $[i = 1, 2, \ldots, n]$. If $r \in R$, then

$$r \cdot b = r \cdot (s_i \cdot a_i) = (r \cdot s_i) \cdot a_i \in (a_i),$$

which shows $(b) \subseteq (a_i)$ for each value of i. Therefore $(b) \subseteq \cap(a_i) = (a)$ and accordingly b must be a multiple of a. Our argument establishes that a is a least common multiple of $a_1, a_2, \ldots, a_n$.

To illustrate this theorem, consider the principal ideals $((4), +, \cdot)$ and $((6), +, \cdot)$ generated by the integers 4 and 6 in the ring $(Z, +, \cdot)$. The reader can easily verify that

$$((4) \cap (6), +, \cdot) = ((12), +, \cdot),$$

where 12 is the least common multiple of 4 and 6.

We now turn our attention to the matter of cosets in a ring. If $(I, +, \cdot)$ is an ideal of the ring $(R, +, \cdot)$, then, since addition is commutative, the system $(I, +)$ is a normal subgroup of $(R, +)$. Thus by the results of Section 2–5, we may construct the quotient group of R by I.

In our present notation, the cosets of I in R assume the form

$$a + I = \{a + i \mid i \in I\},$$

where $a \in R$. By Theorem 2–27, two cosets $a + I$ and $b + I$ are equal if and only if $a - b \in I$.

As before, the collection of distinct cosets of I in R shall be denoted by R/I. It follows from Theorem 2–33 and Problem 14, Section 2–5, that if addition of cosets is defined by the rule

$$(a + I) + (b + I) = (a + b) + I,$$

then $(R/I, +)$ becomes a commutative group. An operation of multiplication can also be introduced in R/I in a natural way with the result that a ring is obtained; all we need to do is to specify

$$(a + I) \cdot (b + I) = (a \cdot b) + I.$$

Because $(I, +, \cdot)$ is an ideal, this definition of coset multiplication is well defined and does not depend on the particular representatives of the cosets used. Indeed, suppose that

$$a + I = a' + I$$

and

$$b + I = b' + I.$$

Then, as observed above, $a - a' = i_1$ and $b - b' = i_2$, where $i_1, i_2 \in I$. From this, we conclude that

$$a \cdot b - a' \cdot b' = a \cdot (b - b') + (a - a') \cdot b' = a \cdot i_2 + i_1 \cdot b' \in I,$$

since both the products $a \cdot i_1$ and $i_2 \cdot b'$ are in I. Consequently,

$$a \cdot b + I = a' \cdot b' + I.$$

The closure of I under multiplication by arbitrary elements of R thus leads to a meaningful definition of coset multiplication; indeed, this is the principal reason for defining an ideal as we did.

Theorem 3–13. If $(I, +, \cdot)$ is an ideal of the ring $(R, +, \cdot)$, then the system $(R/I, +, \cdot)$ is a ring, known as the *quotient ring* of R by I.

We omit the details of the proof and merely point out that the zero element of $(R/I, +, \cdot)$ is the coset $0 + I = I$, while $-(a + I) = (-a) + I$.

Example 3–17. In the ring $(Z, +, \cdot)$ of integers, consider the principal ideal $((n), +, \cdot)$, where n is a nonnegative integer. The cosets of (n) in Z take the form

$$a + (n) = \{a + kn \mid k \in Z\} = [a].$$

That is, the cosets are precisely the congruence classes modulo n. It follows from the definition of coset addition and multiplication that the quotient ring of Z by (n) is merely the ring of integers modulo n:

$$(Z_n, +_n, \cdot_n) = (Z/(n), +, \cdot).$$

A homomorphism between two rings $(R, +, \cdot)$ and $(R', +', \cdot')$, as one might expect, is a function $f: R \to R'$ which preserves both ring operations. This amounts to applying the familiar homomorphism concept to the additive groups $(R, +)$ and $(R', +')$, and to the multiplicative semigroups $(R, \cdot)$ and $(R', \cdot')$. The precise definition follows.

Definition 3–12. Let $(R, +, \cdot)$ and $(R', +', \cdot')$ be two rings and f a function from R into R'; in symbols, $f: R \to R'$. Then f is said to be a (ring) *homomorphism* from $(R, +, \cdot)$ into $(R', +', \cdot')$ if and only if

$$f(a + b) = f(a) +' f(b),$$
$$f(a \cdot b) = f(a) \cdot' f(b)$$

for every pair of elements $a, b \in R$.

Before proving any theorems concerning homomorphisms between rings, we pause to examine a few examples.

Example 3–18. Let $(R, +, \cdot)$ and $(R', +', \cdot')$ be arbitrary rings and $f: R \to R'$ be the function that maps each element of R onto the zero element $0'$ of $(R', +', \cdot')$. A simple calculation shows that f is operation-preserving:

$$f(a + b) = 0' = 0' +' 0' = f(a) +' f(b),$$
$$f(a \cdot b) = 0' = 0' \cdot' 0' = f(a) \cdot' f(b), \qquad a, b \in R.$$

As with the case of groups, this mapping is called the *trivial* homomorphism.

Example 3–19. The mapping $f: Z \to Z_e$ defined by $f(a) = 2a$ is not a homomorphism from $(Z, +, \cdot)$ into $(Z_e, +, \cdot)$, for while addition is preserved, multiplication is not:

$$f(a + b) = 2(a + b) = 2a + 2b = f(a) + f(b),$$

but

$$f(a \cdot b) = 2(a \cdot b) \neq (2a) \cdot (2b) = f(a) \cdot f(b).$$

Example 3–20. Consider $(Z, +, \cdot)$, the ring of integers, and $(Z_n, +_n, \cdot_n)$, the ring of integers modulo n. Define $f \colon Z \to Z_n$ by taking $f(a) = [a]$; that is, map each integer into the congruence class containing it. Then

$$f(a + b) = [a + b] = [a] +_n [b] = f(a) +_n f(b),$$
$$f(a \cdot b) = [a \cdot b] = [a] \cdot_n [b] = f(a) \cdot_n f(b),$$

so that f is a homomorphic mapping.

Example 3–21. Let $(R, +, \cdot)$ be any ring with identity. For each invertible element $a \in R^*$, the function $f_a \colon R \to R$ given by

$$f_a(x) = a \cdot x \cdot a^{-1}$$

is a homomorphism from $(R, +, \cdot)$ into itself. Indeed, if $x, y \in R$, we see that

$$f_a(x + y) = a \cdot (x + y) \cdot a^{-1} = a \cdot x \cdot a^{-1} + a \cdot y \cdot a^{-1} = f_a(x) + f_a(y),$$
$$f_a(x \cdot y) = a \cdot (x \cdot y) \cdot a^{-1} = (a \cdot x \cdot a^{-1}) \cdot (a \cdot y \cdot a^{-1}) = f_a(x) \cdot f_a(y),$$

showing that f_a has the asserted property.

The next theorem gives the ring-theoretic analogs of Theorems 2–38 and 2–39. We shall give no details, since the proof follows the lines of the corresponding results obtained for groups. The parts of the theorem concerning addition carry over with just a change in notation.

Theorem 3–14. Let f be a homomorphism from the ring $(R, +, \cdot)$ into the ring $(R', +', \cdot')$. Then the following hold:

1) $f(0) = 0'$, where $0'$ is the zero element of $(R', +', \cdot')$.
2) $f(-a) = -f(a)$ for all $a \in R$.
3) The triple $\bigl(f(R), +', \cdot'\bigr)$ is a subring of $(R', +', \cdot')$.

If, in addition, $(R, +, \cdot)$ and $(R', +', \cdot')$ are rings with identity elements 1 and $1'$, respectively, and $f(R) = R'$, then

4) $f(1) = 1'$,
5) $f(a^{-1}) = f(a)^{-1}$ for each invertible element $a \in R$.

Two comments regarding part (4) of the theorem are in order. First, it is evident that

$$f(a) \cdot' 1' = f(a) = f(a \cdot 1) = f(a) \cdot' f(1)$$

for all a in R. From this, one might be tempted to (incorrectly) invoke the cancellation law to conclude that $f(1) = 1'$. What is actually required is the fact that multiplicative identities are unique.

Secondly, if the hypothesis that f maps onto the set R' is omitted, then it can only be inferred that $f(1)$ is the identity of the subring $\bigl(f(R), +', \cdot'\bigr)$. The element $f(1)$ need not serve as an identity for the entire ring $(R', +', \cdot')$; in fact, it may very well happen that $f(1) \neq 1'$.

We also observe, in passing, that by statement (2),

$$f(a - b) = f(a) - f(b), \qquad a, b \in R.$$

That is to say, a homomorphism preserves differences as well as sums and products. We shall need this fact presently.

If f is a homomorphism from the ring $(R, +, \cdot)$ into the ring $(R', +', \cdot')$, then the *kernel* of f is the set

$$\ker (f) = \{a \in R \mid f(a) = 0'\},$$

where, as usual, $0'$ designates the zero element of $(R', +', \cdot')$. Ignoring the multiplication operations in the rings, this is just the usual definition of the kernel of a homomorphism between the additive groups $(R, +)$ and $(R', +')$. As before, f is a one-to-one mapping if and only if $\ker (f) = \{0\}$.

For our analogy between ideals and normal subgroups to be meaningful, one would anticipate that the kernel of a homomorphism is an ideal. This is indeed the content of the following theorem.

Theorem 3–15. If f is a homomorphism from the ring $(R, +, \cdot)$ into the ring $(R', +', \cdot')$, then the triple $(\ker (f), +, \cdot)$ is an ideal of $(R, +, \cdot)$.

Proof. By part (1) of Theorem 3–14, $0 \in \ker (f)$, so that the kernel is nonempty. Now, consider any two elements a and b in $\ker (f)$; by definition, $f(a) = 0' = f(b)$. Since any homomorphic mapping between rings preserves differences, it follows that

$$f(a - b) = f(a) - f(b) = 0' - 0' = 0',$$

and consequently $a - b \in \ker (f)$. If r is an arbitrary member of R, then

$$f(r \cdot a) = f(r) \cdot' f(a) = f(r) \cdot' 0' = 0'.$$

Accordingly, the product $r \cdot a \in \ker (f)$. In a like manner, we also conclude that $r \cdot a$ lies in $\ker (f)$. This is sufficient for $(\ker (f), +, \cdot)$ to be an ideal of $(R, +, \cdot)$.

Example 3–22. Consider an arbitrary ring $(R, +, \cdot)$ with identity element 1 and the mapping $f \colon Z \to R$ given by $f(n) = n1$. A simple computation shows that f, so defined, is a homomorphism from the ring of integers $(Z, +, \cdot)$ into the ring $(R, +, \cdot)$:

$$f(n + m) = (n + m)1 = n1 + m1 = f(n) + f(m),$$

$$f(nm) = (nm)1 = (nm)1^2 = (n1) \cdot (m1) = f(n) \cdot f(m).$$

Since $(\ker (f), +, \cdot)$ is then an ideal of $(Z, +, \cdot)$, it follows at once from

Theorem 3–11 that

$$\ker (f) = \{n \in Z \mid n1 = 0\} = (m)$$

for some nonnegative integer m. A moment's reflection will convince the reader that the integer m must be the characteristic of the ring $(R, +, \cdot)$. In other words, the ideal $(\ker (f), +, \cdot)$ is nothing more than the principal ideal generated by the characteristic of $(R, +, \cdot)$.

In agreement with our previous use of the term, two rings $(R, +, \cdot)$ and $(R', +', \cdot')$ are said to be *isomorphic* if there exists a one-to-one homomorphism from the ring $(R, +, \cdot)$ onto the ring $(R', +', \cdot')$. We indicate this by writing $(R, +, \cdot) \simeq (R', +', \cdot')$. The last example, for instance, implies that any ring $(R', +', \cdot')$ with identity which is of characteristic zero contains a subring isomorphic to the integers; more specifically, $(Z, +, \cdot) \simeq (Z1, +', \cdot')$, where 1 is the identity element of $(R', +', \cdot')$.

As we have seen, many aspects of ring theory are considerably simplified when a multiplicative identity exists. The next theorem shows that there is no real loss in generality in assuming the presence of such an element, for every ring is isomorphic to a subring of a ring with identity. Because this result is often phrased differently, we require another definition.

Definition 3–13. A ring $(R, +, \cdot)$ is *imbedded* in a ring $(R', +', \cdot')$ if there exists some subring $(S, +', \cdot')$ of $(R', +', \cdot')$ such that $(R, +, \cdot) \simeq (S, +', \cdot')$.

Theorem 3–16. Any ring can be imbedded in a ring with identity.

Proof. Let $(R, +, \cdot)$ be an arbitrary ring and consider the Cartesian product

$$R \times Z = \{(r, n) \mid r \in R, n \in Z\},$$

where, as usual, Z designates the integers. If addition and multiplication are defined in $R \times Z$ by means of the equations

$$(a, n) + (b, m) = (a + b, n + m),$$

$$(a, n) \cdot (b, m) = (a \cdot b + ma + nb, nm),$$

then it is a simple matter to verify that the enlarged system $(R \times Z, +, \cdot)$ forms a ring. This ring has a multiplicative identity, namely the pair $(0, 1)$; for

$$(a, n) \cdot (0, 1) = (a \cdot 0 + 1a + n\,0, n\,1) = (a, n),$$

and, similarly,

$$(0, 1) \cdot (a, n) = (a, n).$$

Next, consider the subset $R \times 0$ of $R \times Z$ consisting of all pairs of the form $(a, 0)$. Since

$$(a, 0) - (b, 0) = (a - b, 0), \qquad (a, 0) \cdot (b, 0) = (a \cdot b, 0),$$

it follows that the triple $(R \times 0, +, \cdot)$ constitutes a subring of $(R \times Z, +, \cdot)$.

The proof is completed by showing $(R \times 0, +, \cdot)$ is isomorphic to the given ring $(R, +, \cdot)$. To this end, define the function $f \colon R \to R \times 0$ by taking

$$f(a) = (a, 0).$$

Evidently, f is a one-to-one mapping of R onto the set $R \times 0$. Furthermore, this function has the property of preserving algebraic structure:

$$f(a + b) = (a + b, 0) = (a, 0) + (b, 0) = f(a) + f(b),$$

$$f(a \cdot b) = (a \cdot b, 0) = (a, 0) \cdot (b, 0) = f(a) \cdot f(b).$$

Whence, $(R, +, \cdot) \simeq (R \times 0, +, \cdot)$ and we may regard the ring $(R, +, \cdot)$ as imbedded in $(R \times Z, +, \cdot)$, a ring with identity.

A point to be emphasized in connection with the preceding theorem is that the imbedding process may be carried out even if the given ring has an identity to start with. Of course, in this case, the construction has no particular merit; indeed, the original identity only serves to introduce divisors of zero into the enlarged system (see Problem 15 of this section).

While Theorem 3–16 shows that we could confine our study to rings with identity, it is nonetheless desirable to develop as much of the theory as possible without the assumption of such an element. Thus, unless an explicit statement is made to the contrary, the subsequent discussion will not presuppose the existence of a multiplicative identity.

Earlier in our study, we saw that to every normal subgroup $(H, *)$ of a group $(G, *)$ there corresponds an homomorphism with H as its kernel; one need only consider the natural mapping onto the quotient group $(G/H, \otimes)$. In the same way, each ideal $(I, +, \cdot)$ of a ring $(R, +, \cdot)$ determines a quotient ring $(R/I, +, \cdot)$ and a natural mapping $\mathrm{nat}_I \colon R \to R/I$ given by

$$\mathrm{nat}_I(a) = a + I$$

for all $a \in R$. Paralleling our work in group theory, it is possible to prove:

Theorem 3–17. The natural mapping nat_I is a homomorphism from $(R, +, \cdot)$ onto $(R/I, +, \cdot)$ with kernel I.

Proof. By the corresponding theorem for groups, Theorem 2–42, nat_I is known to be a group homomorphism of $(R, +)$ onto $(R/I, +)$ such that $\ker (\mathrm{nat}_I) = I$. Thus, we need simply show that products are preserved by nat_I. This follows immediately from the fact that, for any $a, b \in R$,

$$\mathrm{nat}_I(a \cdot b) = a \cdot b + I = (a + I) \cdot (b + I) = \mathrm{nat}_I (a) \cdot \mathrm{nat}_I (b).$$

Hence, nat_I is a ring homomorphism.

Without further delay, let us now derive the ring-theoretic version of the Fundamental Theorem for Groups.

Theorem 3–18. If f is a homomorphism from the ring $(R, +, \cdot)$ onto the ring $(R', +', \cdot')$, then $(R/\ker (f), +, \cdot) \simeq (R', +', \cdot')$.

Proof. Just as in the group case, we define a function $\bar{f}: R/\ker (f) \to R'$, the induced mapping, by taking $\bar{f}(a + \ker (f)) = f(a)$; it is this function which establishes the desired isomorphism. From the proof of Theorem 2–47, we already know that $(R/\ker (f), +) \simeq (R', +')$ by $\bar{f}$. To complete the argument, it remains only to settle the question of whether $\bar{f}$ preserves the multiplication operation in $(R/\ker (f), +, \cdot)$; but this is straightforward:

$$\bar{f}\big((a + \ker (f)) \cdot (b + \ker (f))\big) = \bar{f}(a \cdot b + \ker (f))$$
$$= f(a \cdot b)$$
$$= f(a) \cdot' f(b)$$
$$= \bar{f}(a + \ker (f)) \cdot' \bar{f}(b + \ker (f)).$$

Incidentally, note that by virtue of the definition of the induced mapping $\bar{f}$, any ring homomorphism f admits the factorization

$$f = \bar{f} \circ \mathrm{nat}_{\ker(f)}.$$

Example 3–23. For a simple, but useful, example illustrating some of these ideas, consider the rings $(Z_4, +_4, \cdot_4)$ and $(Z_2, +_2, \cdot_2)$. We define the function $f: Z_4 \to Z_2$ as follows:

$$f(0) = f(2) = 0, \qquad f(1) = f(3) = 1.$$

It is a lengthy procedure to verify that f is a homomorphism and we pass over the details. The reader should check several possibilities to satisfy himself that this property actually holds.

In the present case, the kernel of f is the two-element set $\{0, 2\}$. Moreover, we see that

$$Z_4/\ker (f) = \big\{\{0, 2\}, \{1, 3\}\big\}.$$

The operation tables for the quotient ring $(Z_4/\ker (f), +, \cdot)$ are as shown:

$+$	$\{0, 2\}$	$\{1, 3\}$
$\{0, 2\}$	$\{0, 2\}$	$\{1, 3\}$
$\{1, 3\}$	$\{1, 3\}$	$\{0, 2\}$

$\cdot$	$\{0, 2\}$	$\{1, 3\}$
$\{0, 2\}$	$\{0, 2\}$	$\{0, 2\}$
$\{1, 3\}$	$\{0, 2\}$	$\{1, 3\}$

Theorem 3–18 asserts that the system $(Z_4/\ker (f), +, \cdot)$ must be isomorphic to the ring of integers modulo 2; indeed, this is reasonably evident from the nature of the foregoing tables.

As an application of Theorem 3–18, we propose to show that each homomorphism onto the ring of integers $(Z, +, \cdot)$ is entirely determined by the set where it assumes the value 0. Contrast this with the case of groups: both i_Z and $-i_Z$ are homomorphisms from the additive group of integers $(Z, +)$ onto itself. The kernel of each of these mappings is $\{0\}$, but clearly $i_Z \neq -i_Z$.

We begin by establishing a lemma which is of independent interest.

Lemma. The only nontrivial homomorphism from the ring of integers $(Z, +, \cdot)$ into itself is the identity map i_Z.

Proof. Consider any homomorphism f having the asserted properties. Because each positive integer n may be written as $1 + 1 + \cdots + 1$ (n summands), the operation-preserving nature of f implies $f(n) = nf(1)$ for each $n \in Z_+$. On the other hand, if n is an arbitrary negative integer, $-n \in Z_+$, and accordingly,

$$f(n) = f(-(-n)) = -f(-n) = -(-n)f(1) = n\,f(1).$$

Finally, $f(0) = 0 = 0\,f(1)$. The net result of all this is that

$$f(n) = n\,f(1)$$

for every n in Z. As the function f is, by hypothesis, not identically zero, we must have $f(1) = 1$. Therefore, $f(n) = n = i_Z(n)$ for all n, so that f is just the identity function on Z.

Corollary. There is at most one homomorphism under which an arbitrary ring $(R, +, \cdot)$ is isomorphic to $(Z, +, \cdot)$.

Proof. Suppose the rings $(R, +, \cdot)$ and $(Z, +, \cdot)$ are isomorphic under two functions f and g, where $f, g : R \to Z$. Then the composition $f \circ g^{-1}$ is a homomorphic mapping from the ring of integers $(Z, +, \cdot)$ onto itself (we leave the verification of this fact as an exercise). It follows at once from the lemma just proved that $f \circ g^{-1} = i_Z$ or $f = g$.

We now have all the necessary information to prove the following result.

Theorem 3–19. Any homomorphism from an arbitrary ring $(R, +, \cdot)$ onto the ring of integers $(Z, +, \cdot)$ is uniquely determined by its kernel.

Proof. Let f and g be two homomorphisms from the ring $(R, +, \cdot)$ onto $(Z, +, \cdot)$ with the property that ker $(f) = $ ker (g). Our aim is to show that f and g must, in actual fact, be the same function. Now, by Theorem 3–18, both the quotient rings $(R/\ker(f), +, \cdot)$ and $(R/\ker(g), +, \cdot)$ are isomorphic to the ring of integers under the induced mappings $\bar{f}$ and $\bar{g}$, respectively. The assumption that f and g have a common kernel, taken in conjunction with the preceding corollary, implies $\bar{f} = \bar{g}$. It then becomes apparent from the factorizations

$$f = \bar{f} \circ \mathrm{nat}_{\ker(f)}, \qquad g = \bar{g} \circ \mathrm{nat}_{\ker(g)}$$

that the functions f and g are themselves identical.

As a final topic in this section, we look briefly at the problem of extending a function from a subsystem to the entire system. In practice, one is usually concerned with extensions which retain the characteristic features of the given function. The next theorem, for instance, presents a situation where it is possible to extend a homomorphism in such a way that its extension also has this property. But first, one more definition is needed (see Problem 17, Section 3–1).

Definition 3–14. The *center* of a ring $(R, +, \cdot)$, denoted by cent R, is the center of the multiplicative semigroup $(R, \cdot)$; that is,

$$\text{cent } R = \{r \in R \mid r \cdot a = a \cdot r \text{ for every } a \in R\}.$$

We are now in a position to state and prove our theorem.

Theorem 3–20. Let $(I, +, \cdot)$ be an ideal of the ring $(R, +, \cdot)$ and f a homomorphism from $(I, +, \cdot)$ onto $(R', +', \cdot')$, a ring with identity. If $I \subseteq$ cent R, then there is a unique homomorphic extension of f to all of R.

Proof. As a starting point, we choose $u \in I$ so that $f(u) = 1'$, where $1'$ is the identity element of the ring $(R', +', \cdot')$. Since $(I, +, \cdot)$ is an ideal, the product $a \cdot u$ will be a member of the set I for each choice of $a \in R$. It is therefore possible to define a new function $g \colon R \to R'$ by setting $g(a) = f(a \cdot u)$, $a \in R$. In particular, if the element a belongs to I, then

$$g(a) = f(a \cdot u) = f(a) \cdot' f(u) = f(a) \cdot 1' = f(a),$$

showing that the restriction $g \mid I$ agrees with f. What we are observing, in effect, is that g extends the given function f to all of R.

The next thing to establish is that both ring operations are preserved by the function g. The case of addition is fairly obvious: if $a, b \in R$, then

$$g(a + b) = f((a + b) \cdot u) = f(a \cdot u + b \cdot u)$$
$$= f(a \cdot u) +' f(b \cdot u) = g(a) +' g(b).$$

As a preliminary step to demonstrating that g also preserves multiplication, note that

$$f((a \cdot b) \cdot u^2) = f((a \cdot b \cdot u) \cdot u) = f((a \cdot b) \cdot u) \cdot' f(u) = f((a \cdot b) \cdot u).$$

In light of this, we are able to conclude

$$g(a \cdot b) = f((a \cdot b) \cdot u) = f((a \cdot b) \cdot u^2)$$
$$= f((a \cdot u) \cdot (b \cdot u)) = f(a \cdot u) \cdot' f(b \cdot u) = g(a) \cdot' g(b).$$

The third equality is justified by the fact that $u \in$ cent R, hence commutes with b.

Only the uniqueness of g remains unproved. Let us therefore suppose the function h is another homomorphic extension of f to the larger set R. Since f and h are required to coincide on I and, more specifically, at the element u,

$$h(u) = f(u) = 1.$$

With this in mind, it follows that

$$h(a) = h(a) \cdot' h(u) = h(a \cdot u) = f(a \cdot u) = g(a)$$

for all a in R, so h and g must be the same function. Hence there is one and only one way of extending f from the ideal $(I, +, \cdot)$ to the entire ring $(R, +, \cdot)$.

PROBLEMS

1. Determine all ideals of $(Z_{12}, +_{12}, \cdot_{12})$, the ring of integers modulo 12.

2. Show by example that if $(I_1, +, \cdot)$ and $(I_2, +, \cdot)$ are both ideals of the ring $(R, +, \cdot)$, then the triple $(I_1 \cup I_2, +, \cdot)$ is not necessarily an ideal.

3. For any ideal $(I, +, \cdot)$ of the ring $(R, +, \cdot)$, define $C(I)$ to be the set

$$C(I) = \{r \in R \mid r \cdot a - a \cdot r \in I \text{ for all } a \in R\}.$$

Determine whether $(C(I), +, \cdot)$ forms a subring of $(R, +, \cdot)$.

4. If $(I_1, +, \cdot)$ and $(I_2, +, \cdot)$ are ideals of the ring $(R, +, \cdot)$ such that $I_1 \cap I_2 = \{0\}$, prove $a \cdot b = 0$ for every $a \in I_1$, $b \in I_2$.

5. a) Verify that the ring of real numbers $(R^{\#}, +, \cdot)$, is a simple ring.
   b) Prove that for each $n \in Z_+$, the ring $(Z_n, +_n, \cdot_n)$ of integers modulo n is a principal ideal ring.

6. Let $(I, +, \cdot)$ be an ideal of the ring $(R, +, \cdot)$ and define

$$\operatorname{ann} I = \{r \in R \mid r \cdot a = 0 \text{ for all } a \in I\}.$$

Prove that the triple $(\operatorname{ann} I, +, \cdot)$ constitutes an ideal of $(R, +, \cdot)$, called the *annihilator ideal* of I.

7. Let $(I, +, \cdot)$ be an ideal of $(R, +, \cdot)$, a commutative ring with identity. For an arbitrary element a in R, the ideal generated by $I \cup \{a\}$ is denoted by $((I, a), +, \cdot)$. Assuming $a \notin I$, show that

$$(I, a) = \{i + r \cdot a \mid i \in I, r \in R\}.$$

8. Suppose $(I_1, +, \cdot)$ and $(I_2, +, \cdot)$ are ideals of the ring $(R, +, \cdot)$. Define

$$I_1 + I_2 = \{a + b \mid a \in I_1, b \in I_2\}.$$

Show that $(I_1 + I_2, +, \cdot)$ is an ideal of the ring $(R, +, \cdot)$; in fact, $(I_1 + I_2, +, \cdot)$ is the ideal generated by $I_1 \cup I_2$.

9. In the ring of integers, consider the principal ideals $((n), +, \cdot)$ and $((m), +, \cdot)$ generated by nonnegative integers n and m. Using the notation of the previous two problems, verify that

$$((n), m) = ((m), n) = (n) + (m) = (\{m, n\}) = (d),$$

where d is the greatest common divisor of n and m.

10. Consider the ring $(P(X), \triangle, \cap)$ of Example 3–4. For a fixed subset $S \subseteq X$, define the function $f: P(X) \to P(X)$ by

$$f(A) = A \cap S.$$

Show that f is a homomorphism and determine its kernel.

11. Utilize Problem 19, Section 3–1, to show that in an integral domain $(R, +, \cdot)$ of characteristic $p > 0$, the mapping

$$f(a) = a^p, \qquad a \in R,$$

is a homomorphism of $(R, +, \cdot)$ into itself.

12. Given that f is a homomorphism from the ring $(R, +, \cdot)$ onto the ring $(R', +', \cdot')$, prove that

a) if $(I, +, \cdot)$ is an ideal of $(R, +, \cdot)$, then the triple $(f(I), +', \cdot')$ is an ideal of $(R', +', \cdot')$,

b) if $(I', +', \cdot')$ is an ideal of $(R', +', \cdot')$, then the triple $(f^{-1}(I'), +, \cdot)$ is an ideal of $(R, +, \cdot)$ with ker $(f) \subseteq f^{-1}(I')$,

c) if $(R, +, \cdot)$ is a principal ideal ring, then the same is true of $(R', +', \cdot')$. [*Hint:* For $a \in R$, $f((a)) = (f(a))$.]

13. Let f be a homomorphism from the ring $(R, +, \cdot)$ into itself and S be the set of elements that are left fixed by f:

$$S = \{a \in R \mid f(a) = a\}.$$

Establish that $(S, +, \cdot)$ is a subring of the ring $(R, +, \cdot)$.

14. For a fixed element a of $(R, +, \cdot)$, a ring with identity, define the *left-multiplication function* $f_a: R \to R$ by taking

$$f_a(x) = a \cdot x, \qquad x \in R.$$

If F_R denotes the set of all such functions, prove the ring analog of Cayley's theorem:

a) The triple $(F_R, +, \circ)$ forms a ring, where $+$ denotes the usual pointwise addition of functions and $\circ$ denotes functional composition.

b) $(R, +, \cdot) \simeq (F_R, +, \circ)$. [*Hint:* Consider the mapping $f(a) = f_a$.]

15. Let $(R, +, \cdot)$ be an arbitrary ring and $(R \times Z, +', \cdot')$ be the ring constructed in Theorem 3–16. Establish that

a) $(R \times 0, +', \cdot')$ is an ideal of $(R \times Z, +', \cdot')$,

b) $(Z, +, \cdot) \simeq (0 \times Z, +', \cdot')$,

c) if a is an idempotent element of R, then the pair $(-a, 1)$ is idempotent in the ring $(R \times Z, +', \cdot')$ and $(a, 0) \cdot' (-a, 1) = (0, 0)$.

16. Suppose $(I_1, +, \cdot)$ and $(I_2, +, \cdot)$ are both ideals of the ring $(R, +, \cdot)$. Define the set $I_1 \cdot I_2$ by

$$I_1 \cdot I_2 = \{\textstyle\sum a_i \cdot b_i \mid a_i \in I_1, b_i \in I_2\},$$

where $\sum$ denotes a finite sum with one or more terms. Prove that $(I_1 \cdot I_2, +, \cdot)$ is an ideal of $(R, +, \cdot)$.

17. Given that $(I, +, \cdot)$ is an ideal of the ring $(R, +, \cdot)$, show that
   a) whenever $(R, +, \cdot)$ is commutative with identity, then so is the quotient ring $(R/I, +, \cdot)$,
   b) the ring $(R/I, +, \cdot)$ may have divisors of zero, even though $(R, +, \cdot)$ does not have any,
   c) if $(R, +, \cdot)$ is a principal ideal ring, then so is the quotient ring $(R/I, +, \cdot)$.

18. Let $(R, +, \cdot)$ be a commutative ring with identity and let N denote the set of nilpotent elements of R. Verify that
   a) the triple $(N, +, \cdot)$ is an ideal of $(R, +, \cdot)$. [*Hint:* If $a^n = b^m = 0$, consider $(a - b)^{n+m}$.]
   b) the quotient ring $(R/N, +, \cdot)$ has no nonzero nilpotent elements.

19. Assume $(R, +, \cdot)$ is a ring with the property that $a^2 + a \in \text{cent } R$ for every element a in R. Show that $(R, +, \cdot)$ is a commutative ring. [*Hint:* Make use of the expression $(a + b)^2 + (a + b)$ to prove, first, that $a \cdot b + b \cdot a$ lies in the center.]

20. Illustrate Theorem 3–18 by considering the rings $(Z_6, +_6, \cdot_6)$, $(Z_3, +_3, \cdot_3)$, and the homomorphism $f\colon Z_6 \to Z_3$ defined by

$$f(0) = f(3) = 0, \qquad f(1) = f(4) = 1, \qquad f(2) = f(5) = 2.$$

21. Let $(S, +, \cdot)$ be a subring and $(I, +, \cdot)$ an ideal of the ring $(R, +, \cdot)$. Assuming $S \cap I = \{0\}$, prove that $(S, +, \cdot)$ is isomorphic to a subring of the quotient ring $(R/I, +, \cdot)$. [*Hint:* Use the mapping $f(a) = a + I$, where $a \in S$, in conjunction with Theorem 3–18.]

22. a) Let f be a homomorphism from the ring $(R, +, \cdot)$ into the ring $(R', +', \cdot')$. Given that $a \in R$ is nilpotent, show its image $f(a)$ is nilpotent in R'.
   b) Suppose $(R, +, \cdot)$ is a ring which has no nonzero nilpotent elements. Deduce that all the idempotent elements of R belong to the center. [*Hint:* If $a^2 = a$, then $(a \cdot r \cdot a - a \cdot r)^2 = (a \cdot r \cdot a - r \cdot a)^2 = 0$ for all $r \in R$.]

23. A ring $(R, +, \cdot)$ is said to be the *direct sum* of the two ideals $(I_1, +, \cdot)$ and $(I_2, +, \cdot)$, indicated by writing $R = I_1 \oplus I_2$, if $R = I_1 + I_2$ with $I_1 \cap I_2 = \{0\}$. Given $R = I_1 \oplus I_2$, show that
   a) $I_1 \cdot I_2 = I_2 \cdot I_1 = \{0\}$,
   b) every element $a \in R$ can be uniquely expressed as a sum

$$a = a_1 + a_2, \qquad \text{where} \qquad a_1 \in I_1, \quad a_2 \in I_2.$$

24. Let $(R, +, \cdot)$ be a commutative ring with identity and $a \in R$ be an idempotent which is different from 0 or 1. Prove that $(R, +, \cdot)$ is the direct sum of the principal ideals $((a), +, \cdot)$ and $((1 - a), +, \cdot)$: $R = (a) \oplus (1 - a)$. [*Hint:* Utilize the fact that $a \cdot (1 - a) = 0$.]

3–3 FIELDS

In the preceding two sections, a hierarchy of special rings has been obtained by imposing more and more restrictions on the multiplicative semigroup of a ring. One might be tempted to require that the multiplicative semigroup actually be a group. Such an assumption would be far too demanding, for this situation can only take place in the trivial ring consisting of the zero element alone. It turns out, however, that there do exist rings in which the nonzero elements form a group under multiplication. This leads us to the notion of a field.

Definition 3–15. A ring $(F, +, \cdot)$ is said to be a *field* provided the pair $(F - \{0\}, \cdot)$ forms a commutative group (the identity of this group will be written as 1).

It should be evident that any field $(F, +, \cdot)$ must contain at least one non-zero element, for $F - \{0\}$ is nonempty, being the set of elements of a group. Moreover, since $a \cdot 0 = 0 = 0 \cdot a$ for every $a \in F$, all the elements of F commute under multiplication and not merely the nonzero elements. In brief, a field is a commutative ring with identity in which each nonzero element has an inverse under multiplication. Observe also that if the zero element were allowed to possess a multiplicative inverse, then $0 = a \cdot 0 = 1$ for some element $a \in F$; this would imply $F = \{0\}$, contrary to our convention that any ring with identity contains more than one member.

As before, to distinguish the two inverses of a nonzero element a in F, we shall denote the multiplicative inverse by a^{-1} and use the notation $-a$ for its inverse relative to addition.

Example 3–24. Both the systems $(R^\#, +, \cdot)$ and $(Q, +, \cdot)$, where $+$ and $\cdot$ indicate ordinary addition and multiplication, are examples of fields.

Example 3–25. Let F be the set of real numbers of the form $a + b\sqrt{3}$, with a and b rational: $F = \{a + b\sqrt{3} \mid a, b \in Q\}$. It is straightforward to check that the triple $(F, +, \cdot)$ is a commutative ring with identity (see Example 3–3). The additive and multiplicative identity elements in this case are

$$0 = 0 + 0\sqrt{3}, \qquad 1 = 1 + 0\sqrt{3}.$$

To show that $(F, +, \cdot)$ is a field, we must verify that each nonzero element of F has an inverse belonging to F. Suppose then that $a + b\sqrt{3} \in F$, where a and b are not both zero. Under these circumstances, $a^2 - 3b^2 \neq 0$, for otherwise $\sqrt{3}$ would be rational. This means that

$$(a + b\sqrt{3})^{-1} = \frac{1}{a + b\sqrt{3}} = \frac{1}{a + b\sqrt{3}} \frac{a - b\sqrt{3}}{a - b\sqrt{3}}$$

$$= \frac{a}{a^2 - 3b^2} + \frac{-b}{a^2 - 3b^2} \sqrt{3} \in F.$$

Since $a/(a^2 - 3b^2)$ and $-b/(a^2 - 3b^2)$ are both rational numbers, the resulting inverse does have the required form to be a member of F.

Note that if a and b were restricted simply to the set of integers, then $(F, +, \cdot)$ would no longer be a field, for then the element

$$\frac{a}{a^2 - 3b^2} + \frac{-b}{a^2 - 3b^2} \sqrt{3}$$

would not necessarily lie in F.

Example 3–26. Consider the set $C = R^{\#} \times R^{\#}$ of ordered pairs of real numbers. To endow C with the structure of a field, we define addition and multiplication by

$$(a, b) + (c, d) = (a + c, b + d),$$

$$(a, b) \cdot (c, d) = (ac - bd, ad + bc).$$

The reader may verify without difficulty that the triple $(C, +, \cdot)$ is a commutative ring with identity. Here the pair $(1, 0)$ serves as the multiplicative identity and $(0, 0)$ is the zero element of the ring. Now, suppose (a, b) is any nonzero member of C. Since $(a, b) \neq (0, 0)$, either $a \neq 0$ or $b \neq 0$, so that $a^2 + b^2 > 0$; thus

$$(a, b)^{-1} = \left(\frac{a}{a^2 + b^2}, \frac{-b}{a^2 + b^2} \right),$$

for we plainly have

$$(a, b) \cdot \left(\frac{a}{a^2 + b^2}, \frac{-b}{a^2 + b^2} \right) = \left(\frac{a^2 + b^2}{a^2 + b^2}, \frac{-ab + ab}{a^2 + b^2} \right) = (1, 0).$$

This shows that the nonzero elements of C have inverses under multiplication, proving the system $(C, +, \cdot)$ to be a field.

The field $(C, +, \cdot)$ contains a subring which is isomorphic to the ring of real numbers. For if

$$R^{\#} \times 0 = \{(a, 0) \mid a \in R^{\#}\},$$

it follows that $(R^{\#}, +, \cdot) \simeq (R^{\#} \times 0, +, \cdot)$ via the mapping f defined by

$$f(a) = (a, 0), \qquad a \in R^{\#}.$$

(Verify this!) As the distinction between these systems is one only of notation, we customarily identify the real number a with the corresponding ordered pair $(a, 0)$; in this sense, $(R^{\#}, +, \cdot)$ may be regarded as a subring of $(C, +, \cdot)$.

The definition of the operations $+$ and $\cdot$ enables us to express any element $(a, b) \in C$ as

$$(a, b) = (a, 0) + (b, 0) \cdot (0, 1),$$

where the pair $(0, 1)$ is such that $(0,1)^2 = (0, 1) \cdot (0, 1) = (-1, 0)$. Introducing the symbol i as an abbreviation for $(0, 1)$, we thus have

$$(a, b) = (a, 0) + (b, 0) \cdot i.$$

If it is agreed to replace pairs of the form $(a, 0)$ by the first component a, this representation becomes

$$(a, b) = a + bi,$$

with $i^2 = -1$. In other words, the field $(C, +, \cdot)$ as defined above is nothing more than the familiar complex number system.

The following theorem shows that a field is without divisors of zero, and consequently is a system in which the cancellation law for multiplication holds (see Theorem 3–5).

Theorem 3–21. If $(F, +, \cdot)$ is a field and $a, b \in F$ with $a \cdot b = 0$, then either $a = 0$ or $b = 0$.

Proof. If $a = 0$, the theorem is already established. So let us suppose that $a \neq 0$ and prove that $b = 0$. By the definition of a field, the element a, being nonzero, must have a multiplicative inverse $a^{-1} \in F$. The hypothesis $a \cdot b = 0$ then yields

$$0 = a^{-1} \cdot 0 = a^{-1} \cdot (a \cdot b) = (a^{-1} \cdot a) \cdot b = 1 \cdot b = b,$$

as desired.

Since a field is a commutative ring with identity, and we have just proved that it contains no divisors of zero, we conclude that any field is an integral domain. There obviously are integral domains which are not fields; for instance, the ring of integers. However, an integral domain having a finite number of elements must necessarily be a field.

Theorem 3–22. Any finite integral domain $(R, +, \cdot)$ is a field.

Proof. Suppose $a_1, a_2, \ldots, a_n$ are the members of the set R. For a fixed non-zero element $a \in R$, consider the n products $a \cdot a_1, a \cdot a_2, \ldots, a \cdot a_n$. These products are all distinct, for if $a \cdot a_i = a \cdot a_j$, then $a_i = a_j$ by the cancellation law. It follows that each element of R is of the form $a \cdot a_i$. In particular, there exists some $a_i \in R$ such that $a \cdot a_i = 1$; since multiplication is commutative, we thus have $a_i = a^{-1}$. This shows that every nonzero element of R is invertible, so $(R, +, \cdot)$ is a field.

It was previously seen that for each positive integer n the system $(Z_n, +_n, \cdot_n)$ is a commutative ring with identity. Our next result indicates for precisely what values of n this ring is a field.

Theorem 3–23. The ring $(Z_n, +_n, \cdot_n)$ of integers modulo n is a field if and only if n is a prime number.

Proof. We first show that if n is not prime, then $(Z_n, +_n, \cdot_n)$ is not a field. Thus assume $n = a \cdot b$, where $0 < a < n$ and $0 < b < n$. It follows at once that

$$[a] \cdot_n [b] = [a \cdot b] = [n] = [0],$$

although both $[a] \neq [0]$, $[b] \neq [0]$. This means that the system $(Z_n, +_n, \cdot_n)$ is not an integral domain, and hence not a field.

On the other hand, suppose that n is a prime number. To show that $(Z_n, +_n, \cdot_n)$ is a field, it suffices to prove here that each nonzero element of Z_n has a multiplicative inverse in Z_n. To this end, let $[a] \in Z_n$, where $0 < a < n$. According to Theorem 1–13, since a and n have no common factors, there exist integers r and s such that

$$a \cdot r + n \cdot s = 1.$$

This implies that

$$
\begin{aligned}
[a] \cdot_n [r] = [a \cdot r] +_n [0] &= [a \cdot r] +_n [n \cdot s] \\
&= [a \cdot r + n \cdot s] \\
&= [1],
\end{aligned}
$$

showing the congruence class $[r]$ to be the multiplicative inverse of $[a]$. Therefore $(Z_n, +_n, \cdot_n)$ is a field, as required.

There is an interesting relationship between fields and the lack of ideals; what we shall show is that fields have as trivial an ideal structure as possible.

Theorem 3–24. Let $(R, +, \cdot)$ be a commutative ring with identity. Then $(R, +, \cdot)$ is a field if and only if $(R, +, \cdot)$ has no nontrivial ideals.

Proof. Assume first that $(R, +, \cdot)$ is a field. We wish to show that the trivial ideals $(\{0\}, +, \cdot)$ and $(R, +, \cdot)$ are its only ideals. Let us assume to the contrary that there exists some nontrivial ideal $(I, +, \cdot)$ of $(R, +, \cdot)$. By our assumption, the subset I is such that $I \neq \{0\}$, and $I \neq R$. This means there is some nonzero element $a \in I$. Since $(R, +, \cdot)$ is a field, a has a multiplicative inverse $a^{-1} \in R$. By the definition of ideal, we thus obtain $a^{-1} \cdot a = 1 \in I$, which in turn implies $I = R$, contradicting our choice of I.

Conversely, suppose that the ring $(R, +, \cdot)$ has no nontrivial ideals. For an arbitrary nonzero element $a \in R$, consider the principal ideal $((a), +, \cdot)$ generated by a:

$$(a) = \{r \cdot a \mid r \in R\}.$$

Now $((a), +, \cdot)$ cannot be the zero ideal, since $a = a \cdot 1 \in (a)$, with $a \neq 0$. It follows from the hypothesis that the only other possibility is $((a), +, \cdot) = (R, +, \cdot)$; that is, $(a) = R$. In particular, since $1 \in (a)$, there exists an element $\bar{r} \in R$ for which $\bar{r} \cdot a = 1$. Multiplication is commutative, so that $\bar{r} = a^{-1}$. Hence each nonzero element of R has a multiplicative inverse in R.

In view of this last result, the ring of integers $(Z, +, \cdot)$ fails to be a field, since it possesses the nontrivial ideal $(Z_e, +, \cdot)$.

Theorem 3–24 is useful in revealing the nature of homomorphisms between fields.

Theorem 3–25. Let f be a homomorphism from the field $(F, +, \cdot)$ onto the field $(F', +', \cdot')$. Then either f is the trivial homomorphism or else $(F, +, \cdot)$ and $(F', +', \cdot')$ are isomorphic.

Proof. The proof consists of noticing that since $(\ker (f), +, \cdot)$ is an ideal of the field $(F, +, \cdot)$, either the set $\ker (f) = \{0\}$ or else $\ker (f) = F$. The condition $\ker (f) = \{0\}$ implies f is a one-to-one function, in which case $(F, +, \cdot) \simeq (F', +', \cdot')$ via f. On the other hand, if it happens that $\ker (f) = F$, then each element of the field $(F, +, \cdot)$ must map onto zero; that is, f is the trivial homomorphism.

Plainly, any ring with identity which is a subring of a field must in fact be an integral domain. We now turn our attention to the converse situation; specifically, one may ask whether each integral domain can be considered (apart from isomorphism) as a subring of some field. More formally, can a given integral domain be imbedded in a field? In the finite case, there is obviously no difficulty, since every finite integral domain already forms a field.

Our concern with this problem arises from the desire to solve equations of the type $a \cdot x = b, a \neq 0$. A major drawback to the notion of an integral domain is that it does not always provide us with a solution. Of course, any such solution would have to be unique for $a \cdot x_1 = b = a \cdot x_2$ implies $x_1 = x_2$ by the cancellation law. It hardly seems necessary to point out that when the integral domain happens to be a field, there is always a solution of the equation $a \cdot x = b$ $(a \neq 0)$, namely $x = a^{-1} \cdot b$.

We begin our discussion of this question with a definition.

Definition 3–16. By a *subfield* of the field $(F, +, \cdot)$ is meant any subring $(F', +, \cdot)$ of $(F, +, \cdot)$ which is itself a field.

For example, the ring $(Q, +, \cdot)$ of rational numbers is a subfield of the field $(R^\#, +, \cdot)$.

Surely, the triple $(F', +, \cdot)$ will be a subfield of the field $(F, +, \cdot)$ provided (1) $(F', +)$ is a subgroup of the additive group $(F, +)$ and (2) $(F' - \{0\}, \cdot)$ is a subgroup of the multiplicative group $(F - \{0\}, \cdot)$. Recalling our minimal set of conditions for determining subgroups (Theorem 2–17), we see that $(F', +, \cdot)$ will be a subfield of $(F, +, \cdot)$ if and only if the following hold:

1) F' is a nonempty subset of F with at least one nonzero element.
2) $a, b \in F'$ implies $a - b \in F'$.
3) $a, b \in F'$, where $b \neq 0$, implies $a \cdot b^{-1} \in F'$.

It should come as no surprise that if $(F_i, +, \cdot)$ is an arbitrary collection of subfields of the field $(F, +, \cdot)$, then $(\cap F_i, +, \cdot)$ is also a subfield.

The next theorem furnishes some clue to the nature of the field in which we wish to imbed a given integral domain.

Theorem 3–26. Let the integral domain $(R, +, \cdot)$ be a subring of the field $(F, +, \cdot)$. If the set F' is defined by

$$F' = \{a \cdot b^{-1} \mid a, b \in R; b \neq 0\},$$

then the triple $(F', +, \cdot)$ forms a subfield of $(F, +, \cdot)$ such that $R \subseteq F'$. In fact, $(F', +, \cdot)$ is the smallest subfield containing R.

Proof. Note first that the definition of the set F' is meaningful; indeed, if $a, b \in R$ with $b \neq 0$, the product $a \cdot b^{-1}$ must be in F by virtue of the fact $(F, +, \cdot)$ is a field. Since $1 = 1 \cdot 1^{-1} \in F'$, $F' \neq \{0\}$. Now consider two arbitrary elements x, y of F'. We then have

$$x = a \cdot b^{-1}, \qquad y = c \cdot d^{-1}$$

for suitable $a, b, c, d \in R$, where $b \neq 0, d \neq 0$. A simple calculation shows

$$x - y = (a \cdot d - b \cdot c) \cdot (b \cdot d)^{-1} \in F'.$$

Also, if y is nonzero (that is, whenever $c \neq 0$),

$$x \cdot y^{-1} = (a \cdot d) \cdot (c \cdot b)^{-1} \in F'.$$

In light of the remarks following Definition 3–16, this is sufficient to establish that the triple $(F', +, \cdot)$ is a subfield of $(F, +, \cdot)$. Furthermore,

$$a = a \cdot 1 = a \cdot 1^{-1} \in F'$$

for each a in R, so that $R \subseteq F'$. Any subfield of $(F, +, \cdot)$ which contains R necessarily includes all products $a \cdot b^{-1}$ with $a, b \neq 0$ in R, hence contains F'.

Theorem 3–26 began with an integral domain already imbedded in a field. In the general case, it is actually necessary to construct the imbedding field. Since the expression $a \cdot b^{-1}$ may not always exist, one must now work with ordered pairs (a, b), where $b \neq 0$. Our thinking is that (a, b) will play a role analogous to $a \cdot b^{-1}$.

As a starting point, let $(R, +, \cdot)$ be an arbitrary integral domain and K the set of ordered pairs,

$$K = \{(a, b) \mid a, b \in R; b \neq 0\}.$$

A notion of equivalence may be introduced in K as follows:

$$(a, b) \equiv (c, d) \qquad \text{if and only if} \qquad a \cdot d = b \cdot c.$$

(We have in mind the foregoing theorem in which $a \cdot b^{-1} = c \cdot d^{-1}$ if and only if $a \cdot d = b \cdot c$.)

It is not difficult to verify that the relation $\equiv$, thus defined, is an equivalence relation in K; that is to say,

1) $(a, b) \equiv (a, b)$,
2) if $(a, b) \equiv (c, d)$, then $(c, d) \equiv (a, b)$,
3) if $(a, b) \equiv (c, d)$ and $(c, d) \equiv (e, f)$, then $(a, b) \equiv (e, f)$.

The least obvious statement is (3). In this case, the hypothesis $(a, b) \equiv (c, d)$ and $(c, d) \equiv (e, f)$ implies that

$$a \cdot d = b \cdot c, \qquad c \cdot f = d \cdot e.$$

Multiplying the first of these equations by f and the second by b, we obtain

$$a \cdot d \cdot f = b \cdot c \cdot f = b \cdot d \cdot e,$$

and, from the commutativity of multiplication, $a \cdot f \cdot d = b \cdot e \cdot d$. Since $d \neq 0$, this factor may be cancelled to yield $a \cdot f = b \cdot e$. But then $(a, b) \equiv (e, f)$, as required.

Next, we label those elements which are equivalent to the pair (a, b) by the symbol $[a, b]$; in other words,

$$[a, b] = \{(c, d) \in K \mid (a, b) \equiv (c, d)\}$$
$$= \{(c, d) \in K \mid a \cdot d = b \cdot c\}.$$

To emphasize the similarity between what follows and the familiar construction of the rational numbers, many authors prefer to write a/b in place of $[a, b]$; the reader will realize the difference is merely a matter of notation.

The collection of all equivalence classes $[a, b]$ relative to $\equiv$ will be designated by F. From Theorem 1–5, we know that the elements of F constitute a partition of the set K. That is, the ordered pairs of K fall into disjoint classes, with each class consisting of equivalent pairs, and nonequivalent pairs belong to different classes. Further, two such classes $[a, b]$ and $[c, d]$ are identical if and only if $a \cdot d = b \cdot c$.

Let us proceed to introduce suitable operations of addition and multiplication in F. We do these by means of the equations

$$[a, b] +' [c, d] = [a \cdot d + b \cdot c, b \cdot d],$$

$$[a, b] \cdot' [c, d] = [a \cdot c, b \cdot d].$$

Note, incidentally, that since $b \neq 0$ and $d \neq 0$ imply $b \cdot d \neq 0$, the right-hand sides of these formulas are actually elements of F.

We must, as usual, first justify that these operations are well-defined. Otherwise expressed, we need to show that the sum and product are independent of the particular elements of R used in the definition. To achieve this, let

$[a, b] = [a', b']$ and $[c, d] = [c', d']$. From the equations

$$a \cdot b' = b \cdot a', \qquad c \cdot d' = d \cdot c',$$

it follows that

$$(a \cdot d + c \cdot b) \cdot (b' \cdot d') - (a' \cdot d' + c' \cdot b') \cdot (b \cdot d)$$
$$= (a \cdot b' - b \cdot a') \cdot (d \cdot d') + (c \cdot d' - d \cdot c') \cdot (b \cdot b')$$
$$= 0 \cdot (d \cdot d') + 0 \cdot (b \cdot b') = 0.$$

Thus, by the definition of equality of classes,

$$[a \cdot d + c \cdot b, b \cdot d] = [a' \cdot d' + c' \cdot b', b' \cdot d'],$$

proving addition to be well-defined. In much the same way, one can show that

$$[a \cdot c, b \cdot d] = [a' \cdot c', b' \cdot d'].$$

The next lemma establishes the algebraic nature of the triple $(F, +', \cdot')$.

Lemma. The system $(F, +', \cdot')$ is a field, generally known as the *field of quotients* of the integral domain $(R, +, \cdot)$.

Proof. It is an entirely straightforward matter to establish that the triple $(F, +', \cdot')$ is a commutative ring. We leave the reader to make the necessary verifications at his leisure, and merely point out that $[0, b]$ serves as the zero element while $[-a, b]$ is the negative of $[a, b]$.

That the equivalence class $[a, a]$, where a is any nonzero element, constitutes the multiplicative identity is evidenced by the following:

$$[a, a] \cdot' [c, d] = [a \cdot c, a \cdot d] = [c, d],$$

with $[c, d]$ arbitrary in F.

To show that every nonzero element of F has an inverse under multiplication, suppose that $[a, b]$ is not the zero of $(F, +', \cdot')$. Then $a \neq 0$, whence the class $[b, a]$ is a member of F. Accordingly,

$$[a, b] \cdot' [b, a] = [a \cdot b, b \cdot a] = [a \cdot b, a \cdot b].$$

Since the product $a \cdot b$ is not zero, $[a \cdot b, a \cdot b]$ is the identity element, so that $[a, b]^{-1} = [b, a]$.

We wish to show next that the field $(F, +', \cdot')$ contains a subsystem isomorphic to $(R, +, \cdot)$; this will establish the required imbedding theorem.

Theorem 3–27. The integral domain $(R, +, \cdot)$ can be imbedded in its field of quotients $(F, +', \cdot')$.

Proof. Consider the subset F' of F consisting of all elements of the form $[a, 1]$, where 1 is the multiplicative identity of $(R, +, \cdot)$:

$$F' = \{[a, 1] \mid a \in R\}.$$

It is readily checked that the triple $(F', +', \cdot')$ is a subring of $(F, +', \cdot')$ and, in actual fact, is an integral domain. Now, let $f: R \to F'$ be the onto mapping defined by

$$f(a) = [a, 1]$$

for each $a \in R$. Since the condition $[a, 1] = [b, 1]$ implies $a \cdot 1 = 1 \cdot b$ or $a = b$, we see that f is a one-to-one function. Moreover, this function preserves addition and multiplication:

$$f(a + b) = [a + b, 1] = [a, 1] +' [b, 1] = f(a) +' f(b),$$
$$f(a \cdot b) = [a \cdot b, 1] = [a, 1] \cdot' [b, 1] = f(a) \cdot' f(b).$$

Accordingly, $(R, +, \cdot) \simeq (F', +', \cdot')$ under f, and the proof is complete.

Several remarks are in order. First, note that any member $[a, b]$ of F can be written in the form

$$[a, b] = [a, 1] \cdot' [1, b] = [a, 1] \cdot' [b, 1]^{-1}.$$

Since the systems $(R, +, \cdot)$ and $(F', +', \cdot')$ are isomorphic, one customarily identifies the element $[a, 1] \in F'$ with the element a of R. The above equation then becomes $[a, b] = a \cdot' b^{-1}$. The point is this: we may now regard the set F as consisting of all *quotients* $a \cdot' b^{-1}$, with a and $b \neq 0$ in R. It should also be observed that for any $a \neq 0$,

$$[a, 1] \cdot' [b, a] = [a \cdot b, a] = [b, 1].$$

Again writing $[a, 1]$ simply as a, we infer that the equation $a \cdot' x = b$ always has a solution in F, namely $x = [b, a] = b \cdot' a^{-1}$.

A final fact of interest is that the field of quotients $(F, +', \cdot')$ is the smallest field in which the integral domain $(R, +, \cdot)$ can be imbedded, in the sense that any field in which $(R, +, \cdot)$ is imbeddable contains a subfield isomorphic to $(F, +', \cdot')$ (Problem 14 of this section).

The field of quotients constructed from the integral domain $(Z, +, \cdot)$ is, of course, the rational number field $(Q, +, \cdot)$.

Definition 3–17. A field which does not have any proper subfields is called a *prime field*.

Example 3–27. The field of rational numbers, $(Q, +, \cdot)$, is a prime field. To see this, suppose $(F, +, \cdot)$ is a subfield of $(Q, +, \cdot)$ and let $a \in F$ be any nonzero element. Since $(F, +, \cdot)$ is a subfield, it must contain the product

$a \cdot a^{-1} = 1$. In turn, $n = n \cdot 1^{-1} \in F$ for any n in Z; in other words, F contains all the integers. It follows then that every rational number $n/m = n \cdot m^{-1}$, $m \neq 0$, also belongs to F, so that $F = Q$.

Example 3–28. For every prime p, the field $(Z_p, +_p, \cdot_p)$ of integers modulo p is a prime field. The reasoning here depends on the fact that the additive group $(Z_p, +_p)$ of $(Z_p, +_p, \cdot_p)$ is a finite group of prime order, and therefore has no nontrivial subgroups.

We conclude this section by showing that the rational number field and the fields $(Z_p, +_p, \cdot_p)$ are, in a certain sense, the only prime fields. The proof relies heavily on earlier results.

Theorem 3–28. Any prime field $(F, +, \cdot)$ is isomorphic either to $(Q, +, \cdot)$, the field of rational numbers, or to one of the fields $(Z_p, +_p, \cdot_p)$, where p is a prime number.

Proof. Let 1 be the identity element of $(F, +, \cdot)$ and define the mapping $f \colon Z \to F$ by

$$f(n) = n1$$

for any integer $n \in Z$. Then f is a homomorphism from $(Z, +, \cdot)$ onto the subring $(f(Z), +, \cdot)$ consisting of integral multiples of 1 (Example 3–22). By Theorem 3–18, we see that

$$(Z/\ker{(f)}, +, \cdot) \simeq (f(Z), +, \cdot).$$

But the triple $(\ker{(f)}, +, \cdot)$ is an ideal of $(Z, +, \cdot)$, a principal ideal ring. Whence, $\ker{(f)} = (n)$ for some nonnegative integer n. The possibility that $n = 1$ may be ruled out, for otherwise f would be the trivial homomorphism; that can only happen if $F = \{0\}$.

Note further that if $n \neq 0$, then n must in fact be a prime number. Suppose to the contrary that $n = n_1 n_2$ where $1 < n_i < n$ $(i = 1, 2)$. Since $n \in \ker{(f)}$,

$$(n_1 1) \cdot (n_2 1) = (n_1 n_2)1 = n1 = 0,$$

yielding the contradiction that the field $(F, +, \cdot)$ has divisors of zero. (This result is not entirely unexpected, because n is the characteristic of $(F, +, \cdot)$ and as such must be prime.)

The preceding discussion indicates that two possibilities arise: either

1) $(f(Z), +, \cdot) \simeq (Z/(p), +, \cdot) = (Z_p, +_p, \cdot_p)$ for some prime p, or
2) $(f(Z), +, \cdot) \simeq (Z/(0), +, \cdot) = (Z, +, \cdot)$.

Turning to a closer analysis of these cases, suppose first that $(f(Z), +, \cdot) \simeq (Z_p, +_p, \cdot_p)$, with p prime. Inasmuch as the ring of integers modulo a prime forms a field, the subring $(f(Z), +, \cdot)$ must itself be a field. But $(F, +, \cdot)$ contains no proper subfields. Accordingly, $f(Z) = F$ and $(F, +, \cdot) \simeq (Z_p, +_p, \cdot_p)$.

Next, consider the situation $(f(Z), +, \cdot) \simeq (Z, +, \cdot)$. Under these circumstances, the subring $(f(Z), +, \cdot)$ is an integral domain, but not a field. Theorem 3–26, in conjunction with the hypothesis $(F, +, \cdot)$ is a prime field, then implies

$$F = \{a \cdot b^{-1} \mid a, b \in f(Z); b \neq 0\}$$
$$= \{(n1) \cdot (m1)^{-1} \mid n, m \in Z; m \neq 0\}.$$

It is now a purely routine matter to show that the fields $(F, +, \cdot)$ and $(Q, +, \cdot)$ are isomorphic under the mapping $g(n/m) = (n1) \cdot (m1)^{-1}$; we leave this as an exercise.

Since each field has a prime subfield, we get the following subsidiary result.

Corollary. Every field contains a subfield which is isomorphic either to the field $(Q, +, \cdot)$ or to one of the fields $(Z_p, +_p, \cdot_p)$, p a prime.

PROBLEMS

1. If $+$ and $\cdot$ denote ordinary addition and multiplication, for which of the following sets F is $(F, +, \cdot)$ a field?
   a) $F = \{a - b\sqrt{2} \mid a, b \in Z\}$
   b) $F = \{a + b\sqrt[3]{2} \mid a, b \in Q\}$
   c) $F = \{a + b\sqrt[3]{2} + c\sqrt[3]{4} \mid a, b, c \in Q\}$

2. In a field $(F, +, \cdot)$, show that the equation $a^2 = a$ implies either $a = 0$ or $a = 1$

3. Define two binary operations $*$ and $\circ$ on the set Z of integers by letting

$$a * b = a + b - 1, \qquad a \circ b = a + b - ab \qquad a, b \in Z.$$

   Prove that the triple $(Z, *, \circ)$ forms a field.

4. In the field $(C, +, \cdot)$ of complex numbers, define the mapping $f: C \rightarrow C$ by the rule $f(a, b) = (a, -b)$; in other words,

$$f(a + bi) = a - bi.$$

   Determine whether the function f is a homomorphism.

5. A *division ring* is a ring with identity in which every nonzero element has a multiplicative inverse. Assuming $(R, +, \cdot)$ is a division ring, prove that (cent $R, +, \cdot$) forms a field.

6. Let $(R, +, \cdot)$ be an integral domain and consider the set $Z1$ of all integral multiples of the identity:

$$Z1 = \{n1 \mid n \in Z\}.$$

   Verify that $(Z1, +, \cdot)$ is a field if and only if $(R, +, \cdot)$ has positive characteristics.

7. a) Prove that every field is a principal ideal ring.
   b) Consider the set of numbers $R = \{a + b\sqrt{2} \mid a, b \in Z\}$. Show that the ring $(R, +, \cdot)$ is not a field by exhibiting a nontrivial ideal of $(R, +, \cdot)$.

8. Derive the following results:
   a) The identity element of a subfield is the same as that of the field.
   b) If $(F_i, +, \cdot)$ is an indexed collection of subfields of the field $(F, +, \cdot)$, then $(\cap F_i, +, \cdot)$ is also a subfield of $(F, +, \cdot)$.

9. Let f be a homomorphism from the field $(F, +, \cdot)$ into itself and K be the set of elements left fixed by f:
$$K = \{a \in F \mid f(a) = a\}.$$

Given $K \neq \{0\}$, verify that the triple $(K, +, \cdot)$ is a subfield of $(F, +, \cdot)$.

10. a) Consider the subset $S \subset R^{\#}$ defined by $S = \{a + b\sqrt{p} \mid a, b \in Q; p \text{ a prime}\}$. Show that $(S, +, \cdot)$ is a subfield of $(R^{\#}, +, \cdot)$.
    b) Prove that any subfield of $(R^{\#}, +, \cdot)$ must contain the rational numbers.

11. Prove that if the field $(F, +, \cdot)$ is of characteristic $p > 0$, then every subfield of $(F, +, \cdot)$ has characteristic p.

12. Let f be a homomorphism of the ring $(R, +, \cdot)$ into the ring $(R', +', \cdot')$ and suppose $(R, +, \cdot)$ has a subring $(F, +, \cdot)$ which is a field. Show that either $F \subseteq \ker(f)$ or else $(R', +', \cdot')$ contains a subring isomorphic to $(F, +, \cdot)$.

13. If $R = \{a + b\sqrt{2} \mid a, b \in Z\}$, then the system $(R, +, \cdot)$ is an integral domain, but not a field. Obtain the field of quotients of $(R, +, \cdot)$.

14. Suppose the integral domain $(R, +, \cdot)$ is imbedded in the field $(F', +', \cdot')$, say $(R, +, \cdot) \simeq (R', +', \cdot')$ under the mapping f. Define the set K by
$$K = \{a' \cdot' (b')^{-1} \mid a', b' \in R'; b' \neq 0\}.$$

Prove (1) $(K, +', \cdot')$ is a subfield of $(F', +', \cdot')$ and (2) $(K, +', \cdot')$ is isomorphic to the field of quotients of $(R, +, \cdot)$. [*Hint:* For (2), consider the function g defined by $g([a, b]) = f(a) \cdot' f(b)^{-1}$ where $a, b \in R, b \neq 0$.]

15. Show that any field is isomorphic to its field of quotients. [*Hint:* Make use of the previous exercise with f as the identity map.]

16. Prove that if $(R, +, \cdot)$ and $(R', +', \cdot')$ are isomorphic integral domains, then their fields of quotients are also isomorphic.

17. From Problem 8(b), deduce that every field $(F, +, \cdot)$ has a unique prime subfield. Is this result still true if $(F, +, \cdot)$ is assumed merely to be a division ring?

18. Establish the following assertion, thereby completing the proof of Theorem 3–28: If $(F, +, \cdot)$ is a field of characteristic zero and $(K, +, \cdot)$ the prime subfield generated by the identity element, then $(Q, +, \cdot) \simeq (K, +, \cdot)$ via the mapping $f(n/m) = (n1) \cdot (m1)^{-1}$, where $n, m \in Z, m \neq 0$.

19. Use the preceding problem to prove that any *finite field* (i.e., a field with a finite number of elements) has nonzero characteristic.

3–4 CERTAIN SPECIAL IDEALS

The present section is largely devoted to a study of certain special types of ideals, most notably maximal and prime ideals. On the whole, our hypothesis will restrict us to commutative rings with identity. The requirement is motivated to some extent by the fact that many of the standard examples of ring theory have this property. A further reason, which is perhaps more important from the conceptual point of view, is that the most satisfactory and complete results occur here. We begin by making the following definition.

Definition 3–18. An ideal $(I, +, \cdot)$ of the ring $(R, +, \cdot)$ is a *maximal ideal* provided $I \neq R$ and whenever $(J, +, \cdot)$ is an ideal of $(R, +, \cdot)$ with $I \subset J \subseteq R$, then $J = R$.

Expressed rather loosely, an ideal is maximal if it is not the whole ring and is not properly contained in any larger nontrivial ideal. The only ideal to contain a maximal ideal properly is the ring itself.

Assume, for the moment, that $(I, +, \cdot)$ is a proper ideal of the ring $(R, +, \cdot)$ and a is an element which does not belong to I. Then the ideal $((I, a), +, \cdot)$, the ideal generated by the set $I \cup \{a\}$, is such that $I \subset (I, a) \subseteq R$. These inclusions imply that if $(I, +, \cdot)$ were a maximal ideal, the set (I, a) must be all of R, $(I, a) = R$. On the other hand, suppose $(J, +, \cdot)$ is an ideal of $(R, +, \cdot)$ for which $I \subset J \subseteq R$. If a is an element of J not in I, then $I \subset (I, a) \subseteq J$. The condition $(I, a) = R$ would therefore force $J = R$ and we could conclude that $(I, +, \cdot)$ is a maximal ideal. Summing up, the ideal $(I, +, \cdot)$ is a maximal ideal of $(R, +, \cdot)$ if and only if $I \neq R$ and $(I, a) = R$ for every element $a \notin I$. This fact will prove quite helpful a little later.

To illustrate the concept, let us show that in the ring of integers the maximal ideals correspond to the prime numbers.

Theorem 3–29. Let $(Z, +, \cdot)$ be the ring of integers and $n > 1$. Then the principal ideal $((n), +, \cdot)$ is maximal if and only if n is a prime number.

Proof. First, suppose $((n), +, \cdot)$ is a maximal ideal of $(Z, +, \cdot)$. If the integer n is not prime, then $n = n_1 n_2$, where $1 < n_1 \leq n_2 < n$. This implies the ideals $((n_1), +, \cdot)$ and $((n_2), +, \cdot)$ are such that

$$(n) \subset (n_1) \subset Z, \qquad (n) \subset (n_2) \subset Z,$$

contrary to the maximality of $((n), +, \cdot)$.

For the opposite direction, assume now that the integer n is prime. If the ideal $((n), +, \cdot)$ is not maximal in $(Z, +, \cdot)$, then either $(n) = Z$ or else there exists some proper ideal $((m), +, \cdot)$ with $(n) \subset (m) \subset Z$. The first case is immediately ruled out by the fact that 1 is not a multiple of a prime number. On the other hand, the alternative possibility $(n) \subset (m)$ means $n = km$ for some integer $k > 1$; this also is untenable, since n is prime, not composite. We therefore conclude that $((n), +, \cdot)$ is a maximal ideal.

An additional illustration may be of some interest: Let R denote the collection of all functions $f \colon R^{\#} \to R^{\#}$. For two such functions f and g, addition and multiplication are defined by the formulas

$$(f + g)(x) = f(x) + g(x), \qquad (f \cdot g)(x) = f(x)g(x), \qquad x \in R^{\#}.$$

Then $(R, +, \cdot)$ is a commutative ring with identity (see Example 3–5). Consider the set M of functions in R which vanish at 0:

$$M = \{f \in R \mid f(0) = 0\}.$$

Evidently, the triple $(M, +, \cdot)$ forms an ideal of $(R, +, \cdot)$; we observe that it is actually a maximal ideal. For, if $f \notin M$ and i is the identity map on $R^{\#}$, one may easily check that $(i^2 + f^2)(x) \neq 0$ for each $x \in R^{\#}$. Hence, the sum $i^2 + f^2$ is an invertible element of R. This implies that

$$(M, f) \supseteq (i, f) = R,$$

and therefore $(M, f) = R$ for every $f \notin M$ [here (i, f) designates the elements of the ideal generated by i and f; that is, $(i, f) = \{r \cdot i + s \cdot f \mid r, s \in R\}$].

Our immediate goal is to obtain a general result assuring the existence of suitably many maximal ideals. As will be seen presently, the crucial step in the proof depends upon the *maximal element principle*, or what is commonly termed Zorn's Lemma. It would take us somewhat far afield to do much more than merely formulate this lemma as an axiom; the reader who wishes to pursue the topic further is directed to the comprehensive discussion in [38].

For ease of reference, let us recall that by a chain is meant a collection $\mathcal{C}$ of sets such that $A, B \in \mathcal{C}$ implies either $A \subseteq B$ or $B \subseteq A$. We now state Zorn's Lemma in a form best suited to our present needs.

Zorn's Lemma. Let $\mathcal{A}$ be a nonempty family of subsets of some fixed set with the property that for each chain $\mathcal{C}$ in $\mathcal{A}$, the union $\cup \mathcal{C}$ also belongs to $\mathcal{A}$. Then $\mathcal{A}$ contains a set which is maximal in the sense that it is not properly contained in any member of $\mathcal{A}$.

The significant point, needless to say, is that this lemma asserts the existence of a certain maximal element without actually giving a constructive process for finding it.

Theorem 3–30. (*Krull-Zorn*). In a commutative ring with identity, each proper ideal is contained in a maximal ideal.

Proof. Let $(I, +, \cdot)$ be any proper ideal of $(R, +, \cdot)$, a commutative ring with identity. Define a family of subsets of R by taking

$$\mathcal{A} = \{J \mid I \subseteq J; (J, +, \cdot) \text{ is a proper ideal of } (R, +, \cdot)\}.$$

This family is obviously nonempty for I itself belongs to $\mathcal{A}$.

Now, consider an arbitrary chain $\{I_i\}$ in $\mathcal{A}$. Our aim, of course, is to establish that $\cup I_i$ is again a member of $\mathcal{A}$. Notice first that $\cup I_i \neq R$, since $1 \notin I_i$ for any i. Next, let the elements $a, b \in \cup I_i$ and $r \in R$. Then there exist indices i and j for which $a \in I_i$, $b \in I_j$. As the collection $\{I_i\}$ forms a chain, either $I_i \subseteq I_j$ or else $I_j \subseteq I_i$; say, for definiteness, $I_i \subseteq I_j$. But $(I_j, +, \cdot)$ is an ideal, so the difference $a - b \in I_j \subseteq \cup I_i$. For the same reason, $r \cdot a \in I_j$. This shows the triple $(\cup I_i, +, \cdot)$ to be a proper ideal of the ring $(R, +, \cdot)$. Finally, $I \subseteq \cup I_i$, hence the union $\cup I_i \in \mathfrak{a}$.

Thus, on the basis of Zorn's Lemma, the family $\mathfrak{a}$ contains a maximal element M. It follows directly from the definition of $\mathfrak{a}$ that the triple $(M, +, \cdot)$ is a proper ideal of the ring $(R, +, \cdot)$ with $I \subseteq M$. We assert $(M, +, \cdot)$ is in fact a maximal ideal. To see this, suppose $(J, +, \cdot)$ is any ideal of $(R, +, \cdot)$ for which $M \subset J \subseteq R$. Since M is a maximal element of the family $\mathfrak{a}$, the set J cannot belong to $\mathfrak{a}$. Accordingly, the ideal $(J, +, \cdot)$ must be improper, which implies $J = R$. We therefore conclude $(M, +, \cdot)$ is a maximal ideal of $(R, +, \cdot)$, completing the proof.

Corollary. An element is invertible if and only if it belongs to no maximal ideal.

Proof. The conclusion is immediate by Theorem 3–7.

One remark: Theorem 3–30 does not extend to rings without identity. The preceding argument is no longer adequate, since the union of a chain in $\mathfrak{a}$ cannot be shown to be a proper subset of R.

Although maximal ideals were defined for arbitrary rings, we shall abandon a degree of generality and henceforth limit our discussion to commutative rings with identity. The advantage in doing so stems from the fact that each ideal, other than the parent ring itself, will be contained in a maximal ideal. Thus, until further notice, we shall assume that

all given rings are commutative with identity,

even when this is not explicitly mentioned. To be sure, some of the subsequent material could be presented without this additional restriction.

In a strict sense, it is incorrect to speak of an ideal being contained in a maximal ideal, for the inclusion actually refers to the underlying sets of elements. Nevertheless, the phrasing is convenient and we commit this inaccuracy freely.

As an application of the Krull-Zorn Theorem, we next give an elementary proof of a somewhat special result; while the fact involved is rather interesting, there will be no occasion to make use of it.

Theorem 3–31. In a ring $(R, +, \cdot)$ having exactly one maximal ideal $(M, +, \cdot)$, the only idempotent elements are 0 and 1.

Proof. Assume the theorem is false; that is, suppose there exists an idempotent $a \in R$ with $a \neq 0, 1$. The relation $a^2 = a$ implies $a \cdot (1 - a) = 0$, so that a and $1 - a$ are zero divisors. Hence, by Problem 8(d), Section 3–1, neither the element a nor $1 - a$ is invertible in R. But this means the principal ideals $((a), +, \cdot)$ and $((1 - a), +, \cdot)$ are both proper ideals of the ring $(R, +, \cdot)$. As such, they must be contained in $(M, +, \cdot)$, the sole maximal ideal of

$(R, +, \cdot)$: $(a) \subseteq M$ and $(1 - a) \subseteq M$. Accordingly, both a and $1 - a$ lie in M, whence
$$1 = a + (1 - a) \in M.$$

This leads at once to the contradiction $M = R$.

While more elementary proofs are possible, Theorem 3–31 can be used to show a field has no idempotents except 0 and 1. A full justification of this statement consists of first establishing that the zero ideal is the only maximal ideal in a field.

We now come to a characterization of maximal ideals in terms of quotient rings, a fundamental result.

Theorem 3–32. Let $(I, +, \cdot)$ be a proper ideal of the ring $(R, +, \cdot)$. Then $(I, +, \cdot)$ is a maximal ideal if and only if the quotient ring $(R/I, +, \cdot)$ is a field.

Proof. To begin with, let $(I, +, \cdot)$ be a maximal ideal of $(R, +, \cdot)$. Since $(R, +, \cdot)$ is a commutative ring with identity, the quotient ring $(R/I, +, \cdot)$ also has these properties. Thus to prove $(R/I, +, \cdot)$ a field, it suffices to show each nonzero element of R/I has a multiplicative inverse. Now, if the coset $a + I \neq 0 + I$, then $a \notin I$. By virtue of the fact $(I, +, \cdot)$ is a maximal ideal, the ideal $((I, a), +, \cdot)$ generated by I and a must be the whole ring $(R, +, \cdot)$:
$$R = (I, a) = \{i + r \cdot a \mid i \in I, r \in R\}.$$

That is to say, every element of R is expressible in the form $i + r \cdot a$, where $i \in I$ and $r \in R$. The identity element 1, in particular, may be written as
$$1 = \bar{i} + \bar{r} \cdot a$$

for suitable choice of $\bar{i} \in I$, $\bar{r} \in R$. But then the difference $1 - \bar{r} \cdot a \in I$. This is obviously equivalent to
$$1 + I = \bar{r} \cdot a + I = (\bar{r} + I) \cdot (a + I),$$

which asserts $\bar{r} + I = (a + I)^{-1}$. Hence $(R/I, +, \cdot)$ is a field.

For the opposite direction, suppose $(R/I, +, \cdot)$ is a field and $(J, +, \cdot)$ is any ideal of $(R, +, \cdot)$ such that $I \subset J \subseteq R$. The argument consists of showing that $J = R$, for then $(I, +, \cdot)$ will be a maximal ideal. Since I is a proper subset of J, there exists an element $a \in J$ with $a \notin I$. Consequently, the coset $a + I \neq 0 + I$, the zero element of $(R/I, +, \cdot)$. As $(R/I, +, \cdot)$ is assumed to be a field, $a + I$ must have an inverse under multiplication,
$$(a + I) \cdot (b + I) = 1 + I$$

for some coset $b + I \in R/I$. It then follows that $1 - a \cdot b \in I \subset J$. But the product $a \cdot b$ also belongs to J (recall a is an element of the ideal $(J, +, \cdot)$), implying the identity $1 \in J$. This in turn yields $J = R$, as desired.

Example 3–29. Consider the ring of even integers, $(Z_e, +, \cdot)$, a commutative ring without identity. In this ring, the principal ideal $((4), +, \cdot)$ generated by the integer 4 is a maximal ideal.

The argument might be expressed as follows: If n is any element not in (4), then n is an even integer not divisible by 4; consequently, the greatest common divisor of n and 4 must be 2. By Problem 9, Section 3–2, we then have

$$((4), n) = (2) = Z_e,$$

so that the ideal generated by (4) and n coincides with the whole ring. This reasoning shows that there is no ideal of $(Z_e, +, \cdot)$ contained strictly between $((4), +, \cdot)$ and $(Z_e, +, \cdot)$.

Now note that in the associated quotient ring $(Z_e/(4), +, \cdot)$,

$$(2 + (4)) \cdot (2 + (4)) = 0 + (4).$$

The ring $(Z_e/(4), +, \cdot)$ therefore has divisors of zero and cannot possibly be a field. The point we wish to make is that the assumption of an identity element is essential to Theorem 3–32.

We now shift our attention from maximal to prime ideals. Before formally defining this notion, let us turn to the ring of integers $(Z, +, \cdot)$ for motivation; specifically, consider the principal ideal $((p), +, \cdot)$ generated by a prime p. If $ab \in (p)$, where $a, b \in Z$, then $ab = np$ for some integer n. Since the product ab is divisible by p, either p divides a or else p divides b (corollary to Theorem 1–4). This being so, it follows that either

$$a = n_1 p \in (p) \qquad \text{or} \qquad b = n_2 p \in (p)$$

for suitable choice of $n_1, n_2 \in Z$. The ideal $((p), +, \cdot)$ thus has the agreeable property that whenever (p) contains a product at least one of the factors must belong to (p). This observation serves to illustrate and partly to suggest the next definition.

Definition 3–19. An ideal $(I, +, \cdot)$ of the ring $(R, +, \cdot)$ is a *prime ideal* if for all $a, b \in R$, $a \cdot b \in I$ implies either $a \in I$ or $b \in I$.

Example 3–30. The prime ideals of the ring $(Z, +, \cdot)$ are precisely the ideals $((p), +, \cdot)$, where p is a prime number, together with the trivial ideals $(\{0\}, +, \cdot)$ and $(Z, +, \cdot)$.

Example 3–31. A commutative ring with identity $(R, +, \cdot)$ is an integral domain if and only if the zero ideal $(\{0\}, +, \cdot)$ is a prime ideal.

The prime ideals of a ring may be characterized in the following manner.

Theorem 3–33. Let $(I, +, \cdot)$ be a proper ideal of the ring $(R, +, \cdot)$. Then $(I, +, \cdot)$ is a prime ideal if and only if the quotient ring $(R/I, +, \cdot)$ is an integral domain.

Proof. First, take $(I, +, \cdot)$ to be a prime ideal of $(R, +, \cdot)$. Since $(R, +, \cdot)$ is a commutative ring with identity, so is the quotient ring $(R/I, +, \cdot)$. It remains therefore only to verify $(R/I, +, \cdot)$ is free of zero divisors. For this, assume that

$$(a + I) \cdot (b + I) = I.$$

In other words, the product of these cosets equals the zero element of the ring $(R/I, +, \cdot)$. The foregoing equation is plainly equivalent to $a \cdot b + I = I$, or what amounts to the same thing, $a \cdot b \in I$. Since $(I, +, \cdot)$ is a prime ideal, one of the factors a or b must lie in I. But this means either the coset $a + I = I$ or else $b + I = I$, hence $(R/I, +, \cdot)$ is without zero divisors.

To prove the converse, we just reverse the argument. Accordingly, suppose $(R/I, +, \cdot)$ is an integral domain and the product $a \cdot b \in I$. We then have

$$(a + I) \cdot (b + I) = a \cdot b + I = I.$$

By hypothesis, $(R/I, +, \cdot)$ contains no divisors of zero, so that either $a + I = I$ or $b + I = I$. In any event, one of a or b belongs to I, forcing $(I, +, \cdot)$ to be a prime ideal.

There is an important class of ideals which are always prime, namely the maximal ideals. From the several ways of proving this result, we choose the argument given below; another approach is indicated in the problems at the end of this section.

Theorem 3–34. In a commutative ring with identity, every maximal ideal is a prime ideal.

Proof. Assume $(I, +, \cdot)$ is a maximal ideal of the ring $(R, +, \cdot)$ and that $a \cdot b \in I$ with $a \notin I$. We propose to show $b \in I$. The maximality of $(I, +, \cdot)$ implies that the ideal generated by I and a must be the whole ring: $R = (I, a)$. Hence there exist elements $i \in I$, $r \in R$ for which

$$1 = i + r \cdot a.$$

Since both $a \cdot b$ and i are in I, we conclude

$$b = (i + r \cdot a) \cdot b = i \cdot b + r \cdot (a \cdot b) \in I,$$

from which it is clear that $(I, +, \cdot)$ is a prime ideal.

We should point out that in rings without an identity element this result does not remain valid; a specific illustration is the ring $(Z_e, +, \cdot)$, where $((4), +, \cdot)$ forms a maximal ideal which is not prime.

One more definition is required: a *principal ideal domain* is a principal ideal ring which is also an integral domain. Otherwise expressed, a principal ideal domain is an integral domain in which every ideal is a principal ideal.

Let us remark that the converse of Theorem 3–34 need not hold; there exist examples of prime ideals which are not maximal ideals. The special properties of the principal ideal domains, however, guarantee that the notions of primeness and maximality are equivalent for this important class of rings. Since every integral domain contains the two trivial prime ideals, the use of the term prime ideal in a principal ideal domain customarily excludes these from consideration.

Theorem 3–35. Let $(R, +, \cdot)$ be a principal ideal domain. A (nontrivial) ideal of $(R, +, \cdot)$ is prime if and only if it is a maximal ideal.

Proof. In view of Theorem 3–34, it is sufficient to show that if $((a), +, \cdot)$ is a prime ideal of $(R, +, \cdot)$, then $((a), +, \cdot)$ is also maximal. To this end, suppose $(I, +, \cdot)$ is any ideal with $(a) \subset I \subseteq R$. Since $(R, +, \cdot)$ is a principal ideal ring, there exists an element $b \in R$ for which $I = (b)$. Now $a \in I = (b)$, hence $a = r \cdot b$ for some choice of r in R. But $((a), +, \cdot)$ is a prime ideal, so either $r \in (a)$ or $b \in (a)$. The possibility that $b \in (a)$ immediately leads to the contradiction $(b) \subseteq (a)$. Therefore $r \in (a)$, which implies $r = s \cdot a$ for suitable $s \in R$, or $a = r \cdot b = (s \cdot a) \cdot b$. Since $a \neq 0$ and $(R, +, \cdot)$ is an integral domain, we then have $1 = s \cdot b$. This means the identity $1 \in (b) = I$, or equivalently, $I = R$. Since no ideal lies between $((a), +, \cdot)$ and the whole ring, we conclude that $((a), +, \cdot)$ is a maximal ideal.

Corollary. A nontrivial ideal of the ring $(Z, +, \cdot)$ is prime if and only if it is maximal.

Note that in asserting the equivalence of prime and maximal ideals, Theorem 3–35 fails to actually identify these ideals. The situation is easily remedied though by introducing the idea of a prime element.

Definition 3–20. A nonzero element a of the ring $(R, +, \cdot)$ is called a *prime element* of R if a is not invertible and in every factorization $a = b \cdot c$ with $b, c \in R$, either b or c is invertible.

The nonprimes thus consist of zero, elements having inverses, and all elements which can be written as the product of two factors neither of which is invertible. In rings such as division rings and fields, where each nonzero element possesses a multiplicative inverse, the concept of a prime element is of no significance.

The theorem providing the bridge between prime elements and prime ideals may now be stated as follows:

Theorem 3–36. Let $(R, +, \cdot)$ be a principal ideal domain. The ideal $((a), +, \cdot)$ is a prime (maximal) ideal of $(R, +, \cdot)$ if and only if a is a prime element of R.

Proof. The structure of the first part of the proof is similar to that of Theorem 3–35. In other words, suppose a is a prime element of R and $(I, +, \cdot)$ is any ideal for which $(a) \subset I \subseteq R$. By hypothesis, $(R, +, \cdot)$ is a principal ideal ring, so there is an element b in R with $I = (b)$. As $a \in (b)$, $a = r \cdot b$ for some $r \in R$. It follows from the fact that a is a prime element that either r or b is invertible. Were r to have a multiplicative inverse, then $b = r^{-1} \cdot a \in (a)$, which implies $I = (b) \subseteq (a)$, an obvious contradiction. Accordingly, the element b must be invertible, so that $(b) = R$. This argument shows that $((a), +, \cdot)$ is a maximal ideal of $(R, +, \cdot)$ and consequently prime, by Theorem 3–34.

On the other hand, let $((a), +, \cdot)$ be a prime ideal of $(R, +, \cdot)$. For a proof by contradiction, assume that a is not a prime element of R. Then a admits the factorization $a = b \cdot c$, where b, $c \in R$, and neither b nor c is invertible. (The alternative possibility that a has an inverse implies $(a) = R$, so it may be ruled out.) Now if the element b were in (a), then $b = r \cdot a$ for some $r \in R$, and $a = b \cdot c = (r \cdot a) \cdot c$. From the cancellation law, we could infer $r \cdot c = 1$. But this results in the contradiction that c is invertible. By the same reasoning, if c lies in (a), then b possesses an inverse, contrary to assumption. We then have $b \cdot c \in (a)$, with $b \notin (a)$ and $c \notin (a)$, which denies that $((a), +, \cdot)$ is a prime ideal. Hence our original supposition is false and a must be a prime element of R.

As might be expected, prime elements in a principal ideal domain play a role analogous to the prime numbers in the ring of integers. To give one illustration, the following generalization of the Fundamental Theorem of Arithmetic can be obtained: every nonzero element of a principal ideal domain is either invertible or can be written as a product of prime elements in an essentially unique way (up to invertible elements as factors and the order of factors); the proof of this fact is omitted.

It would seem inappropriate to conclude this section without some brief mention of the radical of a ring. The notion can be characterized in various ways and in more generality than is done here, but at the cost of cumbersome arguments. For our present purposes, a definition phrased in terms of maximal ideals is preferable.

Definition 3–21. The *radical* of a ring $(R, +, \cdot)$, denoted by rad R, is the set

$$\text{rad } R = \cap \{M \mid (M, +, \cdot) \text{ is a maximal ideal of } (R, +, \cdot)\}.$$

If rad $R = \{0\}$, then we say $(R, +, \cdot)$ is a ring *without radical* or is a *semisimple ring*.

The radical always exists, since we know by Theorem 3–30 that any ring contains at least one maximal ideal. It is also immediate from the definition that the triple (rad $R, +, \cdot$) forms an ideal of $(R, +, \cdot)$.

Example 3–32. The ring of integers $(Z, +, \cdot)$ is a semisimple ring. For, according to Theorem 3–36, the maximal ideals of $(Z, +, \cdot)$ are precisely the principal ideals $((p), +, \cdot)$, where p is a prime; that is,

$$\text{rad } Z = \cap\{(p) \mid p \text{ a prime number}\}.$$

Since no nonzero integer is divisible by every prime, rad $Z = \{0\}$.

First, let us establish a connection between the radical and invertibility of ring elements. At the risk of being repetitious, we recall our convention that "ring" always means commutative ring with identity.

Theorem 3–37. Let $(I, +, \cdot)$ be an ideal of the ring $(R, +, \cdot)$. Then the set $I \subseteq \text{rad } R$ if and only if each element of the coset $1 + I$ has an inverse in R.

Proof. We begin by assuming that $I \subseteq \text{rad } R$ and that there is some element $a \in I$ for which $1 + a$ is not invertible. Our object, of course, is to derive a contradiction. By the corollary to Theorem 3–30, the element $1 + a$ must belong to some maximal ideal $(M, +, \cdot)$ of the ring $(R, +, \cdot)$. Since $a \in \text{rad } R$, a is also contained in M, and therefore $1 = (1 + a) - a$ is in M. But this means $M = R$, which is clearly impossible.

To prove the converse, suppose each member of $1 + I$ has a multiplicative inverse, but $I \nsubseteq \text{rad } R$. By definition of the radical, there will exist a maximal ideal $(M, +, \cdot)$ of $(R, +, \cdot)$ with $I \nsubseteq M$. If a is any element of I which is not in M, the maximality of $(M, +, \cdot)$ implies that $(M, a) = R$. The identity element 1 can therefore be expressed in the form

$$1 = m + r \cdot a$$

for suitable choice of $m \in M$ and $r \in R$. But then $m = 1 - r \cdot a \in 1 + I$, so that m possesses an inverse. The conclusion is untenable, since no proper ideal contains an invertible element.

The form this result takes when $(I, +, \cdot)$ is the principal ideal generated by an element $a \in \text{rad } R$ deserves special attention. While actually a corollary to the theorem just proved, it is important enough to be singled out as a theorem.

Theorem 3–38. In any ring $(R, +, \cdot)$, an element $a \in \text{rad } R$ if and only if $1 + r \cdot a$ has an inverse for each $r \in R$.

This theorem adapts itself to many uses. Three fairly short and instructive applications are presented below.

Corollary 1. An element a is invertible in the ring $(R, +, \cdot)$ if and only if the coset $a + \text{rad } R$ is invertible in the quotient ring $(R/\text{rad } R, +, \cdot)$.

Proof. Assume the coset $a + \text{rad } R$ has an inverse in $(R/\text{rad } R, +, \cdot)$, so that

$$(a + \text{rad } R) \cdot (b + \text{rad } R) = 1 + \text{rad } R$$

for some $b \in R$. Then $a \cdot b - 1$ lies in rad R. We next appeal to Theorem 3–38, with $r = 1$, to conclude that the product $a \cdot b = 1 + 1 \cdot (a \cdot b - 1)$ is invertible; this, in turn, forces the element a to have an inverse. The other direction is essentially trivial.

Corollary 2. The only idempotent in the radical of the ring $(R, +, \cdot)$ is 0.

Proof. Let the element $a \in R$ with $a^2 = a$. Taking $r = -1$ in the preceding theorem, we see that $1 - a$ has an inverse in R; say, for purposes of argument, that $(1 - a) \cdot b = 1$, where $b \in R$. This leads to

$$a = a^2 + a \cdot b - a \cdot b = a \cdot (a + a \cdot b - b) = a \cdot (a - 1) = 0,$$

which completes the proof.

Corollary 3. Let N denote the set of all noninvertible elements of R. Then the triple $(N, +, \cdot)$ is an ideal of the ring $(R, +, \cdot)$ if and only if $N = \operatorname{rad} R$.

Proof. The inclusion $\operatorname{rad} R \subseteq N$ clearly holds. Suppose, therefore, that the element $a \in N$. If the system $(N, +, \cdot)$ forms an ideal of $(R, +, \cdot)$, then $r \cdot a \in N$ for any $r \in R$. Moreover, the element $1 + r \cdot a \notin N$, for otherwise $1 = (1 + r \cdot a) - (r \cdot a)$ would be in N. From the definition of N, it follows that $1 + r \cdot a$ must be invertible, implying $a \in \operatorname{rad} R$. This shows $N \subseteq \operatorname{rad} R$, whence the equality $N = \operatorname{rad} R$. The other direction of the corollary is immediate.

We close this section with a result which provides a convenient method for manufacturing semisimple rings. Its proof utilizes both implications of the last theorem.

Theorem 3–39. For any ring $(R, +, \cdot)$, the quotient ring $(R/\operatorname{rad} R, +, \cdot)$ is semisimple.

Proof. Before becoming involved in details, let us remark that since $(\operatorname{rad} R, +, \cdot)$ is an ideal of $(R, +, \cdot)$, we may certainly form the quotient ring $(R/\operatorname{rad} R, +, \cdot)$. To simplify notation somewhat, we will denote $\operatorname{rad} R$ by I.

Suppose the coset $a + I \in \operatorname{rad}(R/I)$. Our strategy is to show that $a \in I$, for then $a + I = I$, which would imply that $\operatorname{rad}(R/I)$ consists of only the zero coset. Since $a + I$ lies in $\operatorname{rad}(R/I)$, Theorem 3–38 asserts

$$(1 + I) + (r + I) \cdot (a + I) = 1 + r \cdot a + I$$

is invertible in R/I for each $r \in R$. Accordingly, there exists a coset $b + I$ (which, of course, depends on both r and a) such that

$$(1 + a \cdot r + I) \cdot (b + I) = 1 + I.$$

This is clearly equivalent to

$$b + a \cdot r \cdot b - 1 \in I = \operatorname{rad} R.$$

Again appealing to Theorem 3–38, we conclude that the element

$$b + a \cdot r \cdot b = 1 + 1 \cdot (b + a \cdot r \cdot b - 1)$$

has an inverse c in R. But then

$$(1 + r \cdot a) \cdot (b \cdot c) = (b + a \cdot r \cdot b) \cdot c = 1,$$

so that $1 + r \cdot a$ is invertible in R. Because this argument holds for every $r \in R$, it follows that $a \in \operatorname{rad} R$, as desired.

PROBLEMS

In the following set of problems, all rings are assumed to be commutative with identity.

1. Show that the only maximal ideal in a field $(F, +, \cdot)$ is the zero ideal $(\{0\}, +, \cdot)$.

2. Given f is a homomorphism from the ring $(R, +, \cdot)$ onto the ring $(R', +', \cdot')$, prove that
   a) if $(I, +, \cdot)$ is a maximal ideal of $(R, +, \cdot)$, then the triple $(f(I), +', \cdot')$ is a maximal ideal of $(R', +', \cdot')$,
   b) if $(I', +', \cdot')$ is a maximal ideal of $(R', +', \cdot')$, then the triple $(f^{-1}(I'), +, \cdot)$ is a maximal ideal of $(R, +, \cdot)$.

3. If f is a homomorphism from the ring $(R, +, \cdot)$ onto the field $(F, +', \cdot')$, show that $(\ker (f), +, \cdot)$ is a maximal ideal of $(R, +, \cdot)$.

4. With the aid of Theorems 3–29 and 3–32, obtain another proof of the fact that $(Z_p, +_p, \cdot_p)$ is a field if and only if p is a prime number.

5. An ideal $(I, +, \cdot)$ of the ring $(R, +, \cdot)$ is said to be *minimal* if $I \neq \{0\}$ and there exists no ideal $(J, +, \cdot)$ of $(R, +, \cdot)$ such that $\{0\} \subset J \subset I$.
   a) Prove the ideal $(I, +, \cdot)$ is a minimal ideal if and only $(a) = I$ for every non-zero element $a \in I$.
   b) Verify that the ring of integers $(Z, +, \cdot)$ has no minimal ideals.

6. For any ideal $(I, +, \cdot)$ of the ring $(R, +, \cdot)$, define the set $\sqrt{I}$ by

$$\sqrt{I} = \{r \in R \mid r^n \in I \text{ for some } n \in Z_+\}.$$

Establish the following assertions:
   a) The triple $(\sqrt{I}, +, \cdot)$ is an ideal of $(R, +, \cdot)$ such that $I \subseteq \sqrt{I}$.
   b) If $(J, +, \cdot)$ is an ideal of $(R, +, \cdot)$ for which $I \subseteq J \subseteq \sqrt{I}$, then $\sqrt{J} = \sqrt{I}$.
   c) If $(I_1, +, \cdot)$ and $(I_2, +, \cdot)$ are both ideals of $(R, +, \cdot)$, then

$$\sqrt{I_1 \cap I_2} = \sqrt{I_1} \cap \sqrt{I_2}.$$

7. If f is a homomorphism from the ring $(R, +, \cdot)$ onto the ring $(R', +', \cdot')$, show the following:
   a) If $(I, +, \cdot)$ is a prime ideal of $(R, +, \cdot)$ with $I \supseteq \ker (f)$, then the triple $(f(I), +', \cdot')$ is a prime ideal of $(R', +', \cdot')$.

b) If $(I', +', \cdot')$ is a prime ideal of $(R', +', \cdot')$, then the triple $(f^{-1}(I'), +, \cdot)$ is a prime ideal of $(R, +, \cdot)$.

8. Let $(I_i, +, \cdot)$ be an indexed collection of prime ideals of the ring $(R, +, \cdot)$. If the family of sets $\{I_i\}$ forms a chain, prove that both $(\cup I_i, +, \cdot)$ and $(\cap I_i, +, \cdot)$ are prime ideals of $(R, +, \cdot)$.

9. Prove that if $(I_1, +, \cdot)$ and $(I_2, +, \cdot)$ are two ideals of the ring $(R, +, \cdot)$ such that neither the set I_1 nor the set I_2 is contained in the other, then the ideal $(I_1 \cap I_2, +, \cdot)$ is not prime. [*Hint:* Pick $a \in I_1 - I_2$, $b \in I_2 - I_1$, and consider $a \cdot b$.]

10. Utilize Theorems 3–32 and 3–33 to give an alternative proof of the fact that every maximal ideal is a prime ideal.

11. An ideal $(I, +, \cdot)$ of a ring $(R, +, \cdot)$ is said to be a *primary ideal* if $a \cdot b \in I$ with $a \notin I$ implies $b^n \in I$ for some positive integer n. Establish the following facts concerning primary ideals:

   a) Every prime ideal is a primary ideal.
   b) If $(I, +, \cdot)$ is a primary ideal of $(R, +, \cdot)$, then the ideal $(\sqrt{I}, +, \cdot)$ is prime.
   c) If the ideal $(I, +, \cdot)$ is such that $(\sqrt{I}, +, \cdot)$ forms a maximal ideal of $(R, +, \cdot)$, then $(I, +, \cdot)$ is a primary ideal.

12. Let $(I, +, \cdot)$ be an ideal of the ring $(R, +, \cdot)$. Prove that $(I, +, \cdot)$ is a primary ideal if and only if every zero divisor of the quotient ring $(R/I, +, \cdot)$ is nilpotent.

13. An ideal is called a *nil ideal* if each of its elements is nilpotent. Prove that if $(I, +, \cdot)$ is a nil ideal of the ring $(R, +, \cdot)$, then $I \subseteq \operatorname{rad} R$. [*Hint:* If $r \in I$ with $r^n = 0$, then $(1 - r) \cdot (1 + r + r^2 + \cdots + r^{n-1}) = 1 - r^n = 1$.]

14. Describe the radical of $(Z_n, +_n, \cdot_n)$. [*Hint:* Consider the prime factorization of n.]

15. Given $(I, +, \cdot)$ is an ideal of the ring $(R, +, \cdot)$ such that the quotient ring $(R/I, +, \cdot)$ is semisimple, prove that $\operatorname{rad} R \subseteq I$. [*Hint:* If $a \in \operatorname{rad} R$, show that $a + I \in \operatorname{rad}(R/I)$ by use of Theorem 3–38.]

16. Prove that if $(I, +, \cdot)$ is an ideal of the ring $(R, +, \cdot)$, then $\operatorname{rad} I = I \cap \operatorname{rad} R$.

17. a) Show that the annihilator of a semisimple ring $(R, +, \cdot)$ is zero; in other words, $\operatorname{ann} R = \{0\}$.
   b) Let $(R, +, \cdot)$ be a ring with the property that $I = \operatorname{ann}(\operatorname{ann} I)$ for every ideal $(I, +, \cdot)$ of $(R, +, \cdot)$. (In general, we only have the inclusion $I \subseteq \operatorname{ann}(\operatorname{ann} I)$.) Prove that if $(M, +, \cdot)$ is a maximal ideal of the ring $(R, +, \cdot)$, then $(\operatorname{ann} M, +, \cdot)$ is a minimal ideal.

18. Let $(I, +, \cdot)$ be an ideal of the ring $(R, +, \cdot)$ and $S \subseteq R$ be a set that is closed under multiplication and is disjoint from I.

   a) Using Zorn's Lemma, show that there exists an ideal $(P, +, \cdot)$ of $(R, +, \cdot)$ which is maximal with respect to these properties:

$$(\text{i}) \ I \subseteq P, \quad (\text{ii}) \ P \cap S = \emptyset.$$

   b) Prove that $(P, +, \cdot)$ is necessarily a prime ideal. [*Hint:* If $a \notin P$, $b \notin P$, then (P, a) and (P, b) intersect S, which implies $a \cdot b \notin P$.]

19. Prove: an ideal $(I, +, \cdot)$ of $(R, +, \cdot)$ is the intersection of prime ideals if and only if $a^2 \in I$ implies $a \in I$. [*Hint:* For each $a \notin I$, there is a prime ideal $(P, +, \cdot)$

of $(R, +, \cdot)$ which is maximal with respect to disjointedness from the set

$$\{a, a^2, \ldots, a^n, \ldots\}$$

and such that $P \supseteq I$.]

20. Verify that an ideal $(I, +, \cdot)$ of $(R, +, \cdot)$ contains a prime ideal if and only if, for every n, $a_1 \cdot a_2 \cdots a_n = 0$ implies that some $a_k \in I$. [*Hint:* Use Problem 18 with $S = \{b_1 \cdot b_2 \cdots b_n \mid b_k \notin I, n \geq 1\}$.]

21. A ring is said to be a *local ring* if it has a unique maximal ideal. If $(R, +, \cdot)$ is a local ring and $(M, +, \cdot)$ is its maximal ideal, prove that any element $a \notin M$ is invertible.

22. If $f : R \to R'$ is a homomorphism of the ring $(R, +, \cdot)$ onto the ring $(R', +', \cdot')$, prove that $f(\text{rad } R) \subseteq \text{rad } R'$ and, whenever $\ker (f) \subseteq \text{rad } R$, that $\text{rad } R = f^{-1}(\text{rad } R')$.

23. If N denotes the set of noninvertible elements of R, prove that the following conditions are equivalent:
    a) $(N, +, \cdot)$ is an ideal of $(R, +, \cdot)$,
    b) the quotient ring $(R/N, +, \cdot)$ is a field,
    c) $(R, +, \cdot)$ is a local ring.

3–5 POLYNOMIAL RINGS

The next step in our program is to apply some of the previously developed theory to a certain class of rings, the so-called polynomial rings. For the moment, we shall merely remark that these are rings whose elements consist of polynomials with coefficients from a fixed, but otherwise arbitrary, ring. (The most interesting results occur when the coefficients are specialized to a field.)

The matter of formalizing the intuitive idea of what is meant by a polynomial always presents a serious problem. We propose first to put this notion on a sound basis, then to discuss the properties of polynomials and polynomial rings. Our investigation will culminate with a survey of the basic facts relating roots of polynomials and field extensions. En route, the reader will see that many of the familiar results of elementary algebra are but special cases of general theorems to be obtained.

For an arbitrary ring $(R, +, \cdot)$, let poly R designate the set of all infinite sequences

$$f = (a_0, a_1, a_2, \ldots)$$

of elements of R in which at most a finite number of the $a_k \neq 0$; in other words, $(a_0, a_1, a_2, \ldots) \in \text{poly } R$ if and only if there is some nonnegative integer N such that $a_k = 0$ for all $k \geq N$. The elements of poly R are called *polynomials over the ring* $(R, +, \cdot)$, or just polynomials over R.

At times, it will be convenient to use the notation

$$(a_0, a_1, \ldots, a_n, 0, 0, \ldots)$$

for the polynomial with last nonzero term a_n; when $n = 0$, we permit $a_0 = 0$ in order to include the *zero polynomial* $(0, 0, 0, \ldots)$ each of whose terms is zero. With this agreement, the set of polynomials over R may be regarded as the set

$$\text{poly } R = \{(a_0, a_1, \ldots, a_n, 0, 0, \ldots) \mid a_k \in R, n \geq 0\}.$$

Thus, the sequence $(1, 1, 1, 0, 0, \ldots)$ would be a polynomial over $(Z_2, +_2, \cdot_2)$, but $(0, 1, 0, 1, \ldots, 0, 1, \ldots)$ would not.

We next introduce operations of addition and multiplication in the set poly R, so that the resulting system is a ring containing $(R, +, \cdot)$ as a subring. Let us first, however, make clear that two polynomials

$$f = (a_0, a_1, a_2, \ldots) \qquad \text{and} \qquad g = (b_0, b_1, b_2, \ldots)$$

are equal if and only if their corresponding terms are equal: $f = g$ if and only if $a_k = b_k$ for every integer $k \geq 0$. Now, define the sum $f + g$ by the rule

$$f + g = (a_0 + b_0, a_1 + b_1, a_2 + b_2, \ldots).$$

The reader may easily verify that the pair (poly $R, +$) forms a commutative group. We state only that the zero element is the zero polynomial $(0, 0, 0, \ldots)$ and that the additive inverse of $(a_0, a_1, a_2, \ldots)$ is $(-a_0, -a_1, -a_2, \ldots)$.

Finally, we specify an operation of multiplication in poly R by taking

$$f \cdot g = (a_0 \cdot b_0, a_0 \cdot b_1 + a_1 \cdot b_0, a_0 \cdot b_2 + a_1 \cdot b_1 + a_2 \cdot b_0, \ldots)$$
$$= (c_0, c_1, c_2, \ldots),$$

where

$$c_k = \sum_{i+j=k} a_i \cdot b_j = a_0 \cdot b_k + a_1 \cdot b_{k-1} + \cdots + a_k \cdot b_0.$$

Note that if $a_i = 0$ for $i > n$ and $b_j = 0$ for $j > m$, then $c_k = 0$ for all $k > n + m$ ($i + j = k > n + m$ implies either $i > n$ or $j > m$), whence $f \cdot g$ is once again a polynomial. A routine computation, which we omit, establishes that this multiplication is associative as well as distributive with respect to addition; in fact, these properties follow almost at once from the corresponding properties in $(R, +, \cdot)$. All this may be summarized in a theorem.

Theorem 3–40. The triple (poly $R, +, \cdot$) forms a ring, known as the *ring of polynomials over* R. Furthermore, the ring (poly $R, +, \cdot$) is commutative with identity if and only if $(R, +, \cdot)$ is a commutative ring with identity.

At the risk of belaboring the obvious, let us point out that while the operations in (poly $R, +, \cdot$) are defined in terms of those of $(R, +, \cdot)$, these are entirely new operations; we have used the same symbols only to avoid unnecessary notational complications.

If S represents the set of all *constant polynomials,* that is, the set

$$S = \{(a, 0, 0, \ldots) \mid a \in R\},$$

then it is not particularly difficult to show that $(S, +, \cdot)$ constitutes a subring of (poly $R, +, \cdot$) which is isomorphic to $(R, +, \cdot)$; one need simply consider the mapping that sends the constant polynomial $(a, 0, 0, \ldots)$ to a. In this sense, (poly $R, +, \cdot$) contains $(R, +, \cdot)$ as a subring.

As a result of the aforementioned imbedding, we shall no longer distinguish between an element $a \in R$ and the constant polynomial $(a, 0, 0, \ldots)$ of poly R.

By developing some additional notation, it is possible to express polynomials in the familiar form usually encountered in elementary courses in algebra. As a first step in this direction, we let ax designate the polynomial

$$(0, a, 0, 0, \ldots).$$

That is, ax is the specific member of poly R which has the element a for its second term and 0 for all other terms. More generally, the symbol ax^n, $n \geq 1$, will denote the polynomial

$$(0, \ldots, 0, a, 0, \ldots),$$

where the element a is the $(n + 1)$st term in this polynomial; for example, we have

$$ax^2 = (0, 0, a, 0, \ldots)$$

and

$$ax^3 = (0, 0, 0, a, 0, \ldots).$$

Utilizing these conventions, each polynomial

$$f = (a_0, a_1, a_2, \ldots, a_n, 0, 0, \ldots)$$

may be uniquely represented in the form

$$f = (a_0, 0, 0, \ldots) + (0, a_1, 0, 0, \ldots) + \cdots + (0, \ldots, 0, a_n, 0, \ldots)$$
$$= a_0 + a_1 x + a_2 x^2 + \cdots + a_n x^n,$$

with, of course, a_0 replacing $(a_0, 0, 0, \ldots)$. Thus, there is no harm in regarding the polynomial ring (poly $R, +, \cdot$) as consisting of all formal expressions

$$f = a_0 + a_1 x + \cdots + a_n x^n,$$

where the elements $a_0, a_1, \ldots, a_n$ (the *coefficients* of f) lie in R.

We should emphasize that according to our definition, x is simply a new symbol, or *indeterminant*, totally unrelated to the ring $(R, +, \cdot)$, and in no sense represents an element of R. To indicate the indeterminant x, it is common practice to write $R[x]$ for the set poly R, and $f(x)$ for any member of the same. From now on, we shall make exclusive use of this notation.

Remark. If the ring $(R, +, \cdot)$ has a multiplicative identity 1, many authors will identify the polynomial $1x$ with the indeterminant x, thereby treating x itself as a specific member of $R[x]$, namely, the polynomial $x = (0, 1, 0, 0, \ldots)$. From this view, ax becomes an actual product of elements in $R[x]$:

$$ax = (a, 0, 0, \ldots) \cdot (0, 1, 0, 0, \ldots).$$

To simplify the writing of a polynomial, it is customary to omit terms with zero coefficients and to replace $(-a_k)x^k$ by $-a_k x^k$. Thus, for example, $1 - 2x^2$ would stand for $1 + 0x + (-2)x^2$.

An important definition in connection with polynomials is that of degree, given below.

Definition 3–22. If

$$f(x) = a_0 + a_1 x + \cdots + a_n x^n, \qquad a_n \neq 0,$$

is a nonzero polynomial in $R[x]$, we call the coefficient a_n the *leading coefficient* of $f(x)$ and the integer n, the *degree* of the polynomial.

The degree of any nonzero polynomial is therefore a nonnegative integer; no degree is assigned to the zero polynomial. It will be observed that the polynomials of degree 0 are precisely the nonzero constant polynomials. If the ring $(R, +, \cdot)$ has an identity element, a nonzero polynomial of degree n whose leading coefficient $a_n = 1$ is said to be a *monic polynomial*; in this case, we take the liberty of dropping the 1 and writing $f(x) = a_0 + a_1 x + \cdots + x^n$.

As a matter of notation, we shall hereafter write $\deg f(x)$ for the degree of any nonzero polynomial $f(x) \in R[x]$.

Suppose $f(x), g(x) \in R[x]$ with $\deg f(x) = n$ and $\deg g(x) = m$, so that

$$f(x) = a_0 + a_1 x + \cdots + a_n x^n, \qquad a_n \neq 0,$$

$$g(x) = b_0 + b_1 x + \cdots + b_m x^m, \qquad b_m \neq 0.$$

From the definition of multiplication, the reader may easily check that all coefficients of $f(x) \cdot g(x)$ beyond the $(n + m)$th are zero, whence

$$f(x) \cdot g(x) = a_0 \cdot b_0 + (a_0 \cdot b_1 + a_1 \cdot b_0)x + \cdots + (a_n \cdot b_m)x^{n+m}.$$

If we assume that at least one of the leading coefficients a_n or b_m is not a divisor of zero in $(R, +, \cdot)$, then $a_n \cdot b_m \neq 0$; accordingly, $f(x) \cdot g(x) \neq 0$ and

$$\deg (f(x) \cdot g(x)) = n + m = \deg f(x) + \deg g(x).$$

This certainly holds if $(R, +, \cdot)$ is an integral domain, or again if $(R, +, \cdot)$ has an identity element and one of the polynomials $f(x)$ or $g(x)$ has an invertible leading coefficient.

The foregoing argument serves to establish the first part of the next theorem; the proof of the second assertion is left as an exercise.

Theorem 3–41. Let $(R, +, \cdot)$ be an integral domain and $f(x)$, $g(x)$ be two nonzero elements of $(R[x], +, \cdot)$. Then

1) $\deg \left(f(x) \cdot g(x) \right) = \deg f(x) + \deg g(x)$, and
2) either $f(x) + g(x) = 0$ or $\deg \left(f(x) + g(x) \right) \leq \max \{ \deg f(x), \deg g(x) \}$.

The notion of degree may be used to prove the following corollary.

Corollary. If the ring $(R, +, \cdot)$ is an integral domain, so also is its polynomial ring $(R[x], +, \cdot)$.

Proof. We observed earlier that whenever $(R, +, \cdot)$ is a commutative ring with identity, these properties carry over to $(R[x], +, \cdot)$. To see that $(R[x], +, \cdot)$ has no zero divisors, choose $f(x) \neq 0$, $g(x) \neq 0$ in $R[x]$. Then $\deg \left(f(x) \cdot g(x) \right) = \deg f(x) + \deg g(x) \geq 0$, hence the product $f(x) \cdot g(x)$ cannot be the zero polynomial.

Example 3–33. As an illustration of what might happen if $(R, +, \cdot)$ has zero divisors, consider $(Z_8, +_8, \cdot_8)$, the ring of integers modulo 8. Taking

$$f(x) = 1 + 2x,$$
$$g(x) = 4 + x + 4x^2,$$

we then have $f(x) \cdot g(x) = 4 + x + 6x^2$, so that

$$\deg \left(f(x) \cdot g(x) \right) = 2 < 1 + 2 = \deg f(x) + \deg g(x).$$

While many of the properties of the ring $(R, +, \cdot)$ carry over to the polynomial ring $(R[x], +, \cdot)$, it should be observed that for no ring $(R, +, \cdot)$ is $(R[x], +, \cdot)$ a field. In fact, no element of $R[x]$ which has positive degree can have a multiplicative inverse. For suppose $f(x) \in R[x]$ with $\deg f(x) > 0$; if $f(x) \cdot g(x) = 1$ for some $g(x) \in R[x]$, we would obtain the contradiction

$$0 = \deg 1 = \deg \left(f(x) \cdot g(x) \right) = \deg f(x) + \deg g(x) \neq 0.$$

For polynomials, we have a result analogous to the division algorithm for integers.

Theorem 3–42. (*Division Algorithm*). Let $(R, +, \cdot)$ be a commutative ring with identity and $f(x)$, $g(x) \neq 0$ be polynomials in $R[x]$, with the leading coefficient of $g(x)$ an invertible element. Then there exist unique polynomials $q(x)$, $r(x) \in R[x]$ such that

$$f(x) = q(x) \cdot g(x) + r(x),$$

where either $r(x) = 0$ or $\deg r(x) < \deg g(x)$.

Proof. The proof proceeds by induction on the degree of $f(x)$. First note that if $f(x) = 0$ or $\deg f(x) < \deg g(x)$, then a representation meeting the requirements of the theorem exists with $q(x) = 0$, $r(x) = f(x)$. Furthermore, if $\deg f(x) = \deg g(x) = 0$, $f(x)$ and $g(x)$ are both elements of R, and it suffices to take $q(x) = f(x) \cdot g(x)^{-1}$, $r(x) = 0$.

So, suppose the theorem is true for polynomials $f(x)$ of degree less than n (the induction hypothesis), and let $\deg f(x) = n$, $\deg g(x) = m$, where $n \geq m$; that is,

$$f(x) = a_0 + a_1 x + \cdots + a_n x^n, \qquad a_n \neq 0,$$

$$g(x) = b_0 + b_1 x + \cdots + b_m x^m, \qquad b_m \neq 0, \quad (n \geq m).$$

The polynomial

$$f_1(x) = f(x) - (a_n \cdot b_m^{-1}) x^{n-m} g(x)$$

lies in $R[x]$ and, since the coefficient of x^n is $a_n - (a_n \cdot b_m^{-1}) \cdot b_m = 0$, has degree less than n. By induction, there are polynomials $q_1(x)$, $r(x) \in R[x]$ such that

$$f_1(x) = q_1(x) \cdot g(x) + r(x),$$

where $r(x) = 0$ or $\deg r(x) < \deg g(x)$. Substituting, we obtain the equation

$$f(x) = \big(q_1(x) + (a_n \cdot b_m^{-1}) x^{n-m}\big) \cdot g(x) + r(x)$$
$$= q(x) \cdot g(x) + r(x),$$

which shows that the desired representation also exists when $\deg f(x) = n$.

As for uniqueness, suppose

$$f(x) = q(x) \cdot g(x) + r(x) = q'(x) \cdot g(x) + r'(x),$$

where $r(x)$ and $r'(x)$ satisfy the requirements of the theorem. Then

$$r(x) - r'(x) = \big(q'(x) - q(x)\big) \cdot g(x).$$

If $r(x) - r'(x) \neq 0$, we would have

$$\deg \big(r(x) - r'(x)\big) = \deg \big(q'(x) - q(x)\big) + \deg g(x)$$
$$\geq \deg g(x).$$

On the other hand, since the degrees of $r(x)$ and $r'(x)$ are both less than that of $g(x)$, it follows that

$$\deg \big(r(x) - r'(x)\big) < \deg g(x).$$

This contradiction implies $r(x) = r'(x)$, which in turn yields $q(x) = q'(x)$.

The polynomials $q(x)$ and $r(x)$ appearing in the representation

$$f(x) = q(x) \cdot g(x) + r(x)$$

given by the Division Algorithm are called, respectively, the *quotient* and *remainder* on dividing $f(x)$ by $g(x)$. Observe also that if $g(x)$ is a monic polynomial, or if $(R, +, \cdot)$ is a field, it is not necessary to assume the leading coefficient of $g(x)$ to be invertible.

Before discussing the consequences of Theorem 3–42, we pause to introduce some additional concepts. To this end, let $(R, +, \cdot)$ be a commutative ring with identity and r be an arbitrary element of R. For each polynomial

$$f(x) = a_0 + a_1 x + \cdots + a_n x^n$$

in $R[x]$, we may define $f(r) \in R$ by

$$f(r) = a_0 + a_1 \cdot r + \cdots + a_n \cdot r^n.$$

The element $f(r)$ is said to be the result of *substituting* r for x in $f(x)$. Suffice it to say, the addition and multiplication used in defining $f(r)$ are those of the ring $(R, +, \cdot)$, not those of $(R[x], +, \cdot)$. If $f(r) = 0$, we call the element r a *root* or *zero* of the given polynomial $f(x)$.

Suppose $f(x)$, $g(x)$ are in $R[x]$ and $r \in R$. The reader should prove that if

$$h(x) = f(x) + g(x), \qquad k(x) = f(x) \cdot g(x),$$

then

$$h(r) = f(r) + g(r), \qquad k(r) = f(r) \cdot g(r).$$

In particular, it may be concluded that the mapping which sends $f(x)$ to $f(r)$ is a homomorphism from $(R[x], +, \cdot)$ into $(R, +, \cdot)$; the range of this homomorphism will be denoted by $R(r)$.

Some difficulty arises when the ring $(R, +, \cdot)$ fails to be commutative; in this case, the above result need not hold. Observe that if we let

$$h(x) = (x - a) \cdot (x - b) = x^2 - (a + b)x + a \cdot b,$$

then

$$h(r) = r^2 - (a + b) \cdot r + a \cdot b.$$

Without the hypothesis of commutativity, it cannot be concluded that

$$(r - a) \cdot (r - b) = r^2 - a \cdot r - r \cdot b + a \cdot b$$

will equal $h(r)$; in other words, $h(x) = f(x) \cdot g(x)$ does not always imply $h(r) = f(r) \cdot g(r)$.

One more definition should be introduced: If $f(x)$ and $g(x) \neq 0$ are in $R[x]$, we say that $g(x)$ is a *factor* of $f(x)$ [or $g(x)$ *divides* $f(x)$] provided there exists some polynomial $h(x) \in R[x]$ for which $f(x) = h(x) \cdot g(x)$.

With this terminology in mind, we come to a series of theorems concerning the factorization properties of $R[x]$.

Theorem 3–43. (*Remainder Theorem*).   Let $(R, +, \cdot)$ be a commutative ring with identity.   If $f(x) \in R[x]$ and $a \in R$, then there is a unique polynomial $q(x)$ in $R[x]$ such that

$$f(x) = (x - a) \cdot q(x) + f(a).$$

Proof. Applying the division algorithm to $f(x)$ and $x - a$, we obtain

$$f(x) = (x - a) \cdot q(x) + r(x),$$

where $r(x) = 0$ or $\deg r(x) < \deg (x - a) = 1$.   It follows in either case that $r(x)$ is a constant polynomial $r \in R$.   Substituting a for x, we have the desired result:

$$f(a) = (a - a) \cdot q(a) + r(a) = 0 + r = r.$$

Corollary. (*Factorization Theorem*).   The polynomial $f(x) \in R[x]$ is divisible by $x - a$ if and only if a is a root of $f(x)$.

Proof. The corollary follows immediately from the theorem, since

$$f(x) = (x - a) \cdot q(x)$$

if and only if $f(a) = 0$.

Let us next show that the number of roots of a polynomial over an integral domain cannot exceed its degree.

Theorem 3–44. Let $(R, +, \cdot)$ be an integral domain and $f(x) \in R[x]$ be a nonzero polynomial of degree n.   Then $f(x)$ has at most n distinct roots in R.

Proof. We proceed by induction on the degree of $f(x)$.   When $\deg f(x) = 0$, the result is trivial, since $f(x)$ cannot have any roots.   If $\deg f(x) = 1$, say $f(x) = ax + b$, $a \neq 0$, then $f(x)$ has at most one root; indeed, if a is invertible, $-a^{-1} \cdot b$ is the only root of $f(x)$.   Now, suppose the theorem is true for all polynomials of degree $n - 1 \geq 1$, and let $\deg f(x) = n$.   If $f(x)$ has a root r, the preceding corollary gives

$$f(x) = (x - r) \cdot q(x),$$

where the polynomial $q(x)$ has degree $n - 1$.   Any root r_1 of $f(x)$ distinct from r must be a root of $q(x)$, for, by substitution,

$$f(r_1) = (r_1 - r) \cdot q(r_1) = 0$$

and, since $(R, +, \cdot)$ has no zero divisors, $q(r_1) = 0$.   From our induction hypothesis, $q(x)$ has at most $n - 1$ distinct roots.   As the only roots of $f(x)$ are r and those of $q(x)$, $f(x)$ cannot have more than n distinct roots in R.

Corollary. Let $f(x)$ and $g(x)$ be nonzero polynomials of degrees $\leq n$ over the integral domain $(R, +, \cdot)$. If there exist $n + 1$ distinct elements $a_k \in R$ ($k = 1, 2, \ldots, n + 1$) for which $f(a_k) = g(a_k)$, then $f(x) = g(x)$.

Proof. The polynomial $h(x) = f(x) - g(x)$ is such that $\deg h(x) \leq n$ and has at least $n + 1$ distinct roots in R. By Theorem 3–44, this is impossible unless $h(x) = f(x) - g(x) = 0$, or $f(x) = g(x)$.

Example 3–34. Consider the polynomial $x^p - x \in Z_p[x]$, where p is a prime number. Since the nonzero elements of $(Z_p, +_p, \cdot_p)$ form a cyclic group, under multiplication, of order $p - 1$, we must have $a^{p-1} = 1$ or $a^p = a$ for every $a \neq 0$. But the last equation clearly holds when $a = 0$, so that every element of Z_p is a root of the polynomial $x^p - x$. This furnishes an illustration of a nonzero polynomial which "vanishes identically."

Using the terminology of the present section, we now state the result known as the Fundamental Theorem of Algebra.

Theorem 3–45. Let $(C, +, \cdot)$ be the field of complex numbers. If $f(x) \in C[x]$ is a polynomial of positive degree, then $f(x)$ has at least one root in C.

While many proofs of this theorem are available, none is strictly algebraic in nature; thus, we shall assume the validity of Theorem 3–45 without proof. The reader may however establish the following corollary.

Corollary. If $f(x) \in C[x]$ is a polynomial of degree $n > 0$, then $f(x)$ can be expressed in $C[x]$ as a product of n (not necessarily distinct) linear factors.

Throughout the remainder of the section, we shall focus our attention on polynomials with coefficients from a field $(F, +, \cdot)$. In this important and interesting case, the associated polynomial ring $(F[x], +, \cdot)$ is an integral domain (but not a field!); in fact, $(F[x], +, \cdot)$ is a principal ideal domain.

Theorem 3–46. If $(F, +, \cdot)$ is a field, then the ring $(F[x], +, \cdot)$ is a principal ideal domain.

Proof. By Theorem 3–41, it is already known that $(F[x], +, \cdot)$ is an integral domain. To see that any ideal $(I, +, \cdot)$ of $(F[x], +, \cdot)$ is principal, we need only mimic the argument of Theorem 2–24: If $I = \{0\}$, the result is trivially true, since $I = (0)$. Otherwise, there is some nonzero polynomial $p(x)$ of lowest degree in I. For each polynomial $f(x) \in I$, we may use the Division Algorithm to write $f(x) = q(x) \cdot p(x) + r(x)$, where either $r(x) = 0$ or $\deg r(x) < \deg p(x)$. Now, $r(x) = f(x) - q(x) \cdot p(x)$ lies in I; if the degree of $r(x)$ were less than that of $p(x)$, a contradiction to the choice of $p(x)$ would result. With this possibility ruled out, $r(x) = 0$ and $f(x) = q(x) \cdot p(x) \in (p(x))$; hence, $I \subseteq (p(x))$. But the opposite inclusion clearly holds, so that $I = (p(x))$.

Corollary. A nontrivial ideal of $(F[x], +, \cdot)$ is maximal if and only if it is a prime ideal.

By custom, the prime elements of the principal ideal domain $(F[x], +, \cdot)$ are referred to as *irreducible polynomials*. Translating Definition 3–20 into the language of the present section, we see that $f(x)$ is an irreducible polynomial if and only if $f(x)$ is of positive degree and in any factorization $f(x) = g(x) \cdot h(x)$, with $g(x)$, $h(x) \in F[x]$, either $g(x)$ or $h(x)$ must be a constant polynomial (recall that the invertible elements of $F[x]$ are precisely the nonzero constant polynomials); the constant polynomials are neither reducible nor irreducible. Let us record this observation as a formal definition.

Definition 3–23. A nonconstant polynomial $f(x) \in F[x]$ is said to be irreducible in $F[x]$ if and only if $f(x)$ cannot be expressed as the product of two polynomials of positive degree. Otherwise, $f(x)$ is reducible in $F[x]$.

The dependence of this definition upon the domain $(F[x], +, \cdot)$ is essential. It may well happen that a given polynomial is irreducible when viewed as an element of one domain, yet reducible in another. One such example is $x^2 + 1$; it is irreducible in $(R^{\#}[x], +, \cdot)$, but reducible in both $(C[x], +, \cdot)$, where $x^2 + 1 = (x + i) \cdot (x - i)$, and $(Z_2[x], +, \cdot)$, where $x^2 + 1 = (x + 1) \cdot (x + 1)$. Thus, to ask merely whether a polynomial $f(x)$ is reducible is incomplete and meaningless. For the question to make sense, one must indicate what coefficients are to be allowed in the factorization.

It is often quite difficult to decide whether a particular polynomial is irreducible relative to a specific field. If $(F, +, \cdot)$ is a finite field, say one of the fields of integers modulo a prime, we may actually examine all of the possible roots. To cite an illustration, $x^3 + x + 1$ is irreducible in $Z_2[x]$; in this case, the only possible roots for a polynomial are 0 and 1, but $0 +_2 0 +_2 1 \neq 0$, $1 +_2 1 +_2 1 = 1 \neq 0$.

Example 3–35. Any *linear* polynomial $f(x) = ax + b$, $a \neq 0$, is irreducible in $F[x]$. Indeed, since the degree of a product of two nonzero polynomials is the sum of the degrees of the factors, it follows that a representation

$$ax + b = g(x) \cdot h(x),$$

with $0 < \deg g(x) < 1, 0 < \deg h(x) < 1$ is impossible. Thus, every reducible polynomial has degree at least 2.

Example 3–36. The polynomial $x^2 - 2$ is irreducible in $Q[x]$, where $(Q, +, \cdot)$ is the field of rational numbers. Otherwise, we would have

$$x^2 - 2 = (ax + b) \cdot (cx + d)$$
$$= (ac)x^2 + (ad + bc)x + bd,$$

where the coefficients $a, b, c, d \in Q$. Accordingly,

$$ac = 1, \qquad ad + bc = 0, \qquad bd = -2,$$

whence $c = 1/a$, $d = -2/b$.   Substituting in the relation $ad + bc = 0$, we obtain

$$0 = -2a/b + b/a = (-2a^2 + b^2)/ab.$$

Thus, $-2a^2 + b^2 = 0$, or $(b/a)^2 = 2$, which is impossible because $\sqrt{2}$ is not a rational number.   While irreducible in $Q[x]$, the polynomial $x^2 - 2$ is nonetheless reducible in $R^\#[x]$; in this case, $x^2 - 2 = (x - \sqrt{2})(x + \sqrt{2})$, where both factors are in $R^\#[x]$.

For ease of reference, let us summarize in the next theorem some of the results of the previous section (specifically, Theorems 3–32 and 3–36) in the case of $(F[x], +, \cdot)$.

Theorem 3–47. If $(F, +, \cdot)$ is a field, the following statements are equivalent:

1) $f(x)$ is an irreducible polynomial in $F[x]$.
2) The principal ideal $((f(x)), +, \cdot)$ is a maximal (prime) ideal of $(F[x], +, \cdot)$.
3) The quotient ring $(F[x]/(f(x)), +, \cdot)$ is a field.

A further fact which we shall require shortly is that every nonconstant polynomial can be factored into irreducible polynomials.

Theorem 3–48. (*Unique Factorization Theorem*).   Each polynomial $f(x) \in F[x]$ of positive degree is the product of a nonzero element of F and irreducible monic polynomials of $F[x]$.   Apart from the order of the factors, this factorization is unique.

Proof. We prove our theorem by induction on the degree n of $f(x)$.   If $n = 1$, then $f(x) = ax + b = a \cdot (x + a^{-1} \cdot b)$, where by Example 3–35, $x + a^{-1} \cdot b$ is a monic irreducible polynomial.   Next, suppose $f(x)$ has degree $n > 1$ and that the theorem holds for all polynomials of degree less than n.   If $f(x)$ is irreducible in $F[x]$, we are through after factoring out its leading coefficient.   Otherwise, $f(x)$ is reducible and it is possible to write $f(x) = g(x) \cdot h(x)$ with $g(x)$, $h(x) \in F[x]$, $0 < \deg g(x) < n$, $0 < \deg h(x) < n$.   Therefore, by the induction hypothesis,

$$g(x) = a_1 \cdot g_1(x) \cdot g_2(x) \cdots g_r(x),$$
$$h(x) = a_2 \cdot h_1(x) \cdot h_2(x) \cdots h_s(x),$$

where a_1, a_2 are nonzero elements of F (in fact, the leading coefficients of $g(x)$ and $h(x)$) and $g_i(x)$, $h_i(x)$ are irreducible monic polynomials.   Thus,

$$f(x) = (a_1 \cdot a_2) \cdot g_1(x) \cdots g_r(x) \cdot h_1(x) \cdots h_s(x)$$

is a factorization satisfying the conditions of the theorem.

The uniqueness of the factors still remains to be shown.   We again proceed by induction on $n = \deg f(x)$.   The result is trivial for $n = 1$: if

$$f(x) = a_1 \cdot (x + b_1) = a_2 \cdot (x + b_2), \qquad a_1, a_2 \neq 0,$$

then $a_1 = a_2$ and $a_1 \cdot b_1 = a_2 \cdot b_2$, whence $b_1 = b_2$ by the cancellation law for multiplication. Now, let $n > 1$ and

$$f(x) = c \cdot p_1(x) \cdot p_2(x) \cdots p_r(x) = d \cdot q_1(x) \cdot q_2(x) \cdots q_s(x)$$

be any two factorizations of $f(x)$ into irreducible monic polynomials. Surely $c = d$, for each is the leading coefficient of $f(x)$. Furthermore, $p_1(x)$ divides the product $q_1(x) \cdot q_2(x) \cdots q_s(x)$ and must therefore divide some $q_i(x)$, for instance, $q_1(x)$. Since these are irreducible monic polynomials, it follows that $p_1(x) = q_1(x)$; hence, we may cancel to conclude that

$$f_1(x) = p_2(x) \cdots p_r(x) = q_2(x) \cdots q_s(x).$$

Since $\deg f_1(x) < n$, its factorization is unique by the induction assumption, so that the sequence $q_2(x), \ldots, q_s(x)$ is simply a rearrangement of $p_2(x)$, $\ldots, p_r(x)$. Together with the observation that $c \cdot p_1(x) = d \cdot q_1(x)$, this completes the proof.

Needless to say, Theorem 3–48 can be made more explicit when one knows, for a given field $(F, +, \cdot)$, exactly what polynomials are irreducible. If $F = C$, for instance, the Fundamental Theorem of Algebra implies that the only irreducible polynomials in $C[x]$ are the linear polynomials. In the event $(F, +, \cdot)$ is the real field, we have the following corollary.

Corollary. If $f(x) \in R^{\#}[x]$ is of positive degree, then $f(x)$ can be factored into linear and irreducible quadratic factors.

Proof. Since $f(x)$ also belongs to $C[x]$, $f(x)$ factors in $C[x]$ into a product of linear polynomials $x - c_k$, $c_k \in C$. If $c_k \in R^{\#}$, then $x - c_k \in R^{\#}[x]$. Otherwise, $c_k = a + bi$, where $a, b \in R^{\#}$ and $b \neq 0$. But the complex roots of real polynomials occur in conjugate pairs [Problem 9(b)], so that $\bar{c}_k = a - bi$ is also a root of $f(x)$. Thus

$$(x - c_k) \cdot (x - \bar{c}_k) = x^2 - 2ax + (a^2 + b^2) \in R^{\#}[x]$$

is a factor of $f(x)$. The quadratic polynomial $x^2 - 2ax + (a^2 + b^2)$ is irreducible in $R^{\#}[x]$, since any factorization in $R^{\#}[x]$ is also valid in $C[x]$ and $(x - c_k) \cdot (x - \bar{c}_k)$ is its unique factorization in $C[x]$.

An interesting remark, to be recorded without proof, is that if $(F, +, \cdot)$ is a finite field, the polynomial ring $(F[x], +, \cdot)$ contains irreducible polynomials of every degree.

By an *extension* $(F', +, \cdot)$ of a field $(F, +, \cdot)$ we simply mean any field which contains $(F, +, \cdot)$ as a subfield. For instance, the field of real numbers is an extension of $(Q, +, \cdot)$, the field of rational numbers. In view of Theorem 3–28, it may be remarked that every field $(F, +, \cdot)$ is an extension of a field isomorphic to $(Q, +, \cdot)$ or to $(Z_p, +_p, \cdot_p)$, according as the characteristic of $(F, +, \cdot)$ is zero or a prime p.

Given a field $(F, +, \cdot)$ and an irreducible polynomial $f(x) \in F[x]$, we may ask whether one can construct an extension field $(F', +, \cdot)$ of $(F, +, \cdot)$ in which $f(x)$, thought of as a member of $F'[x]$, has a root. (If $\deg f(x) = 1$, then, in a trivial sense, $(F, +, \cdot)$ is itself the required extension.) Our next theorem answers this question in the affirmative.

Theorem 3–49. (*Kronecker*). If $f(x)$ is an irreducible polynomial in $F[x]$, then there is an extension field of $(F, +, \cdot)$ in which $f(x)$ has a root.

Proof. Let $(I, +, \cdot)$ denote the principal ideal of $(F[x], +, \cdot)$ generated by the polynomial $f(x)$; that is to say, $I = (f(x))$. Since $f(x)$ is assumed to be irreducible, the corresponding quotient ring $(F[x]/I, +, \cdot)$ is a field. To see that $(F[x]/I, +, \cdot)$ constitutes an extension of $(F, +, \cdot)$, consider the natural mapping $\mathrm{nat}_I\colon F[x] \to F[x]/I$. According to Theorem 3–25, either the restriction $\mathrm{nat}_I \mid F$ is the trivial homomorphism or else the triple $(\mathrm{nat}_I\,(F), +, \cdot)$ is a field isomorphic to $(F, +, \cdot)$, where

$$\mathrm{nat}_I\,(F) = \{a + I \mid a \in F\}.$$

But the first possibility is immediately excluded by the fact that

$$\mathrm{nat}_I\,(1) = 1 + I \neq I,$$

the zero element of $F[x]/I$. Therefore, $(F, +, \cdot)$ is imbeddable in the quotient field $(F[x]/I, +, \cdot)$ and, in this sense, $(F[x]/I, +, \cdot)$ becomes an extension of $(F, +, \cdot)$.

Next, we need to show that the polynomial $f(x)$ actually has a root in $F[x]/I$. If

$$f(x) = a_0 + a_1 x + \cdots + a_n x^n,$$

then, from the definitions of coset addition and multiplication,

$$(a_0 + I) + (a_1 + I) \cdot (x + I) + \cdots + (a_n + I) \cdot (x + I)^n$$
$$= a_0 + a_1 x + \cdots + a_n x^n + I$$
$$= f(x) + I = 0 + I.$$

Using the identification, justified above, of the coset $a_k + I$ with the corresponding element $a_k \in F$, we obtain

$$a_0 + a_1(x + I) + \cdots + a_n(x + I)^n = 0$$

or $f(x + I) = 0$. In other words, the coset $x + I = 1x + I$ is the desired root of $f(x)$.

Since each polynomial of positive degree has an irreducible factor (Theorem 3–48), we may drop the restriction that $f(x)$ be irreducible.

Corollary. If the polynomial $f(x) \in F[x]$ is of positive degree, then there exists an extension field of $(F, +, \cdot)$ containing a root of $f(x)$.

Before illustrating this theorem, let us take a closer look at the nature of the cosets of $I = (f(x))$ in $F[x]$, with the view of expressing $F[x]/I$ in a more convenient way. As usual, these cosets are of the form $g(x) + I$, with $g(x) \in F[x]$. By the Division Algorithm, for each $g(x)$ there is a unique polynomial $r(x)$ such that $g(x) = q(x) \cdot f(x) + r(x)$, where $r(x) = 0$ or $\deg r(x) < \deg f(x)$. Evidently $g(x) - r(x) = q(x) \cdot f(x) \in I$, which implies $g(x)$ and $r(x)$ must belong to the same coset,

$$g(x) + I = r(x) + I.$$

From this, we draw the following conclusion: each coset of I in $F[x]$ contains exactly one polynomial which either is the zero polynomial or has degree less than that of $f(x)$. In fact, the cosets of I are uniquely determined by remainders upon division by $f(x)$, in the sense that $g(x) + I = h(x) + I$ if and only if $g(x)$ and $h(x)$ leave the same remainder when divided by $f(x)$.

If $\deg f(x) = n > 1$, say $f(x) = a_0 + a_1 x + \cdots + a_n x^n$, the quotient field $(F[x]/I, +, \cdot)$ may therefore be described by

$$F[x]/I = \{b_0 + b_1 x + \cdots + b_{n-1} x^{n-1} + I \mid b_k \in F\}.$$

Identifying $b_k + I$ with the element b_k, we see that a typical coset can be (uniquely) represented in the form

$$b_0 + b_1(x + I) + \cdots + b_{n-1}(x + I)^{n-1}.$$

As a final simplification, let us replace $x + I$ by some new symbol λ, so that the elements of $F[x]/I$ become polynomials in λ:

$$F[x]/I = \{b_0 + b_1 \lambda + \cdots + b_{n-1} \lambda^{n-1} \mid b_k \in F\}.$$

Observe that since $\lambda = x + I$ is a root of $f(x)$ in $F[x]/I$, calculations are carried out with the aid of the relation $a_0 + a_1 \lambda + \cdots + a_n \lambda^n = 0$.

We pause now to examine two concrete examples of the ideas just introduced.

Example 3–37. Consider $(Z_2, +_2, \cdot_2)$, the field of integers modulo 2, and the polynomial $f(x) = x^3 + x + 1 \in Z_2[x]$. Since neither of the elements 0 or 1 is a root of $x^3 + x + 1$, $f(x)$ is irreducible in $Z_2[x]$. Theorem 3–49 thus guarantees the existence of an extension of $(Z_2, +_2, \cdot_2)$, specifically the field

$$\big(Z_2[x]/(f(x)), +, \cdot\big),$$

in which the given polynomial has a root. Denoting this root by λ, the discussion above tells us that

$$\begin{aligned}
Z_2[x]/(f(x)) &= \{a + b\lambda + c\lambda^2 \mid a, b, c \in Z_2\} \\
&= \{0, 1, \lambda, 1 + \lambda, \lambda^2, 1 + \lambda^2, \lambda + \lambda^2, 1 + \lambda + \lambda^2\},
\end{aligned}$$

where, of course, $\lambda^3 + \lambda + 1 = 0$.

As an example of operating in this field, let us calculate the inverse of $1 + \lambda + \lambda^2$. Before starting, observe that by using the relations

$$\lambda^3 = -(\lambda + 1) = \lambda + 1, \qquad \lambda^4 = \lambda^2 + \lambda$$

(our coefficients come from Z_2, whence $-1 = 1$), the degree of any product can be kept less than 3. Now, the problem at hand is to determine elements $a, b, c \in Z_2$ for which

$$(1 + \lambda + \lambda^2) \cdot (a + b\lambda + c\lambda^2) = 1.$$

Carrying out the multiplication and substituting for λ^3, λ^4 in terms of 1, λ and λ^2, we obtain

$$(a + b + c) + a\lambda + (a + b)\lambda^2 = 1.$$

Since 1 is uniquely represented by $1 = 1 + 0\lambda + 0\lambda^2$, this yields the system of linear equations

$$a + b + c = 1, \qquad a = 0, \qquad a + b = 0$$

with solution $a = b = 0$, $c = 1$; therefore, $(1 + \lambda + \lambda^2)^{-1} = \lambda^2$.

Finally, note that $x^3 + x + 1$ factors completely into linear factors in $Z_2[x]/(f(x))$ and has the three roots λ, λ^2, and $\lambda + \lambda^2$:

$$x^3 + x + 1 = (x - \lambda) \cdot (x - \lambda^2) \cdot (x - (\lambda + \lambda^2)).$$

Example 3–38. The quadratic polynomial $x^2 + 1$ is irreducible in $R^{\#}[x]$. For, if $x^2 + 1$ were reducible, it would be of the form

$$x^2 + 1 = (ax + b) \cdot (cx + d) = acx^2 + (ad + bc)x + bd,$$

where $a, b, c, d \in R^{\#}$. It follows at once that $ac = bd = 1$ and $ad + bc = 0$. Therefore $bc = -(ad)$, and

$$1 = (ac)(bd) = (ad)(bc) = -(ad)^2$$

or rather, $(ad)^2 = -1$, which is impossible.

In this instance, the extension field $(R^{\#}[x]/(x^2 + 1), +, \cdot)$ is described by

$$R^{\#}[x]/(x^2 + 1) = \{a + b\lambda \mid a, b \in R^{\#}; \lambda^2 + 1 = 0\}.$$

Performing the usual operations for polynomials, we see that

$$(a + b\lambda) + (c + d\lambda) = (a + c) + (b + d)\lambda$$

and

$$(a + b\lambda) \cdot (c + d\lambda) = (ac - bd) + (ad + bc)\lambda + bd(\lambda^2 + 1)$$
$$= (ac - bd) + (ad + bd)\lambda.$$

The similarity of these formulas to the rules for addition and multiplication of complex numbers should be obvious. As a matter of fact, the field $(R^{\#}[x]/(x^2 + 1), +, \cdot)$ is actually isomorphic to $(C, +, \cdot)$ under the mapping $\Phi \colon R^{\#}[x]/(x^2 + 1) \to C$ given by

$$\Phi(a + b\lambda) = a + bi.$$

Before proceeding, two comments are in order. First, Example 3–37 shows that there exist finite fields other than the fields $(Z_p, +_p, \cdot_p)$ of integers modulo a prime p. The fact that the field of this example has $2^3 = 8$ elements is typical of the general situation: given a prime number p and a positive integer n, there is exactly one (up to isomorphism) field with p^n elements. Indeed, if $f(x)$ is any irreducible polynomial of degree n in $Z_p[x]$, the quotient field $(Z_p[x]/(f(x)), +, \cdot)$ consists of all polynomials $b_0 + b_1\lambda + \cdots + b_{n-1}\lambda^{n-1}$, where $b_k \in Z_p$; since there are only p choices for each coefficient b_k, we thus obtain a finite field with p^n members.

Second, the construction of Theorem 3–49 yields an extension of a field $(F, +, \cdot)$ in which a given polynomial $f(x) \in F[x]$ splits off one linear factor. By repeated application of this procedure, we can build up an extension $(F', +, \cdot)$ of $(F, +, \cdot)$ in which $f(x)$, thought of as a member of $F'[x]$, factors into a product of linear factors; that is, the field $(F', +, \cdot)$ is large enough to contain all the roots of $f(x)$ (technically speaking, the polynomial *splits completely* in $F'[x]$). We phrase this result in the form of an existence theorem.

Theorem 3–50. If $f(x) \in F[x]$ is a polynomial of positive degree, then there exists an extension field $(F', +, \cdot)$ of $(F, +, \cdot)$ in which $f(x)$ factors completely into linear polynomials.

Proof. The proof is by induction on $n = \deg f(x)$. If $n = 1$, $f(x)$ is already linear and $(F, +, \cdot)$ is itself the required field. Therefore, assume that $n > 1$ and that the theorem is true for all polynomials of degree less than n. Now, the polynomial $f(x)$ must have some irreducible factor $g(x)$. By Theorem 3–49, there is an extension field $(F_1, +, \cdot)$ of $(F, +, \cdot)$ in which $g(x)$, and hence $f(x)$, has a root a_1; specifically, $F_1 = F[x]/(g(x))$. Thus, $f(x)$ can be written in $F_1[x]$ as $f(x) = (x - a_1) \cdot f_1(x)$. Since $\deg f_1(x) = n - 1$, there exists, by our induction hypothesis, an extension field $(F', +, \cdot)$ of $(F_1, +, \cdot)$ in which $f_1(x) = a_0(x - a_2)(x - a_3) \cdots (x - a_n)$, with $a_k \in F'$, $a_0 \neq 0$. From this, we see that $f(x)$ can be completely factored into linear factors in $F'[x]$.

Corollary. Let $f(x) \in F[x]$ with $\deg f(x) = n > 0$. Then there exists an extension of $(F, +, \cdot)$ in which $f(x)$ has n roots.

Example 3–39. To illustrate this situation, let us consider the polynomial $f(x) = x^4 - 5x^2 + 6 = (x^2 - 2) \cdot (x^2 - 3)$ over the field $(Q, +, \cdot)$ of rational numbers. From Example 3–36, $x^2 - 2$ (and similarly $x^2 - 3$) is already known to be irreducible in $Q[x]$. So we first extend $(Q, +, \cdot)$ to the field $(F_1, +, \cdot)$, where

$$F_1 = Q[x]/(x^2 - 2) = \{a + b\lambda \mid a, b \in Q; \lambda^2 - 2 = 0\},$$

and obtain the factorization

$$
\begin{aligned}
f(x) &= (x - \lambda) \cdot (x + \lambda) \cdot (x^2 - 3) \\
&= (x - \sqrt{2}) \cdot (x + \sqrt{2}) \cdot (x^2 - 3).
\end{aligned}
$$

(As $\lambda^2 = 2$, one customarily identifies λ with $\sqrt{2}$.)

However, $f(x)$ does not factor completely, since the polynomial $x^2 - 3$ is irreducible in $F_1[x]$. For, suppose to the contrary that $x^2 - 3$ has a root in F_1, say $c + d\sqrt{2}$, with $c, d \in Q$. Substituting, we find that

$$(c^2 + 2d^2 - 3) + 2cd\sqrt{2} = 0,$$

hence

$$c^2 + 2d^2 - 3 = 0, \qquad cd = 0.$$

This latter equation implies that either $c = 0$ or $d = 0$; but neither c nor d can be zero, since otherwise we would have $d^2 = 3/2$ or $c^2 = 3$, which is impossible. Thus $x^2 - 3$ remains irreducible in $F_1[x]$.

In order to factor $f(x)$ into linear factors, it is necessary to extend the coefficient field further. We therefore construct the extension $(F_2, +, \cdot)$, where

$$F_2 = F_1[x]/(x^2 - 3) = \{\alpha + \beta\mu \mid \alpha, \beta \in F_1; \mu^2 - 3 = 0\}.$$

The elements of F_2 may alternatively be expressed in the form

$$(a + b\sqrt{2}) + (c + d\sqrt{2})\sqrt{3} = a + b\sqrt{2} + c\sqrt{3} + d\sqrt{6}.$$

It follows at once that the original polynomial factors in $F_2[x]$ as

$$
\begin{aligned}
f(x) &= (x - \lambda) \cdot (x + \lambda) \cdot (x - \mu) \cdot (x + \mu) \\
&= (x - \sqrt{2}) \cdot (x + \sqrt{2}) \cdot (x - \sqrt{3}) \cdot (x + \sqrt{3}).
\end{aligned}
$$

Observe that the four roots all lie in F_2.

Let $f(x) \in F[x]$. An extension $(F', +, \cdot)$ of $(F, +, \cdot)$ is said to be a *splitting field* for $f(x)$ over F provided $f(x)$ can be factored completely into linear factors in $F'[x]$, but not so factored over any proper subfield of $(F', +, \cdot)$ containing $(F, +, \cdot)$. Loosely speaking, a splitting field is the smallest extension field in which a given polynomial decomposes as a product of linear factors. To obtain a splitting field for any polynomial $f(x) \in F[x]$ of positive degree, we need only return to Theorem 3–50 and consider the family $(F_i, +, \cdot)$ of all subfields of

$(F', +, \cdot)$ in which $f(x)$ factors completely (the theorem guarantees the existence of such extensions); then $(\cap F_i, +, \cdot)$ serves as a splitting field for $f(x)$ over F.

Having thus indicated the existence of splitting fields, it is natural to inquire about their uniqueness. As a final topic for this section, we shall prove that any two splitting fields of the same (nonconstant) polynomial are isomorphic; this being so, one is justified in using the definite article and speaking of *the* splitting field of a given polynomial.

Before presenting the main theorem, two preparatory results of a somewhat technical nature are needed. As previously noted, if r is a fixed element of a field $(K, +, \cdot)$ and $F \subseteq K$, we write $F(r)$ for the set of finite sums:

$$F(r) = \{a_0 + a_1 \cdot r + \cdots + a_n \cdot r^n \mid a_k \in F, n \geq 1\}.$$

Lemma. Let $f(x)$ be an irreducible polynomial in $F[x]$ and r be a root of $f(x)$ in some extension field $(K, +, \cdot)$ of $(F, +, \cdot)$. Then $(F(r), +, \cdot) \simeq \big(F[x]/(f(x)), +, \cdot\big)$ under an isomorphism whereby the element r corresponds to the coset $x + (f(x))$.

Proof. The mapping $\nu \colon F[x] \to K$ defined by setting $\nu f(x) = f(r)$ is easily checked to be a homomorphism of $(F[x], +, \cdot)$ onto the ring $(F(r), +, \cdot)$. It follows at once that

$$f(x) \in \ker(\nu) = \{g(x) \in F[x] \mid g(r) = 0\},$$

whence $(f(x)) \subseteq \ker(\nu)$. One observation is quite pertinent: the possibility that $\ker(\nu) = F[x]$ does not arise, since the identity element of $(F[x], +, \cdot)$ is not mapped onto zero. As $f(x)$ is assumed to be irreducible in $F[x]$, $\big((f(x)), +, \cdot\big)$ is a maximal ideal of $(F[x], +, \cdot)$, so that $(f(x)) = \ker(\nu)$; in other words, $(f(x))$ simply consists of all polynomials in $F[x]$ having the element r as a root. Thus, by the fundamental homomorphism theorem for rings (Theorem 3–18), there exists an isomorphism θ of $\big(F[x]/(f(x)), +, \cdot\big)$ onto $(F(r), +, \cdot)$ such that $\nu = \theta \circ \mathrm{nat}_{(f(x))}$. As regards the last assertion of the theorem, we evidently have

$$r = \nu(x) = (\theta \circ \mathrm{nat}_{(f(x))})(x) = \theta\big(x + (f(x))\big).$$

Although of some interest in its own right, the value of this lemma is that it leads almost immediately to the following theorem:

Theorem 3–51. Let ϕ be an isomorphism from the field $(F, +, \cdot)$ onto the field $(F', +', \cdot')$. Also let $f(x) = a_1 + a_1 x + \cdots + a_n x^n$ be an irreducible polynomial in $F[x]$ and $f'(y) = \phi(a_0) + \phi(a_1)y + \cdots + \phi(a_n)y^n$ be the corresponding polynomial in $F'[y]$. Then $f'(y)$ is irreducible in $F'[y]$. Furthermore, if r is a root of $f(x)$ in some extension field of $(F, +, \cdot)$ and r' is a root of $f'(y)$ in some extension field of $(F', +', \cdot')$, then ϕ can be extended to an isomorphism Φ of $(F(r), +, \cdot)$ onto $(F'(r'), +', \cdot')$ with $\Phi(r) = r'$.

Proof. Let us first extend ϕ to a mapping $\bar\phi$ between the polynomial rings $(F[x], +, \cdot)$ and $(F'[y], +', \cdot')$ by taking

$$\bar\phi g(x) = \bar\phi(b_0 + b_1 x + \cdots + b_n x^n) = \phi(b_0) + \phi(b_1)y + \cdots + \phi(b_n)y^n$$

for every polynomial $g(x) = b_0 + b_1 x + \cdots + b_n x^n \in F[x]$. Using the fact that ϕ is an isomorphism, it is an easy matter to verify that $\bar\phi$ is an isomorphism of $(F[x], +, \cdot)$ onto $(F'[y], +', \cdot')$; we leave the reader to supply the necessary details. Notice that for any polynomial $g(x)$ in $F[x]$, an element $a \in F$ is a root of $g(x)$ if and only if $\phi(a)$ is a root of $\bar\phi g(x)$. Indeed, if $g(x) = b_0 + b_1 x + \cdots + b_n x^n$, we have

$$\begin{aligned}
(\bar\phi g(x))(\phi(a)) &= \phi(b_0) + \phi(b_1) \cdot \phi(a) + \cdots + \phi(b_n) \cdot \phi(a)^n \\
&= \phi(b_0 + b_1 \cdot a + \cdots + b_n \cdot a^n) \\
&= \phi(g(a)),
\end{aligned}$$

from which the assertion follows. In particular, the given polynomial $f(x)$ is irreducible in $F[x]$ if and only if $f'(y) = \bar\phi f(x)$ is irreducible in $F'[y]$.

Now, by the foregoing lemma, we know that there exist isomorphisms

$$\alpha \colon F(r) \to F[x]/(f(x)) \qquad \text{and} \qquad \beta \colon F'(r') \to F'[y]/(f'(y)).$$

Furthermore, it is not difficult to show that there is also an isomorphism τ of $(F[x]/(f(x)), +, \cdot)$ onto $(F'[y]/(f'(y)), +', \cdot')$ defined by

$$\tau(g(x) + (f(x))) = \bar\phi g(x) + (f'(y)), \qquad g(x) \in F[x].$$

Observe, particularly, that τ carries the coset $x + (f(x))$ onto $y + (f'(y))$. We contend that $(F(r), +, \cdot) \simeq (F'(r'), +', \cdot')$ via the composition

$$\Phi = \beta^{-1} \circ \tau \circ \alpha,$$

where $\Phi \colon F(r) \to F'(r')$; this situation is portrayed in the diagram below:

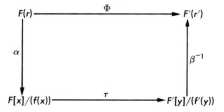

Certainly Φ is an isomorphism of $(F(r), +, \cdot)$ onto $(F'(r'), +', \cdot')$, for the individual mappings α, τ, and β^{-1} are themselves isomorphisms. If a is an arbitrary element of F, then

$$\begin{aligned}
\Phi(a) &= (\beta^{-1} \circ \tau)(\alpha(a)) = (\beta^{-1} \circ \tau)(a + (f(x))) \\
&= \beta^{-1}(\phi(a) + (f'(y))) = \phi(a),
\end{aligned}$$

whence Φ is actually an extension of ϕ to $F(r)$. Finally, we point out that

$$\Phi(r) = (\beta^{-1} \circ \tau)(\alpha(r)) = (\beta^{-1} \circ \tau)\big(x + (f(x))\big)$$
$$= \beta^{-1}\big(y + (f'(y))\big) = r'$$

as required, and the theorem is proved in its entirety.

For a simple illustration of this result, let both $(F, +, \cdot)$ and $(F', +', \cdot')$ be the real number field $(R^{\#}, +, \cdot)$; take $f(x) \in R^{\#}[x]$ to be the irreducible polynomial $f(x) = x^2 + 1$, so that $f'(y) = y^2 + 1$ [recall that the identity map is the only isomorphism of $(R^{\#}, +, \cdot)$ onto itself.] Finally, we let $r = i$ and $r' = -i$. Theorem 3–51 then asserts that

$$(R^{\#}(i), +, \cdot) \simeq (R^{\#}(-i), +, \cdot)$$

under an isomorphism which carries i onto $-i$. Since $C = R^{\#}(i) = R^{\#}(-i)$, this mapping is just the correspondence between a complex number and its conjugate.

We are now in a position to show the uniqueness, to within isomorphism, of splitting fields; actually, we shall prove a somewhat more general result:

Theorem 3–52. Let ϕ be an isomorphism of the field $(F, +, \cdot)$ onto the field $(F', +', \cdot')$. Let $f(x) = a_0 + a_1 x + \cdots + a_n x^n \in F[x]$ and $f'(y) = \phi(a_0) + \phi(a_1)y + \cdots + \phi(a_n)y^n$ be the corresponding polynomial in $F'[y]$. If $(K, +, \cdot)$ is a splitting field for $f(x)$ and $(K', +', \cdot')$ is a splitting field for $f'(y)$, then ϕ can be extended to an isomorphism Φ of $(K, +, \cdot)$ onto $(K', +', \cdot')$.

Proof. Our argument proceeds by induction on the number n of roots of $f(x)$ that lie outside of F, but, needless to say, in K. When $n = 0$, all the roots of $f(x)$ belong to F and $(F, +, \cdot)$ is itself the splitting field of $f(x)$; that is, $K = F$. This in turn induces a splitting of the polynomial $f'(y)$ into a product of linear factors in $F'[y]$, so that $K' = F'$. Thus, in the case $n = 0$, the isomorphism ϕ itself is the desired extension to the splitting fields.

Let us next assume, inductively, that the theorem holds true for any pair of corresponding polynomials $f(x)$ and $f'(y)$ over isomorphic base fields $(E, +, \cdot)$ and $(E', +', \cdot')$, provided the number of roots of $f(x)$ outside of E is less than n ($n \geq 1$).

If $f(x) \in F[x]$ is a polynomial having n roots outside of F, then not all the irreducible factors of $f(x)$ can be linear in $F[x]$; for otherwise, $f(x)$ would split completely in F, contrary to assumption. Accordingly $f(x)$ must have some factor $g(x)$ of degree $m > 1$ which is irreducible in $F[x]$. Let $g'(y)$ denote the corresponding irreducible factor of $f'(y)$. Since $(K, +, \cdot)$ is a splitting field of $f(x)$ over F, $g(x)$ in particular must have a root in K, call it r. Similarly, one of the roots of the polynomial $f'(y)$, say r', is a root of $g'(y)$ in K'. By Theorem 3–51, ϕ can be extended to an isomorphism ϕ' between the fields $(F(r), +, \cdot)$ and $(F'(r'), +', \cdot')$. Now $(K, +, \cdot)$ is a splitting field of $f(x)$ viewed as a polynomial with coefficients from the field $(F(r), +, \cdot)$; in a like manner, $(K', +', \cdot')$ can be regarded as a splitting field of $f'(y)$ over $F'(r')$. Because the number of roots of $f(x)$ outside of $F(r)$ is less than n, the induction hypothesis permits us to extend the isomorphism ϕ' (itself an extension of ϕ) to an isomorphism Φ of $(K, +, \cdot)$ onto $(K', +', \cdot')$. This completes the induction step and thus the proof of the theorem.

Corollary. Any two splitting fields of a nonconstant polynomial $f(x) \in F[x]$ are isomorphic by an isomorphism Φ such that $\Phi \mid F$ is the identity map.

Proof. This is an immediate consequence of the theorem on taking $(F, +, \cdot) = (F', +', \cdot')$ and ϕ to be the identity isomorphism i_F.

Let us complete the picture by giving a brief application of these ideas.

Theorem 3–53. Any two fields having p^n elements, p a prime, are isomorphic.

Proof. In view of the preceding corollary, it is enough to establish that any field $(F, +, \cdot)$ with p^n elements is a splitting field of the polynomial $x^{p^n} - x \in Z_p[x]$. [We remind the reader that $(F, +, \cdot)$, being of prime characteristic p, has a subfield isomorphic to $(Z_p, +_p, \cdot_p)$.] Now, the multiplicative group $(F^*, \cdot)$ of nonzero elements of F has order $p^n - 1$. By Lagrange's Theorem, one sees that $r^{p^n-1} = 1$ for all $r \in F^*$ and consequently $r^{p^n} - r = 0$ for every member of F, including 0. In other words, the polynomial $x^{p^n} - x \in Z_p[x]$ possesses p^n distinct roots in F. Since the degree of $x^{p^n} - x$ is p^n, this polynomial must split completely into linear factors in $F[x]$. Needless to say, it cannot split in any proper subfield of $(F, +, \cdot)$, for no proper subfield contains p^n elements. Hence $(F, +, \cdot)$ is a splitting field of $x^{p^n} - x$ over Z_p, as asserted.

A related result, which we shall not stop to prove here, is that any finite field has p^n elements for some $n > 0$, where the prime number p is the characteristic of the field. Granting this, Theorem 3–53 may be interpreted as asserting that any two finite fields having the same number of elements are isomorphic.

PROBLEMS

1. For an arbitrary ring $(R, +, \cdot)$ with identity, prove that
   a) the polynomial $1x^n \in$ cent $R[x]$,
   b) if $(I, +, \cdot)$ is an ideal of $(R, +, \cdot)$, then $(I[x], +, \cdot)$ is an ideal of the polynomial ring $(R[x], +, \cdot)$,
   c) if $(R, +, \cdot)$ and $(R', +', \cdot')$ are isomorphic rings, then $(R[x], +, \cdot)$ is isomorphic to $(R'[x], +', \cdot')$.

2. Given $(R, +, \cdot)$ is an integral domain, show that
   a) the only invertible elements of $R[x]$ are the constant polynomials determined by the invertible elements of R,
   b) the characteristic of $(R[x], +, \cdot)$ is equal to the characteristic of $(R, +, \cdot)$.

3. Prove that no monic polynomial can be a zero divisor in $(R[x], +, \cdot)$.

4. Show that the relation $\sim$ defined by taking $f(x) \sim g(x)$ if and only if

$$\deg f(x) \,=\, \deg g(x)$$

is an equivalence relation in the set of nonzero polynomials of $R[x]$.

5. a) Let P be the set of all polynomials in $Z[x]$ with constant term 0:

$$P \,=\, \{a_1 x + a_2 x^2 + \cdots + a_n x^n \mid a_k \in Z;\, n \geq 1\}.$$

   Establish that the triple $(P, +, \cdot)$ is a prime ideal of $(Z[x], +, \cdot)$.
   b) Show the principal ideal $((1x), +, \cdot)$ is a prime ideal of the polynomial ring $(Z[x], +, \cdot)$, but not a maximal ideal.

6. If $(R, +, \cdot)$ is a commutative ring with identity, prove that the polynomial $1 + ax$ is invertible in $R[x]$ if and only if the element a is nilpotent.

7. Let $(R, +, \cdot)$ be a commutative ring with identity and the element $r \in R$ be fixed.

   a) If $R(r)$ denotes the set

   $$R(r) \,=\, \{f(r) \mid f(x) \in R[x]\},$$

   prove that the triple $(R(r), +, \cdot)$ forms a subring of $(R, +, \cdot)$.
   b) Show that the mapping $\phi \colon R[x] \to R(r)$ defined by $\phi(f(x)) = f(r)$ is a homomorphism of $(R[x], +, \cdot)$ onto $(R(r), +, \cdot)$.

8. a) Given that $f(x) = x^4 + 2x^3 - 4x + 1$ and $g(x) = 2x^2 + 4x + 1$, find polynomials $q(x),\, r(x) \in Z_5[x]$ for which $f(x) = q(x) \cdot g(x) + r(x)$.
   b) Returning to the ring $(R, +, \cdot)$ of Example 3–8, show that the polynomial $(a, 0)x^2 \in R[x]$ has infinitely many roots in R.

9. For $f(x) = a_0 + a_1 x + \cdots + a_n x^n \in C[x]$, define the polynomial $\bar{f}(x)$ by

$$\bar{f}(x) \,=\, \bar{a}_0 + \bar{a}_1 x + \cdots + \bar{a}_n x^n,$$

where $\bar{a}_k$ indicates the complex conjugate of a_k. Prove that
   a) $r \in C$ is a root of $f(x)$ if and only if $\bar{r}$ is a root of $\bar{f}(x)$. [*Hint:* $\overline{f(r)} = \bar{f}(\bar{r})$.]
   b) if $f(x) \in R^{\#}[x] \subseteq C[x]$ and $r \in C$ is a complex root of $f(x)$, then $\bar{r}$ is also a root of $f(x)$.

10. Assume that p/q (where p and q are relatively prime) is a rational root of the polynomial $f(x) = a_0 + a_1 x + \cdots + a_n x^n \in Z[x]$. Verify that $p \mid a_0$ and $q \mid a_n$.

11. Let $(R, +, \cdot)$ be a commutative ring with identity and $f(x)$, $g(x)$ be two polynomials in $R[x]$ which are not both zero. Then $d(x) \in R[x]$ is said to be a *greatest common divisor* (gcd) of $f(x)$ and $g(x)$ provided

   i) $d(x)$ is a divisor of both $f(x)$ and $g(x)$, and
   ii) every polynomial which is a divisor of $f(x)$ and $g(x)$ also divides $d(x)$.

   Prove that any two polynomials $f(x)$, $g(x) \in R[x]$, not both zero, have a unique monic gcd $d(x)$ in $R[x]$ which can be expressed in the form

$$d(x) \,=\, f(x) \cdot p(x) + g(x) \cdot q(x)$$

   for some $p(x)$, $q(x) \in R[x]$. [*Hint:* Follow the pattern of Theorem 1–12.]

12. Let $(R, +, \cdot)$ be a commutative ring with identity, and let $f(x) \in R[x]$. The function $\tilde{f}: R \to R$ defined by taking $\tilde{f}(r) = f(r)$ for all $r \in R$ is called the *polynomial function associated with* $f(x)$. Assuming that S denotes the set of all polynomial functions associated with elements of $R[x]$, prove that

   a) the triple $(S, +, \cdot)$ forms a ring,
   b) the mapping $\alpha: R[x] \to S$ given by $\alpha f(x) = \tilde{f}$ is a homomorphism of the ring $(R[x], +, \cdot)$ onto $(S, +, \cdot)$,
   c) if $r \in R$ is fixed and $I_r = \{\tilde{f} \in S \mid \tilde{f}(r) = 0\}$, then $(I_r, +, \cdot)$ is an ideal of $(S, +, \cdot)$.

13. a) Show that if the integral domain $(R, +, \cdot)$ has an infinite number of elements, then distinct polynomials in $R[x]$ induce distinct polynomial functions.
   b) Give an example of two distinct polynomials which induce the same polynomial function.

14. Let $(R, +, \cdot)$ be a commutative ring with identity. Let the function $\delta: R[x] \to R[x]$, the so-called *derivative function*, be defined as follows: if

$$f(x) = a_0 + a_1 x + \cdots + a_n x^n \in R[x],$$

   then

$$\delta f(x) = a_1 + 2a_2 x + \cdots + n a_n x^{n-1}.$$

   For any $f(x)$, $g(x) \in R[x]$ and any $a \in R$, verify that
   a) $\delta\big(f(x) + g(x)\big) = \delta f(x) + \delta g(x)$,
   b) $\delta\big(af(x)\big) = a\delta f(x)$,
   c) $\delta\big(f(x) \cdot g(x)\big) = \delta f(x) \cdot g(x) + f(x) \cdot \delta g(x)$. [*Hint:* Induct on the number of nonzero terms of $f(x)$.]

15. Let $(R, +, \cdot)$ be a commutative ring with identity, and let $r \in R$ be a root of the nonzero polynomial $f(x) \in R[x]$. We call r a *multiple root* of $f(x)$ if

$$f(x) = (x - r)^n \cdot g(x), \qquad n > 1,$$

   where $g(x) \in R[x]$ is a polynomial such that $g(r) \neq 0$. Prove that an element $r \in R$ is a multiple root of $f(x)$ if and only if r is a root of both $f(x)$ and $\delta f(x)$.

16. Determine

   a) all irreducible polynomials of degree 2 in $Z_3[x]$, and
   b) all irreducible polynomials of degree 3 in $Z_2[x]$.

17. Let $(F, +, \cdot)$ be a field and $f(x) \in F[x]$ be a polynomial of degree 2 or 3. Establish that $f(x)$ is irreducible in $F[x]$ if and only if $f(x)$ has no root in F. Give an example which shows that this result need not be true if $\deg f(x) \geq 4$.

18. Prove that if $f(x)$ is an irreducible polynomial in $Z[x]$, then $f(x)$ is also irreducible when regarded as an element of $Q[x]$.

19. Derive the following analog of Euclid's Lemma: Let $(R, +, \cdot)$ be a commutative ring with identity and $f(x)$ be an irreducible polynomial in $R[x]$. If $f(x)$ divides the product $g_1(x) \cdot g_2(x) \cdots g_n(x)$, then $f(x)$ divides $g_k(x)$ for some k, $1 \leq k \leq n$.

20. In regard to Problem 7, show that the ring $(R(r), +, \cdot)$ is a field if and only if $\ker(\phi) = (f(x))$ where $f(x)$ is an irreducible polynomial in $R[x]$.

21. a) Prove the Eisenstein Criterion for irreducibility: If

$$f(x) = a_0 + a_1 x + \cdots + a_n x^n \in Z[x]$$

and p is a prime number such that $p \mid a_k$ ($k = 0, 1, \ldots, n - 1$), $p \nmid a_n$, $p^2 \nmid a_0$, then $f(x)$ is irreducible in $Z[x]$. [*Hint:* Proof is by contradiction.]

   b) Use part (a) to show that the polynomial $2x^5 - 6x^3 + 9x^2 - 15$ is irreducible in $Z[x]$.

22. Given $f(x) = x^2 + x + 2$, an irreducible polynomial in $Z_3[x]$, construct the multiplication table for the field $(Z_3[x]/(f(x)), +, \cdot)$.

23. Verify that the polynomial $f(x) = x^3 + x^2 + 1 \in Z_2[x]$ factors into linear factors in $Z_2[x]/(f(x))$.

24. Prove that the triple $(Q[x]/(x^2 - 2), +, \cdot)$ forms a field isomorphic to the field $(F, +, \cdot)$, where $F = \{a + b\sqrt{2} \mid a, b \in Q\}$.

25. Describe the splitting fields of the following polynomials:

   a) $x^3 - 3 \in Q[x]$,
                 b) $x^2 + x + 1 \in Z_5[x]$,
   c) $x^4 + 2x^2 + 1 \in R^{\#}[x]$,
         d) $(x^2 - 2)(x^2 + 1) \in Q[x]$.

26. Let $f(x) \in F[x]$ be irreducible and r, s be two roots of $f(x)$ in some splitting field. Show that $(F(r), +, \cdot) \simeq (F(s), +, \cdot)$ by a unique isomorphism that leaves every element of F fixed.

27. Show that if $g(x)$ is a factor of the polynomial $f(x) \in F[x]$, then any splitting field of $f(x)$ over F contains a subfield which is a splitting field of $g(x)$.

28. Prove: An extension field $(K, +, \cdot)$ of $(F, +, \cdot)$ is a splitting field of the polynomial $f(x) \in F[x]$ if and only if both

   i) $f(x)$ factors completely into linear factors in $K[x]$, and also
   ii) $(K, +, \cdot)$ is generated by F and all the roots of $f(x)$ in K.

29. Let $f_1(x)$, $f_2(x)$ be two irreducible polynomials of degree n in $Z_p[x]$, p a prime number. If r_i is a root of $f_i(x)$ in some splitting field ($i = 1, 2$), establish that $(Z_p(r_1), +, \cdot) \simeq (Z_p(r_2), +, \cdot)$.

30. Derive Fermat's Little Theorem: If p is a prime number and $a \not\equiv 0 \pmod{p}$, then $a^{p-1} \equiv 1 \pmod{p}$.

3–6 BOOLEAN RINGS AND BOOLEAN ALGEBRAS

The theory of Boolean algebras is an algebraic counterpart to the logical theory of the calculus of propositions. Its origins lie in the work of the English mathematician George Boole (1815–1864), who first attempted to give a systematic treatment of logic by abstract methods. Since such a structure may be viewed as the postulational abstraction of the rules governing the algebra of sets, it provides a suitable topic with which to conclude our discussion of two-operational systems. Indeed, as will be evidenced shortly, Boolean algebras may be subsumed under the general theory of rings.

We begin by studying the properties of a special class of rings, which we shall designate as Boolean rings.

Definition 3–24. A *Boolean ring* $(R, +, \cdot)$ is a ring with identity every element of which is idempotent; that is, $a^2 = a$ for every $a \in R$.

It should be pointed out that the existence of an identity is frequently omitted in the definition of a Boolean ring. (One can show that if the number of elements in a Boolean ring is finite, then an identity element always exists.) The definition given here, however, will be more convenient for the applications we have in mind.

Let us pause to give several examples of the concept just introduced.

Example 3–40. The ring of integers modulo 2, $(Z_2, +_2, \cdot_2)$, forms a Boolean ring, since $0 \cdot_2 0 = 0$ and $1 \cdot_2 1 = 1$.

Example 3–41. The ring $(P(X), \triangle, \cap)$ of subsets of a nonempty set X is easily verified to be a Boolean ring. In this case, we have $A \cap A = A$ for every subset $A \subseteq X$.

Example 3–42. For a less obvious example of a Boolean ring, let R consist of all functions from an arbitrary nonempty set X to Z_2, with the operations defined pointwise; specifically, if f and g are in R, then

$$(f + g)(x) = f(x) +_2 g(x),$$
$$(f \cdot g)(x) = f(x) \cdot_2 g(x), \qquad (x \in X).$$

Under these operations, the triple $(R, +, \cdot)$ is a commutative ring with identity; the proof is straightforward and will not be given in detail. To establish the idempotency condition, we proceed as follows: If the function $f \in R$ is such that $f(x) = 0$, then

$$(f^2)(x) = f(x) \cdot_2 f(x) = 0 \cdot_2 0 = 0.$$

While if $f(x) = 1$, then

$$(f^2)(x) = f(x) \cdot_2 f(x) = 1 \cdot_2 1 = 1.$$

In any event, $(f^2)(x) = f(x)$ for every x in X, whence $f^2 = f$.

Our ultimate purpose is to prove the celebrated theorem of Stone which asserts that each Boolean ring may be represented by a ring of sets. Looking forward to this result, we first develop a number of the fundamental properties of Boolean rings necessary to the proof. While the conclusions obtained are somewhat restrictive (Boolean rings have an almost embarrassingly rich structure), they bring together much of the material developed earlier.

Theorem 3–54. Every Boolean ring $(R, +, \cdot)$ is a commutative ring of characteristic 2.

Proof. If a and b are arbitrary elements of R, then

$$a + b = (a + b)^2 = a^2 + a \cdot b + b \cdot a + b^2 = a + a \cdot b + b \cdot a + b,$$

and hence $a \cdot b + b \cdot a = 0$. In particular, setting $a = b$, we obtain

$$2a = a + a = a^2 + a^2 = 0$$

for every $a \in R$. This shows that $(R, +, \cdot)$ is of characteristic 2. But then by adding $a \cdot b$ to both sides of the equation $a \cdot b + b \cdot a = 0$, we obtain

$$a \cdot b = a \cdot b + a \cdot b + b \cdot a = b \cdot a.$$

We proved earlier that, in any commutative ring with identity, maximal ideals are automatically prime ideals. For Boolean rings, the converse is also true.

Theorem 3–55. Let $(R, +, \cdot)$ be a Boolean ring. A proper ideal $(I, +, \cdot)$ of $(R, +, \cdot)$ is prime if and only if it is a maximal ideal.

Proof. It is sufficient to show that if the ideal $(I, +, \cdot)$ is prime, then $(I, +, \cdot)$ is also maximal. To see this, suppose $(J, +, \cdot)$ is an ideal of $(R, +, \cdot)$ with the property $I \subset J \subseteq R$; what we must prove is that $J = R$. If a is any element of J not in I, then $a \cdot (1 - a) = 0 \in I$. Using the fact that $(I, +, \cdot)$ is a prime ideal with $a \notin I$, we conclude

$$1 - a \in I \subset J.$$

As both the elements a and $1 - a$ lie in J, it follows that

$$1 = a + (1 - a) \in J.$$

The ideal $(J, +, \cdot)$ thus contains the identity, and consequently $J = R$.

A natural undertaking is to determine which Boolean rings are also fields. We may dispose of this question rather easily: up to isomorphism, the only Boolean field is the ring of integers modulo 2.

Theorem 3–56. A Boolean ring $(R, +, \cdot)$ is a field if and only if $(R, +, \cdot) \simeq (Z_2, +_2, \cdot_2)$.

Proof. Let $(R, +, \cdot)$ be a Boolean field. For any nonzero element $a \in R$, we then have

$$a = a \cdot 1 = a \cdot (a \cdot a^{-1}) = a^2 \cdot a^{-1} = a \cdot a^{-1} = 1.$$

This argument shows that the only nonzero element of R is the identity; in other words, $R = \{0, 1\}$. But any two-element field is isomorphic to $(Z_2, +_2, \cdot_2)$. The opposite direction of the theorem is fairly obvious.

Corollary. A proper ideal $(I, +, \cdot)$ of the Boolean ring $(R, +, \cdot)$ is a maximal ideal if and only if $(R/I, +, \cdot) \simeq (Z_2, +_2, \cdot_2)$.

Proof. First, note that the quotient ring $(R/I, +, \cdot)$ is itself a Boolean ring, since

$$(a + I)^2 = a^2 + I = a + I$$

for each element a in R. By Theorem 3–32, $(I, +, \cdot)$ is a maximal ideal if and only if $(R/I, +, \cdot)$ is a (Boolean) field. An appeal to the above theorem now completes the proof.

The next theorem is a major one and requires a preliminary lemma of some difficulty.

Lemma. Let $(R, +, \cdot)$ be a Boolean ring. For each nonzero element $a \in R$, there exists a homomorphism f from $(R, +, \cdot)$ onto the field $(Z_2, +_2, \cdot_2)$ such that $f(a) = 1$.

Proof. Let $(I, +, \cdot)$ be the principal ideal generated by the element $1 + a$, that is,

$$I = \{r \cdot (1 + a) \mid r \in R\}.$$

The set $I \neq R$, since the identity is not a member of I. Indeed, if $1 \in I$, then

$$1 = r \cdot (1 + a)$$

for some choice of r in R; this means

$$1 = r \cdot (1 + a)^2 = \big(r \cdot (1 + a)\big) \cdot (1 + a) = 1 \cdot (1 + a),$$

from which it follows that $a = 0$, contrary to hypothesis.

Because $(I, +, \cdot)$ is a proper ideal, Theorem 3–30 assures the existence of a maximal ideal $(M, +, \cdot)$ of $(R, +, \cdot)$ such that $I \subseteq M$. In light of the result just proved, the associated quotient ring $(R/M, +, \cdot)$ will be isomorphic to $(Z_2, +_2, \cdot_2)$ via some homomorphism g.

We may therefore define a function $f \colon R \to Z_2$ by taking $f = g \circ \mathrm{nat}_M$, where nat_M is simply the natural mapping of R onto R/M. The situation is conveniently depicted by the following diagram of maps:

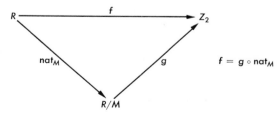

The remainder of the proof amounts to showing that the function f, so defined, has the properties asserted in the statement of the theorem. Plainly, f is both an onto map and a homomorphism being the composition of two such functions. Since $1 + a \in I \subseteq M$, the coset $1 + a + M = M$, so that

$$
\begin{aligned}
1 +_2 f(a) &= f(1) +_2 f(a) \\
&= f(1 + a) \\
&= g(1 + a + M) = g(M) = 0.
\end{aligned}
$$

But, $1 +_2 f(a) = 0$ if and only if $f(a) = 1$, which finishes the proof.

An immediate consequence of this lemma is the following corollary.

Corollary. Every Boolean ring $(R, +, \cdot)$ is a semisimple ring; that is to say, rad $R = \{0\}$.

Proof. In order to arrive at a contradiction, we assume that $a \in$ rad R with $a \neq 0$. Then there exists a homomorphism f from $(R, +, \cdot)$ onto $(Z_2, +_2, \cdot_2)$ for which $f(a) = 1$. It follows that the ideal $(\ker (f), +, \cdot)$ must be a proper ideal of the ring $(R, +, \cdot)$. Hence there is some maximal ideal $(M, +, \cdot)$ of $(R, +, \cdot)$ with $\ker (f) \subseteq M$. In particular, the element $1 - a \in \ker (f) \subseteq M$. But also $a \in$ rad $R \subseteq M$, which implies

$$
1 = a + (1 - a) \in M.
$$

This leads at once to $M = R$, the desired contradiction.

Having assembled the necessary machinery, we now set ourselves the principal task, that of showing that each Boolean ring is essentially a ring of sets. This theorem, now considered a landmark, was first proved in 1936 by the American mathematician, Marshall Stone.

Theorem 3–57. (*Stone Representation Theorem*). Every Boolean ring $(R, +, \cdot)$ is isomorphic to a ring of subsets of some fixed set.

Proof. To begin the attack, let H denote the collection of all homomorphisms from $(R, +, \cdot)$ onto the field $(Z_2, +_2, \cdot_2)$. Next define a function $h: R \to P(H)$ by assigning to each element $a \in R$ those members of H which assume the value 1 at a; in other words,

$$
h(a) = \{f \in H \mid f(a) = 1\}.
$$

While the notation is perfectly clear, let us emphasize that h is a set-valued function in the sense that its functional values are certain subsets of H. By means of this function, we shall establish the isomorphism mentioned in the theorem.

Let us now give some details: For any $f \in H$, the product $f(a) \cdot_2 f(b) = 1$ if and only if both $f(a) = 1$ and $f(b) = 1$. This being so, we conclude

$$
\begin{aligned}
h(a \cdot b) &= \{f \in H \mid f(a \cdot b) = 1\} \\
&= \{f \in H \mid f(a) \cdot_2 f(b) = 1\} \\
&= \{f \in H \mid f(a) = 1\} \cap \{f \in H \mid f(b) = 1\} = h(a) \cap h(b),
\end{aligned}
$$

showing that the function h preserves multiplication. The verification that

$$h(a + b) = h(a) \; \Delta \; h(b)$$

is equally straightforward, depending chiefly upon the observation that the sum $f(a) +_2 f(b) = 1$ if and only if one of $f(a)$ or $f(b)$ is 1, while the other is 0; the reader may easily fill in the steps for himself. These remarks demonstrate the fact that h is a homomorphism from $(R, +, \cdot)$ into the ring of sets $(P(H), \Delta, \cap)$.

All that is needed to complete the proof is to show that h is a one-to-one function or, what amounts to the same thing, that ker $(h) = \{0\}$. But this follows immediately from the preceding lemma which asserts that the set $h(a)$ is empty if and only if $a = 0$, whence,

$$\text{ker } (h) = \{a \in R \mid h(a) = \emptyset\} = \{0\}.$$

The pieces all fall into place, and we see that the ring $(R, +, \cdot)$ is isomorphic to a subring of $(P(H), \Delta, \cap)$.

The definition of a Boolean algebra which we are about to present is based on a structure introduced by E. V. Huntington in 1904. A variety of other sets of postulates could be chosen that would define the algebra equally well; indeed, few areas of mathematics have received more diverse postulational treatment. Aesthetically speaking, it seems desirable to build our theory on as few assumptions as possible. The axiom system quoted below was therefore selected with the intention that no axiom could be derived from the others.

Definition 3–25. A *Boolean algebra* is a mathematical system $(B, \vee, \wedge)$ consisting of a nonempty set B and two binary operations $\vee$ and $\wedge$ defined on B such that

(P$_1$) Each of the operations $\vee$ and $\wedge$ is commutative; that is,

$$a \vee b = b \vee a, \qquad a \wedge b = b \wedge a \qquad \text{for all} \quad a, b \in B.$$

(P$_2$) Each operation is distributive over the other; that is,

$$a \vee (b \wedge c) = (a \vee b) \wedge (a \vee c),$$
$$a \wedge (b \vee c) = (a \wedge b) \vee (a \wedge c) \qquad \text{for all} \quad a, b, c \in B.$$

(P$_3$) There exist distinct identity elements 0 and 1 relative to the operations $\vee$ and $\wedge$, respectively; that is,

$$a \vee 0 = a, \qquad a \wedge 1 = a \qquad \text{for all} \quad a \in B.$$

(P$_4$) For each element $a \in B$, there exists an element $a' \in B$, called the *complement* of a, such that

$$a \vee a' = 1, \qquad a \wedge a' = 0.$$

Example 3–43. An obvious example of a Boolean algebra, but nonetheless an important one, is the system $(P(X), \cup, \cap)$, where X is a nonempty set. It is apparent that we should take $0 = \emptyset$, $1 = X$, and whenever $A \subseteq X$, $A' = X - A$. More generally, if B is any family of subsets of X, including $\emptyset$, which is closed under unions and complements, then $(B, \cup, \cap)$ will be a Boolean algebra, in fact, a Boolean subalgebra of $(P(X), \cap, \cup)$.

Example 3–44. For an illustration quite removed from the algebra of sets, consider the set B of positive integral divisors of 10, that is, $B = \{1, 2, 5, 10\}$. Given elements $a, b \in B$, we define $a \vee b$ to be the least common multiple (lcm) of a and b, $a \wedge b$ to be the greatest common divisor (gcd) of a and b:

$$a \vee b = \text{lcm}\,(a, b), \qquad a \wedge b = \text{gcd}\,(a, b).$$

The tables for these operations are given below.

$\vee$	1	2	5	10
1	1	2	5	10
2	2	2	10	10
5	5	10	5	10
10	10	10	10	10

$\wedge$	1	2	5	10
1	1	1	1	1
2	1	2	1	2
5	1	1	5	5
10	1	2	5	10

The formal verification that the triple $(B, \vee, \wedge)$ constitutes a Boolean algebra is left as an exercise. (We should caution the reader that in this example the integer 1 plays the role of the identity element for the operation $\vee$, while the integer 10 serves as the identity element for the operation $\wedge$.) A quick inspection of the foregoing tables will reveal the various complements to be

$$1' = 10, \qquad 2' = 5, \qquad 5' = 2, \qquad 10' = 1.$$

We call attention to the fact that a' is simply the quotient when 10 is divided by a.

The first thing one notices on inspection of the axiom system for a Boolean algebra is the perfect symmetry or *duality* between the properties of the two operations $\vee$ and $\wedge$. That is to say, if $\vee$ and $\wedge$ are interchanged in the axioms and if, at the same time, 0 and 1 are also interchanged, then the properties are merely permuted amongst themselves. This principle of duality permits us to state all theorems in dual pairs (unless, of course, a statement happens to be its own dual) and guarantees that the proof of one of the pair of statements will be sufficient for the establishment of both; the proof of the dual theorem is obtained by making the appropriate interchange of symbols in the proof of the original theorem.

We now proceed to deduce from the postulated properties of the operations in a Boolean algebra a series of further properties, including, for instance, the associative laws for $\vee$ and $\wedge$. Dual statements are placed side by side; in view of the principle of duality, only one statement from each dual pair need be proved. In order to condense the demonstrations, we shall arrange the steps so far as possible one under another, citing to the right those propositions used in passing across successive equality signs.

Theorem 3–58. In any Boolean algebra $(B, \vee, \wedge)$, the following properties hold:

1) The elements 0 and 1 are unique.
2) For each element $a \in B$,

$$a \vee a = a, \qquad a \wedge a = a.$$

3) For each element $a \in B$,

$$a \vee 1 = 1, \qquad a \wedge 0 = 0.$$

4) For each pair of elements $a, b \in B$,

$$a \vee (a \wedge b) = a, \qquad a \wedge (a \vee b) = a.$$

Proof. To establish (1), we need only appeal to Theorem 2–1. The proof of (2) is indicated below:

$$
\begin{aligned}
a &= a \vee 0 && \text{(by } P_3\text{)} \\
&= a \vee (a \wedge a') && \text{(by } P_4\text{)} \\
&= (a \vee a) \wedge (a \vee a') && \text{(by } P_2\text{)} \\
&= (a \vee a) \wedge 1 && \text{(by } P_4\text{)} \\
&= a \vee a && \text{(by } P_3\text{)}.
\end{aligned}
$$

We obtain (3) as follows:

$$
\begin{aligned}
1 &= a \vee a' && \text{(by } P_4\text{)} \\
&= a \vee (a' \wedge 1) && \text{(by } P_3\text{)} \\
&= (a \vee a') \wedge (a \vee 1) && \text{(by } P_2\text{)} \\
&= 1 \wedge (a \vee 1) && \text{(by } P_4\text{)} \\
&= a \vee 1 && \text{(by } P_3\text{)}.
\end{aligned}
$$

The proof of (4) requires the use of (3):

$$
\begin{aligned}
a &= a \wedge 1 && \text{(by } P_3\text{)} \\
&= a \wedge (b \vee 1) && \text{(by 3)} \\
&= (a \wedge b) \vee (a \wedge 1) && \text{(by } P_2\text{)} \\
&= (a \wedge b) \vee a && \text{(by } P_3\text{)} \\
&= a \vee (a \wedge b) && \text{(by } P_1\text{)}.
\end{aligned}
$$

We did not include the associative laws for $\lor$ and $\land$ among our axioms for a Boolean algebra, as is frequently done, since they are logical consequences of the properties listed. This is demonstrated in our next theorem.

Theorem 3–59. In any Boolean algebra $(B, \lor, \land)$, each of the operations $\lor$ and $\land$ is associative; that is, for every triple of elements $a, b, c \in B$,

$$a \lor (b \lor c) = (a \lor b) \lor c, \qquad a \land (b \land c) = (a \land b) \land c.$$

Proof. First, set $x = a \lor (b \lor c)$ and $y = (a \lor b) \lor c$. We wish, of course, to prove that $x = y$. Note that

$$\begin{aligned}
a \land x &= (a \land a) \lor [a \land (b \lor c)] && \text{(by } P_2) \\
&= a \lor [a \land (b \lor c)] && \text{[by Theorem 3–58(2)]} \\
&= a && \text{[by Theorem 3–58(4)]}
\end{aligned}$$

and also

$$\begin{aligned}
a \land y &= [a \land (a \lor b)] \lor (a \land c) && \text{(by } P_2) \\
&= a \lor (a \land c) && \text{[by Theorem 3–58(4)]} \\
&= a && \text{[by Theorem 3–58(4)].}
\end{aligned}$$

Therefore $a \land x = a \land y$. Now,

$$\begin{aligned}
a' \land x &= (a' \land a) \lor [a' \land (b \lor c)] && \text{(by } P_2) \\
&= 0 \lor [a' \land (b \lor c)] && \text{(by } P_1, P_4) \\
&= a' \land (b \lor c) && \text{(by } P_3)
\end{aligned}$$

and also

$$\begin{aligned}
a' \land y &= [a' \land (a \lor b)] \lor (a' \land c) && \text{(by } P_2) \\
&= [(a' \land a) \lor (a' \land b)] \lor (a' \land c) && \text{(by } P_2) \\
&= [0 \lor (a' \land b)] \lor (a' \land c) && \text{(by } P_1, P_4) \\
&= (a' \land b) \lor (a' \land c) && \text{(by } P_3).
\end{aligned}$$

Therefore $a' \land x = a' \land y$. From these observations, we conclude that

$$\begin{aligned}
(a \land x) \lor (a' \land x) &= (a \land y) \lor (a' \land y) \\
(a \land a') \lor x &= (a \land a') \lor y && \text{(by } P_1, P_2) \\
1 \lor x &= 1 \lor y && \text{(by } P_4) \\
x &= y && \text{(by } P_3),
\end{aligned}$$

proving the associative law for the operation $\lor$; that $\land$ is also associative follows by a dual argument.

As yet nothing has been said about the properties of complementation. In the next group of results, we shall prove, among other things, that each element has a unique complement; thus, $'$ may be viewed as a function from B into itself (as a matter of fact, onto the set B).

Theorem 3–60. In any $a \in B$ Boolean algebra $(B, \vee, \wedge)$, the following hold:

1) Each element $a \in B$ has a unique complement.
2) For each element $a \in B$, $a'' = a$.
3) $0' = 1$ and $1' = 0$.
4) For all $a, b \in B$,

$$(a \vee b)' = a' \wedge b', \qquad (a \wedge b)' = a' \vee b'.$$

Proof. For (1), assume there are two elements x and y of B such that

$$a \vee x = 1, \qquad a \wedge x = 0,$$
$$a \vee y = 1, \qquad a \wedge y = 0.$$

We then have

$$
\begin{aligned}
x &= x \wedge 1 && \text{(by } P_3) \\
&= x \wedge (a \vee y) && \text{(by hypothesis)} \\
&= (x \wedge a) \vee (x \wedge y) && \text{(by } P_2) \\
&= (a \wedge x) \vee (x \wedge y) && \text{(by } P_1) \\
&= 0 \vee (x \wedge y) && \text{(by hypothesis)} \\
&= x \wedge y && \text{(by } P_3).
\end{aligned}
$$

In the same manner, $y = y \wedge x = x \wedge y$, so that $x = y$. Accordingly, any two elements associated with a as specified by axiom P_4 must be equal; in other words, the complement a' is uniquely determined by a.

From the definition of the complement of a, $a \vee a' = 1$ and $a \wedge a' = 0$. Hence, by P_1,

$$a' \vee a = 1 \qquad \text{and} \qquad a' \wedge a = 0.$$

From this, we conclude that the element a is the complement of a':

$$a'' = (a')' = a.$$

Using the uniqueness of the complement and the relations

$$0 \vee 1 = 1, \qquad 0 \wedge 1 = 0,$$

it follows that $0' = 1$. But then $0 = 0'' = 1'$.

Finally, we prove the first statement of (4). Note that, since complements are unique, it is enough to establish

$$(a \lor b) \lor (a' \land b') = 1, \qquad (a \lor b) \land (a' \land b') = 0$$

Now,

$(a \lor b) \lor (a' \land b')$

$$
\begin{aligned}
&= [(a \lor b) \lor a'] \land [(a \lor b) \lor b'] &&\text{(by } P_2) \\
&= [(a \lor a') \lor b] \land [a \lor (b \lor b')] &&\text{[by } P_1, \text{ Theorem 3–59]} \\
&= (1 \lor b) \land (a \lor 1) &&\text{(by } P_4) \\
&= 1 \land 1 &&\text{[by Theorem 3–58(3)]} \\
&= 1 &&\text{(by } P_3).
\end{aligned}
$$

Furthermore,

$(a \lor b) \land (a' \land b')$

$$
\begin{aligned}
&= (a' \land b') \land (a \lor b) &&\text{(by } P_1) \\
&= [(a' \land b') \land a] \land [(a' \land b') \land b] &&\text{(by } P_2) \\
&= [(a' \land a) \land b'] \land [a' \land (b' \land b)] &&\text{[by } P_1, \text{ Theorem 3–59]} \\
&= (0 \land b') \land (a' \land 0) &&\text{(by } P_1, P_4) \\
&= 0 \land 0 &&\text{[by Theorem 3–58(3)]} \\
&= 0 &&\text{(by } P_3).
\end{aligned}
$$

These considerations imply that $(a \lor b)' = a' \land b'$.

The last three theorems do not, in any sense, exhaust the theory of Boolean algebras; we could continue to deduce a large number of results. This brief outline should serve, however, to give some idea of the structure of the system, as well as to prepare the way for our final objective—that of showing that every Boolean algebra can be transformed into a Boolean ring and vice versa.

As a first step in this direction, we indicate how, by the introduction of suitable definitions of addition and multiplication, a Boolean algebra may be converted into a Boolean ring. The argument relies heavily on the results of the previous three theorems.

Theorem 3–61. Every Boolean algebra $(B, \lor, \land)$ becomes a Boolean ring $(B, +, \cdot)$ on defining addition and multiplication by the formulas

$$a + b = (a \land b') \lor (a' \land b), \qquad a \cdot b = a \land b, \qquad (a, b \in B).$$

Proof. It is obvious that addition as defined above is commutative, for

$$a + b = (a \land b') \lor (a' \land b) = (b' \land a) \lor (b \land a')$$
$$= (b \land a') \lor (b' \land a) = b + a.$$

Furthermore,

$$a + 0 = (a \wedge 0') \vee (a' \wedge 0)$$
$$= (a \wedge 1) \vee (a' \wedge 0)$$
$$= a \vee 0 = a$$

and

$$a + a = (a \wedge a') \vee (a' \wedge a) = 0 \vee 0 = 0.$$

This shows that the element 0 acts as the identity for the system $(B, +)$, while each element is its own (additive) inverse.

To establish the associativity of addition, let us first perform a preparatory calculation:

$$(a + b)' = [(a \wedge b') \vee (a' \wedge b)]'$$
$$= (a \wedge b')' \wedge (a' \wedge b)'$$
$$= (a' \vee b) \wedge (a \vee b')$$
$$= [(a' \vee b) \wedge a] \vee [(a' \vee b) \wedge b']$$
$$= (a \wedge b) \vee (a' \wedge b').$$

Utilizing this relation, we then have

$$(a + b) + c = [(a + b) \wedge c'] \vee [(a + b)' \wedge c]$$
$$= [((a \wedge b') \vee (a' \wedge b)) \wedge c] \vee [((a \wedge b) \vee (a' \wedge b')) \wedge c]$$
$$= (a \wedge b' \wedge c) \vee (a' \wedge b \wedge c) \vee (a \wedge b \wedge c) \vee (a' \wedge b' \wedge c).$$

Note, however, that the foregoing expression is symmetric in a, b and c; that is to say, it is unaltered by permuting these elements. Thus, after interchanging a and c, we obtain

$$(a + b) + c = (c + b) + a$$
$$= a + (b + c).$$

From all this, one may infer that the pair $(B, +)$ is a commutative group.

Turning next to a discussion of multiplication, it is evident that both the commutative and associative laws hold, while 1 serves as the multiplicative identity. Because

$$a^2 = a \cdot a = a \wedge a = a,$$

each element a in B is also idempotent.

Finally, to establish that the triple $(B, +, \cdot)$ is a Boolean ring, it remains only to verify that multiplication is distributive over addition. We may dispose of this rather easily, since

$$a \cdot (b + c) = a \wedge [(b \wedge c') \vee (b' \wedge c)]$$
$$= (a \wedge b \wedge c') \vee (a \wedge b' \wedge c),$$

whereas

$$a \cdot b + a \cdot c = (a \wedge b) + (a \wedge c)$$
$$= [(a \wedge b) \wedge (a \wedge c)'] \vee [(a \wedge b)' \wedge (a \wedge c)]$$
$$= [(a \wedge b) \wedge (a' \vee c')] \vee [(a' \vee b') \wedge (a \wedge c)]$$
$$= (a \wedge b \wedge a') \vee (a \wedge b \wedge c') \vee (a' \wedge a \wedge c) \vee (b' \wedge a \wedge c)$$
$$= (a \wedge b \wedge c') \vee (a \wedge b' \wedge c).$$

The proof of the theorem is therefore complete.

We now reverse this process; in other words, we start with a Boolean ring and transform it into a Boolean algebra by suitably defining the operations $\vee$ and $\wedge$.

Theorem 3–62. Every Boolean ring $(B, +, \cdot)$ becomes a Boolean algebra $(B, \vee, \wedge)$ on defining

$$a \vee b = a + b + a \cdot b, \qquad a \wedge b = a \cdot b, \qquad (a, b \in B).$$

Proof. That $\vee$ and $\wedge$ are both commutative follows immediately from the commutativity of the operations in $(B, +, \cdot)$. A simple calculation will show that $\wedge$ is distributive over $\vee$:

$$a \wedge (b \vee c) = a \cdot (b + c + b \cdot c)$$
$$= a \cdot b + a \cdot c + (a \cdot b) \cdot (a \cdot c)$$
$$= (a \cdot b) \vee (a \cdot c) = (a \wedge b) \vee (a \wedge c).$$

The verification of the other distributive law relies on the fact that, since $2x = 0$ for every element of the ring $(R, +, \cdot)$, it is unnecessary to distinguish between addition and subtraction:

$$(a \vee b) \wedge (a \vee c) = (a + b + a \cdot b) \cdot (a + c + a \cdot c)$$
$$= a + a \cdot b + a \cdot b + a \cdot c + b \cdot c + a \cdot b \cdot c + a \cdot c$$
$$\quad + a \cdot b \cdot c + a \cdot b \cdot c$$
$$= a + b \cdot c + a \cdot b \cdot c$$
$$= a \vee (b \cdot c) = a \vee (b \wedge c).$$

If 0 and 1 are the additive and multiplicative identities of $(B, +, \cdot)$, then

$$a \vee 0 = a + 0 + a \cdot 0 = a, \qquad a \wedge 1 = a \cdot 1 = a$$

for every $a \in B$. Finally, we have

$$a \vee (1 + a) = a + (1 + a) + a \cdot (1 + a) = 1 + 4a = 1,$$
$$a \wedge (1 + a) = a \cdot (1 + a) = a + a^2 = 2a = 0,$$

which implies $1 + a$ is the complement of a in $(B, \vee, \wedge)$, that is

$$a' = 1 + a.$$

These computations show that the postulates of Definition 3–25 are all satisfied and, consequently, the triple $(B, \vee, \wedge)$ is a Boolean algebra.

Taken together, Theorems 3–61 and 3–62 indicate that the theory of Boolean algebras is equivalent to the theory of Boolean rings. What is to be considered remarkable is the identification of a notion arising out of questions of logic and set theory with a system amenable to the powerful techniques of modern algebra.

PROBLEMS

1. Prove that in a Boolean ring $(R, +, \cdot)$, every triple of elements $a, b, c \in R$ satisfies the identity
$$(a + b) \cdot (b + c) \cdot (c + a) = 0.$$

2. If a Boolean ring $(R, +, \cdot)$ has at least three elements, show that every nonzero element except the identity is a divisor of zero. [*Hint:* For $a, b \in R$, consider the product $(a + b) \cdot a \cdot b$.]

3. Prove that any ring $(R, +, \cdot)$ in which each element is idempotent can be imbedded in a Boolean ring. [*Hint:* Let $R' = R \times Z_2$ and mimic the argument of Theorem 3–16.]

4. a) Let $(R, +, \cdot)$ be a commutative ring with identity and S the set of idempotents of R. For $a, b \in S$, define the operation $*$ by taking
$$a * b = a + b - 2(a \cdot b).$$

   Prove that the triple $(S, *, \cdot)$ forms a Boolean ring, known as the *idempotent Boolean ring* of $(R, +, \cdot)$.

   b) In particular, obtain the idempotent Boolean ring of $(Z_{12}, +_{12}, \cdot_{12})$.

5. Suppose $(I, +, \cdot)$ is an ideal of the Boolean ring $(R, +, \cdot)$. Show that $(I, +, \cdot)$ is a proper prime (maximal) ideal if and only if for each element a in R, either $a \in I$ or $1 - a \in I$, but not both.

6. Given $(R, +, \cdot)$ is a Boolean ring. For an element $a \in R$, define the set $I(a)$ by
$$I(a) = \{ I \mid (I, +, \cdot) \text{ is a maximal ideal of } (R, +, \cdot); a \notin I \}.$$

   Verify that the sets $I(a)$ have the following properties:
   a) $I(a) \neq \emptyset$ whenever $a \neq 0$.
   b) $I(a + b) = I(a) \triangle I(b)$.
   c) $I(a \cdot b) = I(a) \cap I(b)$.
   d) $I(a) = I(b)$ if and only if $a = b$.
   [*Hint:* $a \notin I$ if and only if $1 - a \in I$.]

7. In reference to Problem 6, prove that if

$$M = \{I \mid (I, +, \cdot) \text{ is a maximal ideal of } (R, +, \cdot)\},$$

then the ring $(R, +, \cdot)$ is isomorphic to a subring of $(P(M), \triangle, \cap)$. [*Hint:* Consider the mapping $f \colon R \to P(M)$ given by $f(a) = I(a)$.]

8. Establish that there is no Boolean ring having exactly three elements.

9. In any Boolean ring $(R, +, \cdot)$, an order relation $\leq$ may be defined by taking $a \leq b$ if and only if $a \cdot b = a$. If the elements $a, b, c, d \in R$, establish the following order-properties:

   a) $a \leq a$, $0 \leq a \leq 1$ for every $a \in R$.
   b) $a \leq b$ and $b \leq c$ imply $a \leq c$.
   c) $a \leq b$ and $b \leq a$ imply $a = b$.
   d) $a \leq c$ and $b \leq d$ imply $a \cdot b \leq c \cdot d$.
   e) $b \cdot c = 0$ implies $a \cdot c = 0$ if and only if $a \leq b$.

10. a) Let $(R, +, \cdot)$ be a Boolean ring and I be a nonempty subset of R. Show that $(I, +, \cdot)$ is an ideal of $(R, +, \cdot)$ if and only if

    i) $a, b \in I$ imply $a + b \in I$,
    ii) $a \in I$ and $r \in R$ with $r \leq a$ imply $r \cdot a \in I$.

    b) If the set I_a is defined by $I_a = \{r \in R \mid r \leq a\}$, verify that the triple $(I_a, +, \cdot)$ forms an ideal of $(R, +, \cdot)$.

11. Suppose that $(S, +, \cdot)$ is a subring of a Boolean ring $(R, +, \cdot)$. Prove that any homomorphism f from $(S, +, \cdot)$ onto the field $(Z_2, +_2, \cdot_2)$ can be extended to all of $(R, +, \cdot)$. [*Hint:* The ideal $(\ker (f), +, \cdot)$ is contained in maximal ideal $(M, +, \cdot)$, where $(R/M, +, \cdot) \simeq (Z_2, +_2, \cdot_2)$.]

12. For elements a, b, and c of a Boolean algebra $(B, \vee, \wedge)$, prove that

    a) $(a \wedge b) \vee (b \wedge c) \vee (c \wedge a) = (a \vee b) \wedge (b \vee c) \wedge (c \vee a)$,
    b) $a \wedge c = b \wedge c$ and $a \wedge c' = b \wedge c'$ imply $a = b$,
    c) $a = b$ if and only if $(a \wedge b') \vee (a' \wedge b) = 0$,
    d) $a = 0$ if and only if $(a \wedge b') \vee (a' \wedge b) = b$,
    e) $a \wedge b = a$ if and only if $a \vee b = b$.

13. Let the set B consist of the positive integral divisors of 30, that is,

$$B = \{1, 2, 3, 5, 6, 10, 15, 30\}.$$

If $\vee$ and $\wedge$ are defined by

$$a \vee b = \operatorname{lcm} (a, b), \qquad a \wedge b = \gcd (a, b),$$

show that the triple $(B, \vee, \wedge)$ is a Boolean algebra.

14. Given that X is an infinite set. Let B be the family of all subsets $A \subseteq X$ such that either A or $X - A$ is finite, plus $\emptyset$ and X. Determine whether the triple $(B, \cup, \cap)$ forms a Boolean algebra.

15. Prove that if $(B, \vee, \wedge)$ is a Boolean algebra having identity element 1 for the operation $\wedge$, then every Boolean subalgebra must contain 1. Contrast this with the case of rings.

16. By means of Theorem 3–61, convert the Boolean algebra $(B, \vee, \wedge)$, as defined below, into a Boolean ring.

$\vee$	a	b	c	d
a	a	b	c	d
b	b	b	b	b
c	c	b	c	b
d	d	b	b	d

$\wedge$	a	b	c	d
a	a	a	a	a
b	a	b	c	d
c	a	c	c	a
d	a	d	a	d

$B = \{a, b, c, d\}$

17. Suppose a Boolean algebra $(B, \vee, \wedge)$ is made into a Boolean ring $(B, +, \cdot)$ via Theorem 3–61, and then $(B, +, \cdot)$ is converted back to a Boolean algebra $(B, \vee_1, \wedge_1)$ via Theorem 3–62. Verify that $(B, \vee, \wedge) = (B, \vee_1, \wedge_1)$.

18. Suppose $(B, \vee, \wedge)$ is a Boolean ring and $\emptyset \neq I \subseteq B$. The triple $(I, \vee, \wedge)$ is said to be a *(Boolean) ideal* of $(B, \vee, \wedge)$ if and only if

   i) $a, b \in I$ implies $a \vee b \in I$,
   ii) $a \in I$ and $b \in B$ imply $a \wedge b \in I$.

   a) Prove that every Boolean algebra $(B, \vee, \wedge)$ has two trivial ideals, namely, $(\{0\}, \vee, \wedge)$ and $(B, \vee, \wedge)$.
   b) If $(I_i, \vee, \wedge)$ is a collection of ideals of $(B, \vee, \wedge)$, show that $(\cap I_i, \vee, \wedge)$ is also an ideal.
   c) Prove that if $(I, \vee, \wedge)$ is an ideal of $(B, \vee, \wedge)$ and $1 \in I$, then $I = B$.

19. Let $(P(X), \cup, \cap)$ be the Boolean algebra of subsets of a nonempty set X and x_0 be any element of X. Prove that

   a) if I is the family of all subsets $A \subseteq X$ such that $x_0 \notin A$, then the triple $(I, \cup, \cap)$ is an ideal of $(P(X), \cup, \cap)$,
   b) if X is infinite and I is the family of all finite subsets $A \subseteq X$, then the triple $(I, \cup, \cap)$ is an ideal of $(P(X), \cup, \cap)$.

20. Let $(B, \vee, \wedge)$ and $(B_1, \vee_1, \wedge_1)$ be two Boolean algebras and f a mapping from B into B_1. Then f is said to be a *Boolean homomorphism* from $(B, \vee, \wedge)$ into $(B_1, \vee_1, \wedge_1)$ provided

$$f(a \vee b) = f(a) \vee_1 f(b),$$
$$f(a \wedge b) = f(a) \wedge_1 f(b),$$
$$f(a') = f(a)'$$

for all elements $a, b \in B$. (The formation of complements may be regarded as a unitary operation.) Show that such a function has the following properties:

   a) $f(0) = 0_1, f(1) = 1_1$.
   b) $(f(B), \vee_1, \wedge_1)$ is a subalgebra of $(B_1, \vee_1, \wedge_1)$.
   c) If $a \leq b$ is taken to mean $a \wedge b = a$, then $f(a) \leq f(b)$ whenever $a \leq b$.
   d) The triple $(\ker(f), \vee, \wedge)$ is an ideal of $(B, \vee, \wedge)$, where

$$\ker (f) = \{a \in B \mid f(a) = 0_1\}.$$

   e) If $(I_1, \vee_1, \wedge_1)$ is an ideal of $(B_1, \vee_1, \wedge_1)$, then $(f^{-1}(I_1), \vee, \wedge)$ is an ideal of $(B, \vee, \wedge)$.

CHAPTER 4

VECTOR SPACES

4–1 THE ALGEBRA OF MATRICES

The theory of matrices has long occupied a strategic position in various branches of mathematics, physics, and engineering. Only in recent years has its importance in the social and biological sciences as well become apparent. The subject today has become an indispensable tool in such new fields as game theory, linear programming, and statistical decision theory. Part of the reason for the widening applicability of matrix theory is no doubt the role it plays in the analysis of discrete observations and the ease with which matric operations may be programmed for modern highspeed computers.

We do not intend to give a complete and systematic account of the problems of matrix theory and its diverse applications. Rather, the operations and the basic properties of vectors and matrices are approached from an algebraic point of view with the aim of illustrating some of the concepts of the previous chapters. One result of such a study will be the formulation of a mathematical system, somewhat more complicated than those studied earlier, known as a vector space.

The basic definition which starts us off is that of a vector, the fundamental object in our study.

Definition 4–1. An n-component or n-dimensional *vector* over a field $(F, +, \cdot)$ is an ordered n-tuple $(a_1, a_2, \ldots, a_n)$ of elements $a_k \in F$.

The elements $a_k \in F$ are called the *components* of the vector and we say n is its *dimension*. Clearly, the set of all one-dimensional vectors over $(F, +, \cdot)$ can be identified with F itself. To have to write out the whole vector is somewhat awkward; hereafter, we will condense our notation and designate the vector with components a_k by (a_k). It is hardly necessary to point out that two n-component vectors (a_k) and (b_k) are equal, in which case we write $(a_k) = (b_k)$, if and only if their corresponding components are equal: $(a_k) = (b_k)$ if and only if $a_k = b_k$ for $k = 1, 2, \ldots, n$.

Definition 4–2. a) The *sum of two n-component vectors* (a_k) and (b_k), denoted by $(a_k) + (b_k)$, is the vector obtained by adding their corresponding components. Thus, $(a_k) + (b_k) = (a_k + b_k)$.

b) The *product of a vector* (a_k) *and an element* r *of* F, denoted by $r(a_k)$, is the vector obtained by multiplying each component of (a_k) by r. Thus, $r(a_k) = (r \cdot a_k)$.

Here, we conform with the standard practice of using the plus sign in two different contexts, for vectors and for their components. It should be perfectly clear in any given situation whether we are adding vectors or elements of F. Note, incidentally, that the difference of two vectors may be expressed in terms of the operations already given:

$$(a_k) - (b_k) = (a_k) + (-1)(b_k).$$

For a simple illustration of these ideas, consider vectors over $(R^{\#}, +, \cdot)$; in this case, we have

$$(1, 2, 3) - 2(1, 0, -1) = (1, 2, 3) + (-2, 0, 2) = (-1, 2, 5).$$

Definition 4–3. Any vector whose components are all zero is called a *zero vector* and is represented by the symbol O.

Let $V_n(F)$ denote the set of all n-component vectors over an arbitrary field $(F, +, \cdot)$. Inasmuch as vector addition enjoys the basic additive properties of its components, the following theorem concerning the algebraic nature of the pair $(V_n(F), +)$ is obvious.

Theorem 4–1. The system $(V_n(F), +)$ is a commutative group, having the zero vector of dimension n as its identity element and $(-a_k)$ as the inverse of a vector $(a_k) \in V_n(F)$.

The operation of multiplication of vectors by elements of F, as defined above, has the following properties: if $r, s \in F$ and (a_k), (b_k) are vectors in $V_n(F)$, then

1) $(r + s)(a_k) = r(a_k) + s(a_k)$,
2) $r[(a_k) + (b_k)] = r(a_k) + r(b_k)$,
3) $r[s(a_k)] = (r \cdot s)(a_k)$; $1(a_k) = (a_k)$; $0(a_k) = O$.

Verification of these facts is not particularly difficult and is left to the reader.

Vectors may also be combined under a rule of composition known as inner product multiplication.

Definition 4–4. The *inner product* of two vectors (a_k), $(b_k) \in V_n(F)$, denoted by $(a_k) \circ (b_k)$, is defined to be

$$(a_k) \circ (b_k) = \sum_{k=1}^{n} a_k \cdot b_k.$$

According to this definition, inner product multiplication $\circ$ may be regarded as a function from $V_n(F) \times V_n(F)$ onto F; that is, the inner product of two vectors is an element of F. Note also that the product of two nonzero vectors may be zero, as in $V_3(R^{\#})$, where

$$(1, 2, -3) \circ (3, 6, 5) = 1 \cdot 3 + 2 \cdot 6 + (-3) \cdot 5 = 0.$$

However, one should not jump to hasty conclusions concerning divisors of zero, for on the right-hand side we have the real number zero and not a 3-component zero vector.

While failing to be even a binary operation, inner product multiplication nonetheless enjoys some interesting properties, several of which are listed in the next theorem.

Theorem 4–2. If $r \in F$ and (a_k), (b_k), (c_k) are vectors in $V_n(F)$, then

1) $(a_k) \circ (b_k) = (b_k) \circ (a_k)$,
2) $O \circ (a_k) = 0 = (a_k) \circ O$,
3) $r[(a_k) \circ (b_k)] = (r \cdot a_k) \circ (b_k) = (a_k) \circ (r \cdot b_k)$,
4) $(a_k) \circ [(b_k) + (c_k)] = (a_k) \circ (b_k) + (a_k) \circ (c_k)$.

Proof. Let us illustrate the type of argument involved by establishing the last statement; the remaining parts of the theorem are left as an exercise. We proceed as follows:

$$(a_k) \circ [(b_k) + (c_k)] = (a_k) \circ (b_k + c_k) = \sum_{k=1}^{n} a_k \cdot [b_k + c_k]$$

$$= \sum_{k=1}^{n} a_k \cdot b_k + \sum_{k=1}^{n} a_k \cdot c_k$$

$$= (a_k) \circ (b_k) + (a_k) \circ (c_k).$$

Definition 4–5. By an $m \times n$ *matrix* (plural: *matrices*) over the field $(F, +, \cdot)$ we mean a function from $\{1, 2, \ldots, m\} \times \{1, 2, \ldots, n\}$ into F.

In the case of matrices, one customarily arranges the functional values block fashion in a table made up of m rows and n columns. Specifically, if the value of the matrix at the ordered pair (i, j) is denoted by a_{ij}, where $1 \leq i \leq m$, $1 \leq j \leq n$, then the matrix is indicated by the following rectangular array:

$$\begin{pmatrix} a_{11} & a_{12} & \cdots & a_{1n} \\ a_{21} & a_{22} & \cdots & a_{2n} \\ \vdots & \vdots & & \vdots \\ a_{m1} & a_{m2} & \cdots & a_{mn} \end{pmatrix}.$$

Abusing terminology, we shall hereafter refer to the above display of mn elements of F as the matrix itself (in the strict sense, this display is simply a representation of the matrix). Further, we will call a_{ij} the *ij*th *entry* or *element* of the matrix, and we shall speak of the integers m and n, the number of rows and columns, as its *dimensions*.

Note that elements are located in the matrix by the use of double subscripts, the first subscript indicating the row, and the second subscript the column in which the element is found. For instance, the element a_{23} is in the second row and third column.

To avoid cumbersome notations, it is convenient to abbreviate a matrix as $(a_{ij})_{m \times n}$, to be read "the matrix of dimension $m \times n$ whose elements are the a_{ij}'s." When the numbers of rows and columns are clearly understood, we may instead simply write (a_{ij}). If $m = n$, the matrix is said to be *square of order n*.

Definition 4–6. Two $m \times n$ matrices (a_{ij}) and (b_{ij}) are equal, for which we write $(a_{ij}) = (b_{ij})$, if and only if their corresponding elements are equal; that is, $a_{ij} = b_{ij}$ for all i and j.

Since the rows of an $m \times n$ matrix may be regarded as elements of the vector space $V_n(F)$, it is not surprising that the operations defined in $V_n(F)$ have natural generalizations to matrix operations.

Definition 4–7. a) The sum of two $m \times n$ matrices (a_{ij}) and (b_{ij}), denoted by $(a_{ij}) + (b_{ij})$, is the matrix obtained by adding their corresponding elements. Thus, $(a_{ij}) + (b_{ij}) = (a_{ij} + b_{ij})$.

b) The product of the matrix (a_{ij}) and the element $r \in F$, denoted by $r(a_{ij})$, is the matrix obtained by multiplying each element of (a_{ij}) by r. Thus, $r(a_{ij}) = (r \cdot a_{ij})$.

Observe that by its definition, addition is a binary operation on the set of all matrices of a given size; that is, the sum of two $n \times m$ matrices is again an $n \times m$ matrix.

Example 4–1. Taking $(R^{\#}, +, \cdot)$ as the base field, let

$$A = \begin{pmatrix} 1 & -6 & 2 \\ 3 & 0 & 1 \end{pmatrix}, \qquad B = \begin{pmatrix} 3 & 4 & 5 \\ 2 & -1 & 2 \end{pmatrix}.$$

Then

$$2A + B = \begin{pmatrix} 2 & -12 & 4 \\ 6 & 0 & 2 \end{pmatrix} + \begin{pmatrix} 3 & 4 & 5 \\ 2 & -1 & 2 \end{pmatrix}$$

$$= \begin{pmatrix} 5 & -8 & 9 \\ 8 & -1 & 4 \end{pmatrix}.$$

A matrix each of whose elements is zero is called a *zero matrix* and is denoted by O. Accordingly, a zero matrix need not be square. For the zero matrix whose dimensions are those of (a_{ij}), we have

$$(a_{ij}) + O = (a_{ij}) = O + (a_{ij}),$$

$$(a_{ij}) + (-1)(a_{ij}) = O = (-1)(a_{ij}) + (a_{ij}).$$

Let us denote the set of all $m \times n$ matrices over the field $(F, +, \cdot)$ by the symbol $M_{mn}(F)$. The following theorem establishes the algebraic properties of $(M_{mn}(F), +)$ under matrix addition.

Theorem 4–3. The system $(M_{mn}(F), +)$ is a commutative group, with the $m \times n$ zero matrix as the identity element and $(-a_{ij})$ as the inverse of a matrix $(a_{ij}) \in M_{mn}(F)$.

Proof. Definition 4–7 indicates that each property of matrix addition is derived from the corresponding additive property in the field $(F, +, \cdot)$. For instance, to establish the commutative law, let (a_{ij}), $(b_{ij}) \in M_{mn}(F)$. Then

$$(a_{ij}) + (b_{ij}) = (a_{ij} + b_{ij}) = (b_{ij} + a_{ij}) = (b_{ij}) + (a_{ij}).$$

The rest of the proof proceeds along similar lines and is left to the reader.

Although multiplication of matrices by a field element is not a binary operation on $M_{mn}(F)$ [unless, of course, $m = n = 1$], this operation has several interesting features. Specifically, if (a_{ij}), $(b_{ij}) \in M_{mn}(F)$ and r, $s \in F$, then

$$r[(a_{ij}) + (b_{ij})] = r(a_{ij}) + r(b_{ij}),$$

$$(r \cdot s)(a_{ij}) = r[s(a_{ij})],$$

$$(r + s)(a_{ij}) = r(a_{ij}) + s(a_{ij}),$$

$$1(a_{ij}) = (a_{ij}), \qquad 0(a_{ij}) = O.$$

Our main purpose for introducing inner product multiplication for vectors becomes apparent with the following definition.

Definition 4–8. If (a_{ij}) is an $m \times n$ matrix and (b_{ij}) is an $n \times r$ matrix, then their *product* $(c_{ij}) = (a_{ij}) \cdot (b_{ij})$ is an $m \times r$ matrix whose elements are given by the formula

$$c_{ij} = \sum_{k=1}^{n} a_{ik} \cdot b_{kj} \qquad \text{for} \quad i = 1, 2, \ldots, m; \quad j = 1, 2, \ldots, r.$$

As the subscripts indicate, the ijth entry c_{ij} in the product matrix $(a_{ij}) \cdot (b_{ij})$ is obtained by taking the inner product of the ith row of (a_{ij}) and the jth column of (b_{ij}):

$$c_{ij} = (a_{i1}, a_{i2}, \ldots, a_{in}) \circ \begin{pmatrix} b_{1j} \\ b_{2j} \\ \vdots \\ b_{nj} \end{pmatrix}.$$

As we observed previously, the inner product of two vectors is defined only if the vectors involved have the same number of components. Thus for the matrix product $(a_{ij}) \cdot (b_{ij})$ to exist, the number of columns in the matrix (a_{ij})

[which determines the number of elements in a row of (a_{ij})] must be equal to the number of rows in the matrix (b_{ij}) [which determines the number of elements in a column of (b_{ij})]. This means that we could not, for example, multiply a 4×3 matrix and a 2×3 matrix.

Restricted to the set of square matrices of order n, matrix multiplication is a binary operation. For if (a_{ij}) and (b_{ij}) are both $n \times n$ matrices, then so is their product $(a_{ij}) \cdot (b_{ij})$.

Before going on, it would be worthwhile to consider an example in detail.

Example 4–2. Again taking $(R^{\#}, +, \cdot)$ as the field, let

$$A = \begin{pmatrix} 2 & 0 & 1 \\ 3 & 2 & -1 \end{pmatrix} \quad \text{and} \quad B = \begin{pmatrix} 3 & 1 \\ -1 & 0 \\ 0 & 2 \end{pmatrix}.$$

Then

$$A \cdot B = \underbrace{\begin{pmatrix} 2 & 0 & 1 \\ 3 & 2 & -1 \end{pmatrix}}_{2 \times 3} \cdot \underbrace{\begin{pmatrix} 3 & 1 \\ -1 & 0 \\ 0 & 2 \end{pmatrix}}_{3 \times 2}$$

$$= \underbrace{\begin{pmatrix} 2 \cdot 3 + 0 \cdot (-1) + 1 \cdot 0 & 2 \cdot 1 + 0 \cdot 0 + 1 \cdot 2 \\ 3 \cdot 3 + 2 \cdot (-1) + (-1) \cdot 0 & 3 \cdot 1 + 2 \cdot 0 + (-1) \cdot 2 \end{pmatrix}}_{2 \times 2} = \begin{pmatrix} 6 & 4 \\ 7 & 1 \end{pmatrix}.$$

On the other hand,

$$B \cdot A = \underbrace{\begin{pmatrix} 3 & 1 \\ -1 & 0 \\ 0 & 2 \end{pmatrix}}_{3 \times 2} \cdot \underbrace{\begin{pmatrix} 2 & 0 & 1 \\ 3 & 2 & -1 \end{pmatrix}}_{2 \times 3}$$

$$= \underbrace{\begin{pmatrix} 3 \cdot 2 + 1 \cdot 3 & 3 \cdot 0 + 1 \cdot 2 & 3 \cdot 1 + 1 \cdot (-1) \\ -1 \cdot 2 + 0 \cdot 3 & -1 \cdot 0 + 0 \cdot 2 & -1 \cdot 1 + 0 \cdot (-1) \\ 0 \cdot 2 + 2 \cdot 3 & 0 \cdot 0 + 2 \cdot 2 & 0 \cdot 1 + 2 \cdot (-1) \end{pmatrix}}_{3 \times 3}$$

$$= \begin{pmatrix} 9 & 2 & 2 \\ -2 & 0 & -1 \\ 6 & 4 & -2 \end{pmatrix}.$$

We next dispose of one natural question that arises here, namely, the question of commutativity of matrix multiplication. First of all, given an $m \times n$ matrix (a_{ij}), the matrix products $(a_{ij}) \cdot (b_{ij})$ and $(b_{ij}) \cdot (a_{ij})$ are both defined if and only if (b_{ij}) is an $n \times m$ matrix. When the latter condition holds and it is at least possible to form these two products, $(a_{ij}) \cdot (b_{ij})$ and $(b_{ij}) \cdot (a_{ij})$ will be of different dimensions unless $m = n$. Even if this is the case, where it is meaningful to ask whether $(a_{ij}) \cdot (b_{ij})$ and $(b_{ij}) \cdot (a_{ij})$ are equal, matrix multiplication will not as a rule be commutative. One need only consider the computation

$$\begin{pmatrix} 0 & 1 \\ 0 & 0 \end{pmatrix} \cdot \begin{pmatrix} 0 & 0 \\ 0 & 1 \end{pmatrix} = \begin{pmatrix} 0 & 1 \\ 0 & 0 \end{pmatrix}$$

$$\neq \begin{pmatrix} 0 & 0 \\ 0 & 0 \end{pmatrix} = \begin{pmatrix} 0 & 0 \\ 0 & 1 \end{pmatrix} \cdot \begin{pmatrix} 0 & 1 \\ 0 & 0 \end{pmatrix}.$$

Due to the asymmetric way in which two matrices combine in a product, such an outcome is not totally unsuspected. It is quite possible, of course, that a particular pair of matrices may commute.

For the zero matrices of appropriate dimensions, $(a_{ij}) \cdot O = O$ and $O \cdot (a_{ij}) = O$. In particular, if both (a_{ij}) and O are square matrices of the same order, then $(a_{ij}) \cdot O = O \cdot (a_{ij}) = O$.

If (a_{ij}) is any square matrix, then that part of the matrix consisting of the the elements a_{ii} is called the (main) *diagonal* of the matrix.

Definition 4–9. The *identity matrix of order* n, designated by I_n, or simply I when there is no chance of confusion, is the square $n \times n$ matrix having ones down its diagonal and zeros elsewhere.

It is helpful to have some notation for the elements of the identity matrix. Consequently, we will denote the element in the ith row and jth column of I_n by the symbol δ_{ij}, where

$$\delta_{ij} = \begin{cases} 1 & \text{for} \quad i = j, \\ 0 & \text{for} \quad i \neq j, \end{cases} \qquad \text{(the Kronecker delta)}$$

and thus write $I_n = (\delta_{ij})$. To illustrate,

$$I_2 = \begin{pmatrix} \delta_{11} & \delta_{12} \\ \delta_{21} & \delta_{22} \end{pmatrix} = \begin{pmatrix} 1 & 0 \\ 0 & 1 \end{pmatrix}.$$

For each positive integer n, the set of all square matrices of order n over the field $(F, +, \cdot)$ will be represented by $M_n(F)$, rather than $M_{nn}(F)$. The identity matrix I_n serves as an identity element for the operation of matrix multiplication in the set $M_n(F)$. Indeed, if $(a_{ij}) \in M_n(F)$, then

$$(a_{ij}) \cdot I_n = (a_{ij}) \cdot (\delta_{ij}) = \left(\sum_{k=1}^{n} a_{ik} \cdot \delta_{kj} \right) = (a_{ij}),$$

and similarly $I_n \cdot (a_{ij}) = (a_{ij})$.

We have just proved part of the following theorem.

Theorem 4–4. The system $(M_n(F), +, \cdot)$ is a ring with identity.

Proof. It has already been observed that $(M_n(F), +)$ is a commutative group and that matrix multiplication is a binary operation on $M_n(F)$. What remains is to verify the associativity of multiplication and the distributive laws. To establish that multiplication is left distributive over addition, let (a_{ij}), (b_{ij}), and $(c_{ij}) \in M_n(F)$. Then

$$(a_{ij}) \cdot [(b_{ij}) + (c_{ij})] = (a_{ij}) \cdot (b_{ij} + c_{ij})$$

$$= \left(\sum_{k=1}^{n} a_{ik} \cdot [b_{kj} + c_{kj}] \right)$$

$$= \left(\sum_{k=1}^{n} a_{ik} \cdot b_{kj} + \sum_{k=1}^{n} a_{ik} \cdot c_{kj} \right)$$

$$= \left(\sum_{k=1}^{n} a_{ik} \cdot b_{kj} \right) + \left(\sum_{k=1}^{n} a_{ik} \cdot c_{kj} \right)$$

$$= (a_{ij}) \cdot (b_{ij}) + (a_{ij}) \cdot (c_{ij}).$$

The rest of the proof offers no difficulty and is omitted.

For our next theorem we need the following notation: define E_{ij} to be the $n \times n$ matrix having 1 as its ijth entry and zeros everywhere else. Thus for $n = 2$,

$$E_{11} = \begin{pmatrix} 1 & 0 \\ 0 & 0 \end{pmatrix}, \qquad E_{12} = \begin{pmatrix} 0 & 1 \\ 0 & 0 \end{pmatrix},$$

$$E_{21} = \begin{pmatrix} 0 & 0 \\ 1 & 0 \end{pmatrix}, \qquad E_{22} = \begin{pmatrix} 0 & 0 \\ 0 & 1 \end{pmatrix}.$$

The reader may readily prove that

$$I_n = E_{11} + E_{22} + \cdots + E_{nn}$$

and

$$E_{ij} \cdot E_{st} = \begin{cases} E_{it} & \text{if } j = s, \\ O & \text{if } j \neq s. \end{cases}$$

This last relation shows, incidentally, that the ring $(M_n(F), +, \cdot)$ has divisors of zero.

The proof of Theorem 3–24 indicates that any commutative ring with identity which is not a field always possesses nontrivial ideals. There is no reason to assume that in the absence of commutativity the same conclusion follows. Indeed, as we shall see, the system $(M_n(F), +, \cdot)$ provides an example of a noncommutative ring without nontrivial ideals.

Theorem 4–5. The ring of matrices $(M_n(F), +, \cdot)$ has no nontrivial ideals; that is, $(M_n(F), +, \cdot)$ is a simple ring.

Proof. Suppose that $(S, +, \cdot)$ is any ideal of the ring $(M_n(F), +, \cdot)$, where $S \neq \{0\}$. Then S must contain some nonzero matrix (a_{ij}), with, say, $a_{st} \neq 0$. Now consider the matrix product

$$E_{ss} \cdot (b_{ij}) \cdot (a_{ij}) \cdot E_{tt},$$

where the matrix (b_{ij}) has the value a_{st}^{-1} down its main diagonal and zeros elsewhere. Due to the presence of all the zero entries in the various factors, this product is equal to E_{st}. Moreover, since $(S, +, \cdot)$ is an ideal, the matrix E_{st} belongs to S. The relation

$$E_{ij} = E_{is} \cdot E_{st} \cdot E_{tj}, \qquad i, j = 1, 2, \ldots, n,$$

shows further that all n^2 of the matrices E_{ij} are contained in S. The set S, being closed under addition, then has the identity matrix I_n as a member, from which we conclude that $S = M_n(F)$, In other words, if $S \neq \{0\}$, then $S = M_n(F)$.

In passing, let us remark that while the ring $(M_n(F), +, \cdot)$ fails to have nontrivial (two-sided) ideals, it may very well possess one-sided ideals. For example, the set of all matrices of the form

$$\begin{pmatrix} a & 0 \\ b & 0 \end{pmatrix}, \qquad a, b \in F,$$

comprises the elements of a left ideal of $(M_2(F), +, \cdot)$.

Matrices which have a multiplicative inverse are said to be *nonsingular*; otherwise they are called *singular*. Since a nonsingular matrix (a_{ij}) commutes with its inverse [by definition $(a_{ij}) \cdot (a_{ij})^{-1} = (a_{ij})^{-1} \cdot (a_{ij}) = I$], it follows that both the matrix and its inverse must be square and of the same order.

While only square matrices can possess an inverse, not every square matrix is nonsingular. For instance, consider the 2×2 matrix

$$\begin{pmatrix} 1 & 1 \\ 1 & 1 \end{pmatrix}.$$

If this matrix were nonsingular, we would then have

$$\begin{pmatrix} -1 & 1 \\ -1 & 1 \end{pmatrix} \cdot \left[\begin{pmatrix} 1 & 1 \\ 1 & 1 \end{pmatrix} \cdot \begin{pmatrix} 1 & 1 \\ 1 & 1 \end{pmatrix}^{-1} \right] = \begin{pmatrix} -1 & 1 \\ -1 & 1 \end{pmatrix} \cdot I_2 = \begin{pmatrix} -1 & 1 \\ -1 & 1 \end{pmatrix}.$$

On the other hand, the associative law yields

$$\left[\begin{pmatrix} -1 & 1 \\ -1 & 1 \end{pmatrix} \cdot \begin{pmatrix} 1 & 1 \\ 1 & 1 \end{pmatrix} \right] \cdot \begin{pmatrix} 1 & 1 \\ 1 & 1 \end{pmatrix}^{-1} = \begin{pmatrix} 0 & 0 \\ 0 & 0 \end{pmatrix} \cdot \begin{pmatrix} 1 & 1 \\ 1 & 1 \end{pmatrix}^{-1} = \begin{pmatrix} 0 & 0 \\ 0 & 0 \end{pmatrix},$$

which leads to an obvious contradiction.

This argument shows that, without further restriction, the system $(M_n(F), \cdot)$ does not constitute a group. The obvious thing to do is to consider only those matrices having multiplicative inverses, so that the object of interest becomes the group of invertible elements of $(M_n(F), +, \cdot)$.

Theorem 4–6. If $M_n^*(F)$ denotes the set of nonsingular matrices of order n, then the pair $(M_n^*(F), \cdot)$ forms a group.

By further limiting the set of matrices under consideration, one can obviously obtain more specialized results, as is evidenced by the next two examples.

Example 4–3. Consider the set S of all matrices in $M_2(F)$ of the form

$$\begin{pmatrix} a & b \\ -b & a \end{pmatrix}, \qquad a, b \in F.$$

We propose to show that the system $(S, +, \cdot)$ is a field. If the matrices

$$\begin{pmatrix} a & b \\ -b & a \end{pmatrix} \qquad \text{and} \qquad \begin{pmatrix} c & d \\ -d & c \end{pmatrix}$$

are arbitrary elements of S, then

$$\begin{pmatrix} a & b \\ -b & a \end{pmatrix} - \begin{pmatrix} c & d \\ -d & c \end{pmatrix} = \begin{pmatrix} a - c & b - d \\ -(b - d) & a - c \end{pmatrix} \in S,$$

$$\begin{pmatrix} a & b \\ -b & a \end{pmatrix} \cdot \begin{pmatrix} c & d \\ -d & c \end{pmatrix} = \begin{pmatrix} a \cdot c - b \cdot d & a \cdot d + b \cdot c \\ -(a \cdot d + b \cdot c) & a \cdot c - d \cdot d \end{pmatrix} \in S.$$

Consequently, S is closed under both differences and products. This makes $(S, +, \cdot)$ a subring of $(M_2(F), +, \cdot)$, the ring of square matrices of order 2. It is easily checked that the elements of S commute under matrix multiplication. Since the 2×2 identity matrix I_2 is plainly a member of S, the triple $(S, +, \cdot)$ thus forms a commutative ring with identity. All that remains is to establish that each nonzero element of S has a multiplicative inverse in S.

Now if

$$\begin{pmatrix} a & b \\ -b & a \end{pmatrix} \neq \begin{pmatrix} 0 & 0 \\ 0 & 0 \end{pmatrix},$$

either $a \neq 0$ or $b \neq 0$, so that $a^2 + b^2 \neq 0$. Accordingly, $(a^2 + b^2)^{-1}$ exists and, as a direct computation will show,

$$\begin{pmatrix} a & b \\ -b & a \end{pmatrix}^{-1} = (a^2 + b^2)^{-1} \begin{pmatrix} a & -b \\ b & a \end{pmatrix} \in S.$$

An interesting observation is that the additive groups $(S, +)$ and $(V_2(F), +)$ are isomorphic under the mapping $f \colon S \to V_2(F)$ given by

$$f\begin{pmatrix} a & b \\ -b & a \end{pmatrix} = (a, b).$$

This function is obviously a homomorphism, for

$$f\left[\begin{pmatrix} a & b \\ -b & a \end{pmatrix} + \begin{pmatrix} c & d \\ -d & c \end{pmatrix} \right] = f\begin{pmatrix} a+c & b+d \\ -(b+d) & a+c \end{pmatrix}$$

$$= (a+c, b+d)$$

$$= (a, b) + (c, d)$$

$$= f\begin{pmatrix} a & b \\ -b & a \end{pmatrix} + f\begin{pmatrix} c & d \\ -d & c \end{pmatrix}.$$

Moreover, if

$$f\begin{pmatrix} a & b \\ -b & a \end{pmatrix} = f\begin{pmatrix} c & d \\ -d & c \end{pmatrix},$$

then from the definition of equality of the vectors (a, b) and (c, d), we must have $a = c$, $b = d$. This implies that

$$\begin{pmatrix} a & b \\ -b & a \end{pmatrix} = \begin{pmatrix} c & d \\ -d & c \end{pmatrix},$$

so f is a one-to-one mapping. It is clearly onto $V_2(F)$, hence $(S, +) \simeq (V_2(F), +)$.

Example 4–4. Let the set T consist of all real matrices of order two having equal integral entries. A routine argument, which we omit, shows the triple $(T, +, \cdot)$ to be a subring of the ring $(M_2(R^\#), +, \cdot)$. Hereafter, a matrix

$$\begin{pmatrix} n & n \\ n & n \end{pmatrix}, \qquad n \in Z,$$

in T will be denoted simply by (n); while this is an incorrect notation, it is much less unwieldly than the correct one.

What we wish to show here is that the mapping $f\colon T \to Z_e$ defined by $f((n)) = 2n$ yields an isomorphism between $(T, +, \cdot)$ and $(Z_e, +, \cdot)$, the ring of even integers. The demonstration that f preserves addition is straightforward, so we shall consider only multiplication: for $n,\, m \in Z$,

$$f((n) \cdot (m)) = f((2nm)) = 4nm = 2n \cdot 2m = f((n)) \cdot f((m)).$$

Thus, the function f is a (ring) homomorphism, and is evidently one-to-one. Next, let m be an arbitrary even integer, so that $m = 2n$ for some $n \in Z$; then, by the manner in which f was defined, $f((n)) = m$. This shows that $f(T) = Z_e$ and indeed $(T, +, \cdot) \simeq (Z_e, +, \cdot)$ via f.

PROBLEMS

1. Determine the values of a and b for which the following matrix equation holds:

$$\begin{pmatrix} 3 & 0 \\ 1 & 1 \\ 5 & 2 \end{pmatrix} \cdot \begin{pmatrix} 4 & 7 \\ 6 & 8 \end{pmatrix} + 2 \begin{pmatrix} a & -3 \\ 0 & 5 \\ 4 & b \end{pmatrix} = \begin{pmatrix} 20 & 15 \\ 10 & 25 \\ 40 & 25 \end{pmatrix}.$$

2. Compute $A \cdot B$, A^2, $B \cdot C$, $C \cdot A$, and $C \cdot B$ for the matrices

$$A = \begin{pmatrix} 0 & 1 & -1 \\ 0 & 0 & 1 \\ 1 & 0 & -1 \end{pmatrix}, \qquad B = \begin{pmatrix} 1 & 2 \\ 3 & 4 \\ 5 & 6 \end{pmatrix}, \qquad C = \begin{pmatrix} 3 & 0 & -1 \\ 4 & -5 & 1 \end{pmatrix}.$$

3. Show that each of the following matrices from $M_2(R^{\#})$ is a solution of the matrix equation $X^2 - 5X + 4I = O$:

$$\begin{pmatrix} 1 & 0 \\ 0 & 1 \end{pmatrix}, \qquad \begin{pmatrix} 4 & 0 \\ 0 & 4 \end{pmatrix}, \qquad \text{and} \qquad \begin{pmatrix} 3 & -2 \\ -1 & 2 \end{pmatrix}.$$

4. a) Find a matrix in $M_2(R^{\#})$ whose square is the matrix

$$\begin{pmatrix} 3 & -4 \\ 1 & -1 \end{pmatrix}.$$

   b) Obtain all matrices that commute with

$$\begin{pmatrix} 1 & 2 \\ 0 & 2 \end{pmatrix}.$$

5. Let G be the set of all elements from $M_2(F)$ of the form

$$\begin{pmatrix} a & b \\ 0 & a^{-1} \end{pmatrix}, \qquad a \neq 0.$$

   a) Show that the pair $(G, \cdot)$ is a group, where $\cdot$ indicates matrix multiplication.
   b) Suppose H and K denote the sets of matrices of the type

$$\begin{pmatrix} a & a - a^{-1} \\ 0 & a^{-1} \end{pmatrix} \quad \text{and} \quad \begin{pmatrix} 1 & b \\ 0 & 1 \end{pmatrix}$$

   respectively. Prove that $(H, \cdot)$ is a subgroup of the group $(G, \cdot)$, while $(K, \cdot)$ is a normal subgroup of $(G, \cdot)$.

6. Given the matrix $(a_{ij}) \in M_{mn}(F)$ and $r, s \in F$, prove that
   a) $(r + s)I_n = rI_n + sI_n$,   b) $(r \cdot s)I_n = (rI_n) \cdot (sI_n)$,
   c) $I_m \cdot (a_{ij}) = (a_{ij}) \cdot I_n = (a_{ij})$.

7. Let the set G consist of the six 3×3 matrices

$$\begin{pmatrix} 1 & 0 & 0 \\ 0 & 1 & 0 \\ 0 & 0 & 1 \end{pmatrix}, \quad \begin{pmatrix} 1 & 0 & 0 \\ 0 & 0 & 1 \\ 0 & 1 & 0 \end{pmatrix}, \quad \begin{pmatrix} 0 & 1 & 0 \\ 0 & 0 & 1 \\ 1 & 0 & 0 \end{pmatrix},$$

$$\begin{pmatrix} 0 & 1 & 0 \\ 1 & 0 & 0 \\ 0 & 0 & 1 \end{pmatrix}, \quad \begin{pmatrix} 0 & 0 & 1 \\ 1 & 0 & 0 \\ 0 & 1 & 0 \end{pmatrix}, \quad \begin{pmatrix} 0 & 0 & 1 \\ 0 & 1 & 0 \\ 1 & 0 & 0 \end{pmatrix}.$$

   Establish that the pair $(G, \cdot)$ forms a group isomorphic to $(S_3, \circ)$, the symmetric group on 3 symbols.

8. Consider sets G and H consisting of all matrices from $M_3(F)$ of the form

$$\begin{pmatrix} 1 & a & b \\ 0 & 1 & c \\ 0 & 0 & 1 \end{pmatrix} \quad \text{and} \quad \begin{pmatrix} 1 & 0 & b \\ 0 & 1 & 0 \\ 0 & 0 & 1 \end{pmatrix}$$

   respectively. Verify that the pair $(G, \cdot)$ is a group and that $(H, \cdot)$ forms a normal subgroup of $(G, \cdot)$.

9. In quantum mechanics, the Pauli theory of electron spin utilizes the following complex matrices:

$$\begin{pmatrix} 1 & 0 \\ 0 & 1 \end{pmatrix}, \quad \begin{pmatrix} -i & 0 \\ 0 & 1 \end{pmatrix}, \quad \begin{pmatrix} 0 & 1 \\ -1 & 0 \end{pmatrix}, \quad \begin{pmatrix} 0 & -i \\ -i & 0 \end{pmatrix},$$

$$\begin{pmatrix} -1 & 0 \\ 0 & -1 \end{pmatrix}, \quad \begin{pmatrix} -i & 0 \\ 0 & -1 \end{pmatrix}, \quad \begin{pmatrix} 0 & -1 \\ 1 & 0 \end{pmatrix}, \quad \begin{pmatrix} 0 & i \\ i & 0 \end{pmatrix},$$

where, of course, $i^2 = -1$. Prove that the Pauli matrices, together with matrix multiplication, consititute a group.

10. A square matrix (a_{ij}) is said to be *diagonal* if $a_{ij} = 0$ for $i \neq j$; in other words, $(a_{ij}) = (a_i \delta_{ij})$. Assuming diag $M_n(F)$ denotes the set of all diagonal matrices of order n, prove that the triple $(\text{diag } M_n(F), +, \cdot)$ forms a commutative subring of $(M_n(F), +, \cdot)$.

11. By a *scalar matrix* is meant any diagonal matrix (a_{ij}) having equal diagonal elements: $(a_{ij}) = (a\delta_{ij})$. If $S_n(F)$ is the set of scalar matrices of order n over the field $(F, +, \cdot)$, show that
    a) the triple $(S_n(F), +, \cdot)$ is a field isomorphic to $(F, +, \cdot)$,
    b) $S_n(F) = \text{cent } M_n(F)$. [*Hint:* Consider the products $(a_{ij}) \cdot E_{st} = E_{st} \cdot (a_{ij})$.]

12. If $M_n^*(F)$ designates the set of nonsingular matrices of order n, verify that the triple $(M_n^*(F), +, \cdot)$ does not form a subring of the ring $(M_n(F), +, \cdot)$.

13. A square matrix (a_{ij}) is *upper triangular* if $a_{ij} = 0$ for $i > j$ and *strictly upper triangular* if $a_{ij} = 0$ for $i \geq j$. Let $T_n(F)$ and $T_n^\delta(F)$ denote the sets of all upper triangular and strictly upper triangular matrices of order n, respectively. Prove the following:
    a) A matrix $(a_{ij}) \in T_n(F)$ is nonsingular if and only if $a_{ii} \neq 0$ for $i = 1, 2, \ldots, n$.
    b) The triple $(T_n(F), +, \cdot)$ is a subring of the ring $(M_n(F), +, \cdot)$.
    c) Each matrix $(a_{ij}) \in T_n^\delta(F)$ is nilpotent; in particular, $(a_{ij})^n = O$.
    d) $(T_n^\delta(F), +, \cdot)$ is an ideal of the ring $(T_n(F), +, \cdot)$.

14. The *transpose* of a matrix (a_{ij}), designated by $(a_{ij})^t$, is the matrix whose ijth entry is the jith entry of (a_{ij}), that is, $(a_{ij})^t = (a_{ji})$. Given matrices $(a_{ij}), (b_{ij}) \in M_n(F)$, verify that
    a) $(a_{ij})^{tt} = (a_{ij})$,   b) $[r(a_{ij}) + s(b_{ij})]^t = r(a_{ij})^t + s(b_{ij})^t$, $r, s \in F$,
    c) $[(a_{ij}) \cdot (b_{ij})]^t = (b_{ij})^t \cdot (a_{ij})^t$,
    d) whenever (a_{ij}) is nonsingular, so also is $(a_{ij})^t$, with $[(a_{ij})^t]^{-1} = [(a_{ij})^{-1}]^t$.

15. Show that the field $(S, +, \cdot)$ of Example 4–3 is isomorphic to the complex numbers $(C, +, \cdot)$ under the mapping

$$f\begin{pmatrix} a & b \\ -b & a \end{pmatrix} = (a, b).$$

16. In the ring $(M_2(C), +, \cdot)$, let D be the set of all matrices having the form

$$\begin{pmatrix} a & b \\ -\bar{b} & \bar{a} \end{pmatrix},$$

where $\bar{a}$ is the complex conjugate of a. Prove that the triple $(D, +, \cdot)$ is a division ring, but not a field.

17. Show that for any element $a \in F$, the following matrices are both idempotents in $(M_2(F), +, \cdot)$:

$$\begin{pmatrix} 1 & 0 \\ a & 0 \end{pmatrix} \quad \text{and} \quad \begin{pmatrix} 0 & 0 \\ -a & 1 \end{pmatrix}.$$

18. A matrix $(a_{ij}) \in M_n(F)$ is said to be *symmetric* if $(a_{ij})^t = (a_{ij})$ and *skew-symmetric* if $(a_{ij})^t = -(a_{ij})$. Establish the following assertions:
   a) If (a_{ij}) and (b_{ij}) are symmetric matrices, so also is $r(a_{ij}) + s(b_{ij})$.
   b) The products $(a_{ij}) \cdot (a_{ij})^t$ and $(a_{ij})^t \cdot (a_{ij})$ are both symmetric.
   c) If (a_{ij}) and (b_{ij}) are symmetric, then $(a_{ij}) \cdot (b_{ij})$ is a symmetric matrix if and only if $(a_{ij}) \cdot (b_{ij}) = (b_{ij}) \cdot (a_{ij})$.
   d) The diagonal elements of a skew-symmetric matrix are all zero.
   e) Every (square) matrix can be written as the sum of a symmetric and skew-symmetric matrix.

19. Let the set G be comprised of the following matrices:

$$I = \begin{pmatrix} 1 & 0 \\ 0 & 1 \end{pmatrix}, \qquad S = \begin{pmatrix} 0 & 1 \\ -1 & 0 \end{pmatrix}, \qquad T = \begin{pmatrix} -1 & 0 \\ 0 & -1 \end{pmatrix},$$

$$U = \begin{pmatrix} 0 & -1 \\ 1 & 0 \end{pmatrix}, \qquad V = \begin{pmatrix} 1 & 0 \\ 0 & -1 \end{pmatrix}, \qquad W = \begin{pmatrix} 0 & 1 \\ 1 & 0 \end{pmatrix},$$

$$X = \begin{pmatrix} -1 & 0 \\ 0 & 1 \end{pmatrix}, \qquad Y = \begin{pmatrix} 0 & -1 \\ -1 & 0 \end{pmatrix}.$$

   a) Prove that the pair $(G, \cdot)$ forms a group.
   b) If $H = \{I, S, T, U\}$, show that $(H, \cdot)$ is a normal subgroup of $(G, \cdot)$ and find the cosets of H in G.

4-2 ELEMENTARY PROPERTIES OF VECTOR SPACES

We saw in the last section that the collection $M_n(F)$ of square matrices of order n over a field $(F, +, \cdot)$, together with the operations of matrix addition and multiplication, constitutes a ring. At the time, our third matrix operation, multiplication of a matrix by an element of F, seemed relatively unimportant—particularly, since it failed to be even a binary operation on $M_n(F)$. However, by abstracting the essential features of this operation, we now define a mathematical structure having the set $M_n(F)$ [more generally, the set $M_{mn}(F)$] under matrix addition and multiplication by a field element as a model. Basically, this is a matter of combining two different algebraic systems into a single entity known as a vector space.

Due to the availability of a number of excellent texts on the subject, there is no need for us to develop the theory of vector spaces in any great detail. Instead, our goal shall be to give a survey of some, but by no means all, of the main ideas. The pace will frequently be brisk and much is left to the reader.

Definition 4-10. A *vector space* (or *linear space*) over a field is an ordered triple $((V, +), (F, +, \cdot), \circ)$ consisting of

1) a commutative group $(V, +)$ whose elements are called *vectors*,
2) a field $(F, +, \cdot)$ whose elements are called *scalars*,

3) an operation ∘ of *scalar multiplication* connecting the group and field which satisfies the properties:

    a) for each $c \in F$ and $x \in V$, there is defined an element $c \circ x \in V$; that is, V is closed under left multiplication by scalars;

    b) $(c_1 + c_2) \circ x = (c_1 \circ x) + (c_2 \circ x)$;

    c) $(c_1 \cdot c_2) \circ x = c_1 \circ (c_2 \circ x)$;

    d) $c \circ (x + y) = (c \circ x) + (c \circ y)$;

    e) $1 \circ x = x$, where 1 is the field identity element.

While the addition symbol has been used in two contexts in the above definition, to designate the operation of the group and one of the operations of the field, no confusion should arise from this practice. It will always be clear in any given situation whether vectors or scalars are being added. When both vector addition and scalar multiplication are involved in an expression, we follow our usual understanding in omitting parentheses: multiplication takes precedence over addition.

In the sequel, a vector space over the field $(F, +, \cdot)$ will be denoted merely by $V(F)$, rather than the correct but cumbersome notation $((V, +), (F, +, \cdot), \circ)$. The convenience resulting from this convention more than outweighs its lack of precision. For further simplicity, we shall hereafter drop the ∘ and write cx for the product $c \circ x$.

It should be apparent that a vector space is markedly different from the previous systems we have discussed in that the products of scalar multiplication employ elements from both F and V. Part (3) of the definition relates the possible ways these products combine the operation $+$ of $(V, +)$ with $+$ and $\cdot$ of $(F, +, \cdot)$. Note also that the hypothesis $1x = x$ is quite essential; without it, every field and commutative group would yield a vector space under the trivial scalar multiplication $cx = 0$ for all $c \in F$, $x \in V$.

Before discussing the implications of the axioms of a vector space, let us give a selection of examples. The formal verification that each example described actually constitutes a vector space is left as an exercise.

Example 4–5. Let the commutative group be $(V_n(F), +)$, where $V_n(F)$ is the set of all n-component row vectors over an arbitrary field $(F, +, \cdot)$ and $+$ is the usual componentwise addition of vectors. For $c \in F$ and $(a_k) \in V_n(F)$, define scalar multiplication by

$$c(a_k) = (c \cdot a_k).$$

In view of the results of the last section, we thus obtain a vector space, which will henceforth be denoted simply by $V_n(F)$.

Example 4–6. If $M_{mn}(F)$ represents the collection of $m \times n$ matrices over $(F, +, \cdot)$ and $+$ is the operation of matrix addition, then $(M_{mn}(F), +)$ is a commutative group. A vector space results on defining scalar multiplication as in the previous example:

$$c(a_{ij}) = (c \cdot a_{ij}), \qquad (a_{ij}) \in M_{mn}(F), \qquad c \in F.$$

The particular vector space which arises when $m = n$ will, in the future, be indicated by $M_n(F)$.

Example 4–7. Given a field $(F, +, \cdot)$, take V to be all functions from an arbitrary set X into F. For f, $g \in V$ and $c \in F$, define the functions $f + g$ and cf by specifying their values at each point of X:

$$(f + g)(x) = f(x) + g(x),$$
$$(cf)(x) = c \cdot f(x), \qquad x \in X.$$

With vector addition and scalar multiplication so defined, we obtain a vector space $V(F)$.

Example 4–8. Let $(F, +, \cdot)$ be a field and $(F[x], +, \cdot)$ be the ring of polynomials in the indeterminant x with coefficients from F. The operations necessary to give $F[x]$ a vector space structure are the expected ones: if

$$p(x) = a_0 + a_1 x + a_2 x^2 + \cdots + a_n x^n$$

and

$$q(x) = b_0 + b_1 x + b_2 x^2 + \cdots + b_m x^m,$$

where $m \geq n$, then

$$p(x) + q(x) = (a_0 + b_0) + (a_1 + b_1)x + \cdots + (a_m + b_m)x^m,$$
$$cp(x) = (c \cdot a_0) + (c \cdot a_1)x + \cdots + (c \cdot a_n)x^n.$$

(Needless to say, in the sum $p(x) + q(x)$, we set $a_k = 0$ for $n + 1 \leq k \leq m$.) Let us retain the symbol $F[x]$ for this vector space, in preference to the correct but awkward $(F[x])(F)$.

Example 4–9. For any field $(F, +, \cdot)$, Example 4–5 may be generalized by using infinitely many elements of F: just take $V_\infty(F)$ to be the totality of all infinite sequences from F. The members of $V_\infty(F)$ may be conveniently identified with row vectors

$$(a_1, a_2, a_3, \ldots), \qquad a_k \in F,$$

having infinitely many components. In this case,

$$(a_1, a_2, a_3, \ldots) = (b_1, b_2, b_3, \ldots) \qquad \text{if and only if} \quad a_k = b_k \quad \text{for all} \quad k \in Z_+.$$

Vector addition and multiplication by a scalar $c \in F$ are performed component-wise:

$$(a_1, a_2, a_3, \ldots) + (b_1, b_2, b_3, \ldots) = (a_1 + b_1, a_2 + b_2, a_3 + b_3, \ldots),$$

$$c(a_1, a_2, a_3, \ldots) = (c \cdot a_1, c \cdot a_2, c \cdot a_3, \ldots).$$

Using these operations, $V_\infty(F)$ becomes a vector space over $(F, +, \cdot)$.

Example 4–10. As a final, and not quite so simple, example of a vector space, consider a commutative group $(V, +)$ in which every nonzero element has order p (p a prime); that is to say, $px = 0$ for all $x \in V$. If $[n] \in Z_p$ and $x \in V$, we take the product $[n]x$ to mean

$$[n]x = x + x + \cdots + x \qquad (n \text{ summands}).$$

With scalar multiplication defined in this way, $V(Z_p)$ may be regarded as a vector space over the field $(Z_p, +_p, \cdot_p)$.

A further comment on notation: To avoid a proliferation of symbols, 0 will be used to designate the zero element both of $(V, +)$ and of $(F, +, \cdot)$. The additive inverse of a scalar $c \in F$ is denoted by $-c$, while the inverse of a vector $x \in V$ is also represented by its negative, $-x$. These conventions should lead to no ambiguity if the reader attends closely to the context in which the notation is employed. For the sake of brevity, we shall frequently speak of a vector space over a field F when, in actual fact, we mean over a field $(F, +, \cdot)$.

Some immediate consequences of Definition 4–10 are embodied in our first theorem.

Theorem 4–7. If $V(F)$ is a vector space and $x \in V$, $c \in F$, then
1) $0x = 0$,
2) $c0 = 0$,
3) $-(cx) = (-c)x = c(-x)$.

Proof. To establish (1), we use the field result $0 + 1 = 1$. Then

$$0x + x = 0x + 1x = (0 + 1)x = 1x = x = 0 + x.$$

Since $(V, +)$ is a group, the cancellation law yields $0x = 0$.

The proof of the second part of the theorem follows from the group result $0 + x = x$. We have

$$c0 + cx = c(0 + x) = cx = 0 + cx.$$

Again the cancellation law gives the desired conclusion.

Finally, to obtain (3), observe that

$$0 = 0x = [c + (-c)]x = cx + (-c)x.$$

This means that $(-c)x = -(cx)$. Similarly,

$$0 = c0 = c[x + (-x)] = cx + c(-x),$$

which proves

$$c(-x) = -(cx).$$

As the reader should expect by now, a formal investigation of vector spaces involves consideration of such notions as subsystems, operation-preserving functions, quotient structures, etc. Following our standard pattern of presentation, we begin the study with the question of subsystems. In the case of vector spaces, the subvector spaces are customarily referred to as subspaces.

Definition 4–11. Let $V(F)$ be a vector space over the field F and $W \subseteq V$ with $W \neq \emptyset$. Then $W(F)$ is a *subspace* of $V(F)$ if, under the operations of $V(F)$, $W(F)$ is itself a vector space.

Since $W \subseteq V$, much of the algebraic structure of $W(F)$ is inherited from $V(F)$. The minimum conditions that $W(F)$ must satisfy to be subspace are:

1) $(W, +)$ is a subgroup of $(V, +)$;
2) W is closed under scalar multiplication.

The usual criterion for deciding whether $(W, +)$ is a subgroup of $(V, +)$ is to see if W is closed under differences. The second of the above conditions implies that $-x = (-1)\, x$ will belong to W whenever x is an element of W. Because $x - y = x + (-y)$, condition (2), together with the closure of W under addition, is sufficient to guarantee that W be closed under differences. This observation allows us to recast Definition 4–11 as follows:

Definition 4–12. $W(F)$ is a subspace of the vector space $V(F)$ if W is a nonempty subset of V such that

1) $x, y \in W$ implies $x + y \in W$,
2) $x \in W$ and $c \in F$ imply $cx \in W$.

Example 4–11. Every vector space $V(F)$ has two *trivial* subspaces, namely $V(F)$ itself and the zero subspace $\{0\}(F)$. Subspaces distinct from $V(F)$ are said to be *proper*.

Example 4–12. Consider the set W of vectors in $V_3(F)$ whose components add up to zero:

$$W = \{(a_1, a_2, a_3) \mid a_1 + a_2 + a_3 = 0\}.$$

If (a_1, a_2, a_3) and (b_1, b_2, b_3) are arbitrary elements of W, then their sum $(a_1 + b_1, a_2 + b_2, a_3 + b_3)$ is such that

$$(a_1 + b_1) + (a_2 + b_2) + (a_3 + b_3) = (a_1 + a_2 + a_3) + (b_1 + b_2 + b_3)$$
$$= 0 + 0 = 0.$$

This establishes the closure of W under addition. It is equally clear that W is closed under scalar multiplication, hence $W(F)$ is a subspace of $V(F)$.

Example 4–13. Let W denote the collection of all elements from the space $M_2(F)$ of the form

$$\begin{pmatrix} a & b \\ -b & a \end{pmatrix}.$$

It follows immediately from the definition of the matrix operations in $M_2(F)$ that $W(F)$ is a subspace, for

$$\begin{pmatrix} a & b \\ -b & a \end{pmatrix} + \begin{pmatrix} c & d \\ -d & c \end{pmatrix} = \begin{pmatrix} a + c & b + d \\ -(b + d) & a + c \end{pmatrix} \in W,$$

$$k\begin{pmatrix} a & b \\ -b & a \end{pmatrix} = \begin{pmatrix} k \cdot a & k \cdot b \\ -(k \cdot b) & k \cdot a \end{pmatrix} \in W.$$

The two conditions of Definition 4–12 may be combined into a single easily applied criterion.

Theorem 4–8. $W(F)$ is a subspace of the vector space $V(F)$ if and only if $\emptyset \neq W \subseteq V$ and $cx + dy \in W$ whenever $x, y \in W$, $c, d \in F$.

Proof. If $W(F)$ is a subspace, then by definition W is nonempty and contains $cx + dy$ for all $x, y \in W$, $c, d \in F$. Conversely, if this condition holds, W must contain $1x + 1y = x + y$ and $cx + 0y = cx$ for every $x, y \in W$, $c \in F$. Accordingly, W is closed with respect to the vector space operations.

We next consider operations on the subspaces of a vector space that produce other subspaces, the most important of which are sum and intersection. If U and W are nonempty subsets of the vector space $V(F)$, their (linear) *sum* is defined to be the set

$$U + W = \{u + w \mid u \in U, w \in W\}.$$

The following simple, but quite useful, fact will be needed on several occasions.

Theorem 4–9. If $U(F)$ and $W(F)$ are subspaces of the vector space $V(F)$, then $(U + W)(F)$ is also a subspace.

Proof. The sum $U + W$ is plainly not empty, for U and W each contain the zero vector, hence $0 = 0 + 0 \in U + W$. Suppose x and y are arbitrary vectors in $U + W$. Then $x = u_1 + w_1$ and $y = u_2 + w_2$, where $u_i \in U$, $w_i \in W$. For scalars $c, d \in F$,

$$cx + dy = c(u_1 + w_1) + d(u_2 + w_2)$$
$$= (cu_1 + du_2) + (cw_1 + dw_2).$$

Since $U(F)$ and $W(F)$ are both subspaces of $V(F)$, it follows that $cu_1 + du_2 \in U$ and $cw_1 + dw_2 \in W$. Thus $cx + dy$ is again in $U + W$, implying that $(U + W)(F)$ is a subspace.

From our earlier work with other subsystems, one would expect the intersection of subspaces to be also a subspace and, indeed, this is the content of the next theorem. As it would be repetitious to present the details again, the proof is left to the reader.

Theorem 4–10. If $W_i(F)$ is an indexed collection of subspaces of the vector space $V(F)$, then $(\cap W_i)(F)$ is a subspace of $V(F)$.

In analogy with the corresponding ideas for groups and rings, this result provides an effective means for generating subspaces: Given a nonempty subset S of the vector space $V(F)$, we define

$$[S] = \cap\{W \mid S \subseteq W; \, W(F) \text{ is a subspace of } V(F)\}.$$

There is at least one subspace containing S, namely the whole space $V(F)$, so that $[S]$ certainly exists and is unique. We infer at once from Theorem 4–10 that $[S](F)$ is a subspace of $V(F)$, called the subspace *generated* or *spanned* by the set S. More important still, $[S](F)$ is the smallest subspace containing S, in the sense of being included in every subspace which contains S.

The coming theorem gives an alternative and more constructive description of $[S](F)$; before obtaining this, one more definition is required.

Definition 4–13. Suppose $V(F)$ is a vector space and $x_1, x_2, \ldots, x_n \in V$. Any finite sum of the form

$$c_1 x_1 + c_2 x_2 + \cdots + c_n x_n,$$

where each $c_i \in F$ is said to be a *linear combination* (over F) of the vectors $x_1, x_2, \ldots, x_n$. A linear combination is called *trivial* if all its coefficients $c_i = 0$ and *nontrivial* if at least one coefficient is different from zero.

Using this new terminology, Theorem 4–8 may be rephrased in another way: $W(F)$ is a subspace of the vector space $V(F)$ if and only if W is a nonempty subset of V which is closed under the formation of linear combinations.

For our present purposes, the significance of the notion of linear combinations stems from the next result.

Theorem 4–11. If S is a nonempty subset of the vector space $V(F)$, then $[S](F)$, the subspace generated by S, consists of all (finite) linear combinations of elements of S:

$$[S] = \left\{ \sum_{k=1}^{n} c_k x_k \mid c_k \in F, \, x_k \in S, \, n \in Z_+ \right\}.$$

Proof. For the moment, let us denote the set on the right by lin S. Evidently a linear combination of linear combinations of elements from S can again be written as a linear combination of members of S, so $(\text{lin } S)(F)$ is itself a subspace of $V(F)$. Moreover, for each $x \in S$, we have $x = 1x \in \text{lin } S$, hence $S \subseteq \text{lin } S$. As $[S](F)$ is the smallest subspace of $V(F)$ to contain S, it follows that $[S] \subseteq \text{lin } S$. On the other hand, since $[S](F)$ is a subspace containing S, it must contain all linear combinations of elements of S. Accordingly, the inclusion lin $S \subseteq [S]$ also holds and the proof is complete.

Example 4–14. Let S be the subset of $V_n(F)$ whose elements are the n vectors $e_1 = (1, 0, \ldots, 0)$, $e_2 = (0, 1, \ldots, 0)$, $\ldots$, $e_n = (0, 0, \ldots, 1)$; in general, e_k is the vector with 1 in the kth component position and 0 elsewhere:

$$e_k = (\delta_{1k}, \delta_{2k}, \ldots, \delta_{nk}), \qquad k = 1, 2, \ldots, n.$$

Here $[S](F)$, the subspace spanned by these vectors, is all of $V_n(F)$. Indeed, for any n-tuple $(a_1, a_2, \ldots, a_n)$ over F, we have

$$
\begin{aligned}
(a_1, a_2, \ldots, a_n) &= a_1(1, 0, \ldots, 0) + a_2(0, 1, \ldots, 0) + \cdots + a_n(0, 0, \ldots, 1) \\
&= a_1 e_1 + a_2 e_2 + \cdots + a_n e_n \in [S].
\end{aligned}
$$

Let us see what happens when we generalize this situation to the sequence space $V_\infty(F)$. In this context, e_k now denotes the infinite sequence whose kth term is 1, while all other terms are 0:

$$e_k = (\delta_{1k}, \delta_{2k}, \delta_{3k}, \ldots), \qquad k = 1, 2, \ldots$$

As before, let S be the set of all e_k. Recall that in forming the linear span $[S]$, only finite linear combinations of elements of S are utilized. It follows therefore that $[S](F)$ is not $V_\infty(F)$, but rather the (proper) subspace consisting of those vectors having only a finite number of nonzero entries:

$$[S] = \{(a_1, a_2, \ldots, a_n, 0, 0, \ldots) \mid a_k \in F, n \in Z_+\}.$$

The first part of this example serves to suggest, as well as to illustrate, the next definition.

Definition 4–14. A vector space $V(F)$ is *finitely generated* when it contains a finite subset which spans V; if V is spanned by the vectors $x_1, x_2, \ldots, x_n$, this will be indicated by writing $V = [x_1, x_2, \ldots, x_n]$.

The union of subspaces, unlike their intersection, is not necessarily a subspace. For instance, in the vector space $M_2(F)$, take U to be the subset consisting of all scalar matrices

$$\begin{pmatrix} a & 0 \\ 0 & a \end{pmatrix}, \qquad a \in F,$$

and W to be the set of all matrices of the form

$$\begin{pmatrix} 0 & b \\ -b & 0 \end{pmatrix}, \qquad b \in F.$$

That $U(F)$ and $W(F)$ are both subspaces of $M_2(F)$ is easily verified. Note, however, that while the matrices

$$\begin{pmatrix} 1 & 0 \\ 0 & 1 \end{pmatrix} \qquad \text{and} \qquad \begin{pmatrix} 0 & 1 \\ -1 & 0 \end{pmatrix}$$

belong to $U \cup W$, their sum

$$\begin{pmatrix} 1 & 0 \\ 0 & 1 \end{pmatrix} + \begin{pmatrix} 0 & 1 \\ -1 & 0 \end{pmatrix} = \begin{pmatrix} 1 & 1 \\ -1 & 1 \end{pmatrix}$$

fails to be a member of the union. From this, we conclude $(U \cup W)(F)$ is not a subspace of $M_2(F)$.

While the union of subspaces need not be a subspace, the subspace generated by the union always exists and equals the sum of the given subspaces. We now establish this fact.

Theorem 4–12. If $U(F)$ and $W(F)$ are subspaces of the vector space $V(F)$, then $(U + W)(F)$ is the smallest subspace containing both U and W; in symbols, $(U + W)(F) = [U \cup W](F)$.

Proof. Since $u + w = 1u + 1w$, any vector in $U + W$ can be expressed as a linear combination of elements from $U \cup W$. But Theorem 4–11 asserts that $[U \cup W]$ consists of all such linear combinations, hence $U + W \subseteq [U \cup W]$. For the opposite inclusion, observe that both $U \subseteq U + W$ and $W \subseteq U + W$, so their union $U \cup W \subseteq U + W$. In other words, $(U + W)(F)$ is a subspace of $V(F)$ which contains $U \cup W$. As $[U \cup W](F)$ is, by definition, the smallest subspace with this property, we conclude that $[U \cup W] \subseteq U + W$.

This characterization of the linear span of $U \cup W$ is usually much easier to apply in specific cases than the definition itself. In the space $M_2(F)$, for example, where U and W consist of matrices of the form

$$\begin{pmatrix} a & 0 \\ 0 & a \end{pmatrix} \qquad \text{and} \qquad \begin{pmatrix} 0 & b \\ -b & 0 \end{pmatrix}$$

respectively, we have

$$[U \cup W] = \left\{ \begin{pmatrix} a & b \\ -b & a \end{pmatrix} \,\middle|\, a, b \in F \right\}.$$

To see this, one need only observe that each of the matrices on the right can be written as

$$\begin{pmatrix} a & b \\ -b & a \end{pmatrix} = \begin{pmatrix} a & 0 \\ 0 & a \end{pmatrix} + \begin{pmatrix} 0 & b \\ -b & 0 \end{pmatrix} \in U + W.$$

Although each vector x belonging to the sum $U + W$ admits a representation $x = u + w$ with $u \in U$ and $w \in W$, this expression is generally not unique. The next theorem provides a necessary and sufficient condition for u and w to be uniquely determined by the vector x.

Theorem 4–13. Let $U(F)$ and $W(F)$ be two subspaces of the vector space $V(F)$. Then the following conditions are equivalent:

1) $U \cap W = \{0\}$.
2) Every vector x of the sum $U + W$ is uniquely representable in the form $x = u + w$, where $u \in U$, $w \in W$.

Proof. We begin by assuming that $U \cap W = \{0\}$. Suppose further that a vector $x \in U + W$ has two representations

$$x = u_1 + w_1 = u_2 + w_2, \qquad u_i \in U, \quad w_i \in W.$$

Then $u_1 - u_2 = w_2 - w_1$. But the left side is in U and the right side is in W, so both sides belong to $U \cap W$. It follows therefore that

$$u_1 - u_2 = w_2 - w_1 = 0 \qquad \text{or} \qquad u_1 = u_2, \quad w_1 = w_2.$$

In other words, x is uniquely expressible in the form $u + w$.

Conversely, assume statement (2) holds and the vector $z \in U \cap W$. We may then express z in two different ways as the sum of a vector in U and a vector in W, namely $z = z + 0$ (here $z \in U$ and $0 \in W$) and $z = 0 + z$ (here $0 \in U$ and $z \in W$). The uniqueness assumption of condition (2) then implies $z = 0$ or, rather, $U \cap W = \{0\}$.

Two comments on Theorem 4–13 are in order. First, even though the intersection of U and W is not empty, we sometimes express condition (1) by referring to the subspaces $U(F)$ and $W(F)$ as *disjoint*; needless to say, U and W can never be disjoint in the set-theoretic sense, for every subspace must contain the zero vector. Secondly, statement (2) assumes, unnecessarily, that each vector of $U + W$ must have a unique representation. This condition could be replaced by the weaker requirement that only the zero vector is uniquely representable. For suppose a vector $x \in U + W$ has two decompositions

$$x = u_1 + w_1 = u_2 + w_2, \qquad u_i \in U, \quad w_i \in W.$$

Subtracting, we obtain

$$(u_1 - u_2) + (w_1 - w_2) = 0 = 0 + 0,$$

where the differences $u_1 - u_2$, $w_1 - w_2$ lie in U and W, respectively. The assumption that the zero vector can be expressed in only one way as a member of $U + W$ would force $u_1 - u_2 = 0$, $w_1 - w_2 = 0$ or $u_1 = u_2$, $w_1 = w_2$.

When the equivalent conditions of Theorem 4–13 are satisfied, the sum $U + W$ is called *direct* and symbolized by writing $U \oplus W$. If $U \oplus W = V$, we say each of the subspaces $U(F)$ and $W(F)$ is complementary [in $V(F)$] to the other. This concept is of sufficient importance to rate a formal definition.

Definition 4–15. Two subspaces $U(F)$ and $W(F)$ of the vector space $V(F)$ are *complementary* if $U \cap W = \{0\}$ and $U + W = V$.

Our next theorem is included for completeness; it is an immediate consequence of Theorem 4–13 and needs no further justification.

Theorem 4–14. Let $U(F)$ and $W(F)$ be two subspaces of the vector space $V(F)$. Every vector $x \in V$ is uniquely expressible in the form $x = u + w$, with $u \in U$, $w \in W$, if and only if $U(F)$ and $W(F)$ are complementary subspaces.

We should call attention to the fact that a given subspace may possess several complementary subspaces. In the case of $V_2(F)$, for example, take

$$U = \{(a, 0) \mid a \in F\}, \qquad W = \{(0, a) \mid a \in F\}, \qquad W' = \{(a, a) \mid a \in F\}.$$

It is not difficult to establish that the subspaces $W(F)$ and $W'(F)$ are both complementary to $U(F)$.

What is quite significant is that every subspace has complementary subspaces, which, to be sure, are not necessarily unique. For the proof of this assertion, we resort to the powerful tool of Zorn's Lemma (see p. 185).

Theorem 4–15. Every subspace $W(F)$ of the vector space $V(F)$ has a complementary subspace.

Proof. Define a family of subsets of V by taking

$$\mathfrak{F} = \{S \mid S \cap W = \{0\} ; S(F) \text{ is a subspace of } V(F)\}.$$

This family is nonempty for, trivially, the set $\{0\}$ satisfies the defining properties.

Now, consider any chain $\{S_i\}$ in $\mathfrak{F}$. Our object, of course, is to show that $\cup S_i$ is again a member of $\mathfrak{F}$. To achieve this, let $x, y \in \cup S_i$ and $c, d \in F$. Then there exist indices i and j for which $x \in S_i$, $y \in S_j$. Because the collection $\{S_i\}$ forms a chain, either $S_i \subseteq S_j$ or else $S_j \subseteq S_i$; say, $S_i \subseteq S_j$, so that both $x, y \in S_j$. Since $S_j(F)$ is a subspace of $V(F)$, we must then have $cx + dy \in S_j \subseteq \cup S_i$. This proves that $(\cup S_i)(F)$ forms a subspace of $V(F)$. Moreover,

$$(\cup S_i) \cap W = \cup(S_i \cap W) = \{0\},$$

whence the union $\cup S_i$ lies in $\mathfrak{F}$.

Thus, on the basis of Zorn's Lemma, the family $\mathfrak{F}$ contains a maximal element U. Our contention is that the subspace $U(F)$ is complementary to $W(F)$. In order to establish this, it suffices merely to show that $U + W = V$. To the contrary, suppose there is some vector $x \in V$ with $x \notin U + W$. But then $[U, x](F)$, the subspace generated by U and x, will be disjoint from $W(F)$, in the sense that $[U, x] \cap W = \{0\}$. (Verify this!) Since U is a proper subset of $[U, x]$, we have arrived at the contradiction to the maximality of U in $\mathfrak{F}$. Accordingly, $V = U + W$, and the proof is complete.

The foregoing ideas are easily generalized to finitely many subspaces: If $W_1(F)$, $W_2(F)$, ..., $W_n(F)$ are each subspaces of $V(F)$, their sum is defined exactly as for two subspaces,

$$W_1 + W_2 + \cdots + W_n = \{w_1 + w_2 + \cdots + w_n \mid w_i \in W_i\}.$$

This may be denoted more compactly by $\sum W_i$. As in Theorem 4–9, we can prove that $(\sum W_i)(F)$ is a subspace of $V(F)$.

The vector space $V(F)$ is said to be the *direct sum* of $W_1(F)$, ..., $W_n(F)$, symbolized by

$$V = W_1 \oplus W_2 \oplus \cdots \oplus W_n$$

if and only if $V = W_1 + W_2 + \cdots + W_n$ and $W_k \cap (\sum_{i \neq k} W_i) = \{0\}$. In this case too, every vector $x \in V$ has a unique representation

$$x = w_1 + w_2 + \cdots + w_n$$

with $w_i \in W$ $(i = 1, 2, \ldots, n)$.

The concept of a quotient structure carries over to vector spaces as expected. In the present context, we encounter one slight, but highly important difference. When forming quotient groups and quotient rings, it was necessary to introduce special subsystems (namely, normal subgroups, and ideals) in order to ensure that the operations of the quotient structure were well-defined. For vector spaces, no such distinguished subsystem need be defined.

To be more concrete, let $W(F)$ be an arbitrary subspace of the vector space $V(F)$. Since $(W, +)$ is a subgroup of the commutative group $(V, +)$, we may form the quotient group $(V/W, +)$. The elements of this group are just the cosets $x + W$, with coset addition given by

$$(x + W) + (y + W) = x + y + W.$$

To equip V/W with the structure of a vector space, a notion of multiplication by scalars is introduced by taking

$$c(x + W) = cx + W, \qquad c \in F.$$

As usual, we must first satisfy ourselves that scalar multiplication is unambiguously defined, depending only on the coset $x + W$ and scalar $c \in F$.

This amounts to showing that whenever $x + W = x' + W$, then $cx + W = cx' + W$. Our aim would obviously be achieved if we knew that

$$cx - cx' = c(x - x') \in W.$$

But this follows directly from the fact that $x - x' \in W$ and that $W(F)$ is assumed to be a subspace, hence closed under multiplication by scalars. Thus scalar multiplication in V/W is independent of coset representatives.

It can easily be checked that $(V/W)(F)$, with the operations so defined, forms a vector space over the field F. Since the pattern of proof is by now familiar, we omit the formal details.

These ideas may be conveniently summarized in the following theorem.

Theorem 4–16. Let $W(F)$ be a subspace of the vector space $V(F)$ and the cosets $x + W$, $y + W$ belong to V/W. If vector addition and scalar multiplication are given by

$$(x + W) + (y + W) = x + y + W,$$

$$c(x + W) = cx + W, \qquad (c \in F),$$

then $(V/W)(F)$ is itself a vector space, known as the *quotient space* of V by W.

Example 4–15. For a concrete example, consider the quotient space $(V_3/W)(R^{\#})$, where

$$W = \{(w, 0, 0) \mid w \in R^{\#}\}.$$

In the situation at hand, the cosets of W in $V_3(R^{\#})$ take the form

$$(x, y, z) + W = \{(x + w, y, z) \mid w \in R^{\#}\}.$$

The subspace $W(R^{\#})$ may be viewed, geometrically, as the x-axis and the coset $(x, y, z) + W$ as a line through the point (x, y, z) parallel to this axis. The elements of V_3/W would therefore consist of all lines parallel to the x-axis. Since such lines may be identified in one-to-one fashion with the points in the yz-plane, and these points in turn correspond to ordered pairs of real numbers, we associate $(V_3/W)(R^{\#})$ with the vector space $V_2(R^{\#})$; that is, we can define a map $f : V_3/W \to V_2$ by $f((x, y, z) + W) = (y, z)$. The notions involved will be formalized shortly.

PROBLEMS

In the exercises below, the symbol F denotes an arbitrary field.

1. If $V(F)$ is a vector space, establish that

$$n(cx) = (nc)x = c(nx)$$

for all $x \in V$, $c \in F$, and $n \in Z$.

2. Prove that in any vector space $V(F)$, if x, $y \in V$ and $c \in F$, then
   a) $c(x - y) = cx - cy$,
   b) $cx = 0$ implies either $c = 0$ or $x = 0$.

3. In any vector space $V(F)$, show that the following cancellation laws hold:
   a) If $x \in V$ with $x \neq 0$, then $c_1 x = c_2 x$ implies $c_1 = c_2$.
   b) If x, y are nonzero elements of V, then $cx = cy$ with $c \neq 0$ implies $x = y$.

4. Prove that $W(F)$ is a subspace of the vector space $V(F)$ if and only if $\emptyset \neq W \subseteq V$ and $ax + y \in W$ for all x, $y \in W$, $a \in F$.

5. For each of the following sets W, determine whether $W(R^{\#})$ is a subspace of the vector space $V_n(R^{\#})$.
   a) $W = \{(a_1, a_2, \ldots, a_n) \mid a_1 + a_2 + \cdots + a_n \neq 0\}$
   b) $W = \{(a_1, a_2, \ldots, a_n) \mid a_1 = a_2 = \cdots = a_n\}$
   c) $W = \{(a_1, a_2, \ldots, a_n) \mid a_1 a_2 = 0\}$
   d) $W = \{(a_1, a_2, \ldots, a_n) \mid a_k \in Z \text{ for all } k\}$

6. Let $U(F)$ and $W(F)$ be subspaces of the vector space $V(F)$. Prove that $(U \cup W)(F)$ forms a subspace of $V(F)$ if and only if $U \subseteq W$ or $W \subseteq U$.

7. Determine whether $W(F)$ is a subspace of the indicated vector space:
   a) $V_3(F)$; for fixed scalars a_1, a_2, $a_3 \in F$,

   $$W = \{(x_1, x_2, x_3) \mid a_1 x_1 + a_2 x_2 + a_3 x_3 = 0\}.$$

   b) $V_\infty(F)$; W consists of sequences where all but a finite number of the terms are equal to zero, that is,

   $$W = \{(a_1, \ldots, a_n, 0, 0, \ldots) \mid a_k \in F, \, n \in Z_+\}.$$

   c) $F[x]$; W consists of all polynomials of degree greater than 4.
   d) $V_n(F)$; for a fixed $n \times n$ matrix (a_{ij}),

   $$W = \{x \in V_n(F) \mid (a_{ij})x = 0\}.$$

   e) $M_3(F)$; W consists of all matrices of the form

   $$\begin{pmatrix} a & b & 0 \\ 0 & a+b & 0 \\ 0 & 0 & b \end{pmatrix}, \quad a, b \in F.$$

   f) $M_n(F)$; W consists of all upper triangular matrices of order n.

8. Find all of the subspaces of $V_2(Z_3)$ and $V_3(Z_2)$.

9. Suppose $U(F)$, $W(F)$, $Y(F)$ are subspaces of the vector space $V(F)$. Prove that
   a) if $U \subseteq Y$, $W \subseteq Y$, then $U + W \subseteq Y$,
   b) $(U \cap Y) + (W \cap Y) \subseteq (U + W) \cap Y$,
   c) if $U \subseteq Y$, then $U + (W \cap Y) = (U + W) \cap Y$.

10. Let $V(R^{\#})$ be the vector space of real-valued functions on the interval $[a, b]$ under pointwise addition and multiplication by a real number.

a) If W is the set of all functions f in V such that $f(a) = 0$, is $W(R^{\#})$ a subspace of $V(R^{\#})$?

b) If W is the set of all functions f in V for which $f(a) = f(b)$, is $W(R^{\#})$ a subspace of $V(R^{\#})$?

11. In $V(Z_3)$, determine all of the vectors in the subspace spanned by two vectors $x_1, x_2 \in V$.

12. If $V(F)$ is a vector space over F, and S, T nonempty subsets of V, establish that

a) $S \subseteq T$ implies $[S] \subseteq [T]$,

b) $[S \cup T] = [S] + [T]$,

c) $[[S]] = [S]$,

d) $S \subseteq [T]$ implies $[S] \subseteq [T]$.

13. In the vector space $V_3(F)$, define the subsets U and W by

$$U = \{(a, b, a + b) \mid a, b \in F\}, \qquad W = \{(c, c, c) \mid c \in F\}.$$

Verify that $V_3(F)$ is the direct sum of the subspaces $U(F)$ and $W(F)$, that is, $V_3 = U \oplus W$.

14. Let $V(R^{\#})$ be the vector space of all functions from $R^{\#}$ into itself and

$$U = \{f \in V \mid f(-x) = f(x)\}, \qquad W = \{f \in V \mid f(-x) = -f(x)\}.$$

Prove that $V = U \oplus W$.

4-3 BASES AND DIMENSION

Perhaps the most far reaching notion in the study of vector spaces and the principal theme of this section is that of a basis. As will soon be evident, this concept is precisely the tool needed to formalize the more or less intuitive idea of what is meant by the dimension of a space. A convenient starting point is the following definition.

Definition 4-16. Let $V(F)$ be a vector space over the field F. A finite set $\{x_1, x_2, \ldots, x_n\}$ of vectors from V is said to be *linearly dependent* (over F) if the zero vector is a nontrivial linear combination of $x_1, x_2, \ldots, x_n$; otherwise, the set $\{x_1, x_2, \ldots, x_n\}$ is termed *linearly independent*.

According to our definition, $\{x_1, x_2, \ldots, x_n\}$ is a linearly dependent set if and only if there exist scalars $c_1, c_2, \ldots, c_n \in F$, not all of which are zero, such that

$$c_1 x_1 + c_2 x_2 + \cdots + c_n x_n = 0.$$

In the contrary case, the zero vector is expressible as a linear combination of independent vectors in only the trivial way where all the coefficients are zero; that is to say, $c_1 x_1 + c_2 x_2 + \cdots + c_n x_n = 0$ implies

$$c_1 = c_2 = \cdots = c_n = 0.$$

While linear dependence and independence are properties of sets of vectors, these terms are frequently applied to the vectors themselves. Thus, we shall speak of $x_1, x_2, \ldots, x_n$ being linearly dependent or independent according as the set $\{x_1, x_2, \ldots, x_n\}$ is dependent or independent.

Two examples should help to clarify matters.

Example 4–16. In $R^{\#}[x]$, the vector space of polynomials in x over $R^{\#}$, consider the three polynomials

$$1 + x + 2x^2, \qquad 2 - x + x^2, \qquad -4 + 5x + x^2$$

of degree two. Since

$$2(1 + x + 2x^2) + (-3)(2 - x + x^2) + (-1)(-4 + 5x + x^2) = 0,$$

the given polynomials are linearly dependent.

Example 4–17. The so-called *unit vectors* $e_1, e_2, \ldots, e_n$, where

$$e_k = (\delta_{1k}, \delta_{2k}, \ldots, \delta_{nk}), \qquad k = 1, 2, \ldots, n,$$

form a linearly independent subset of $V_n(F)$. In this case,

$$c_1 e_1 + c_2 e_2 + \cdots + c_n e_n = (c_1, 0, \ldots, 0) + (0, c_2, \ldots, 0) + \cdots + (0, 0, \ldots, c_n)$$
$$= (c_1, c_2, \ldots, c_n);$$

hence the condition $\sum_{k=1}^{n} c_k e_k = (0, 0, \ldots, 0)$ implies $c_1 = c_2 = \cdots = c_n = 0$.

The essence of this concept lies in the fact that if $\{x_1, x_2, \ldots, x_n\}$ is a linearly independent set, then any vector $x \in [x_1, x_2, \ldots, x_n]$ is uniquely expressible as a linear combination of the x_k's. Indeed, suppose there are two such representations,

$$x = b_1 x_1 + b_2 x_2 + \cdots + b_n x_n = c_1 x_1 + c_2 x_2 + \cdots + c_n x_n;$$

this leads to the relation

$$(b_1 - c_1)x_1 + (b_2 - c_2)x_2 + \cdots + (b_n - c_n)x_n = 0.$$

The hypothesized linear independence of the vectors $x_1, x_2, \ldots, x_n$ then forces

$$b_k - c_k = 0 \qquad \text{or} \qquad b_k = c_k \qquad \text{for all } k.$$

Definition 4–16, as stated, applies only to finite sets of vectors. It is no great step to extend these concepts: Given a vector space $V(F)$, a nonempty subset $S \subseteq V$ is linearly dependent (over F) if it contains some finite subset which is linearly dependent. In the contrary case, S is a linearly independent set; that is to say, S is linearly independent if every finite subset is linearly independent. While S may be infinite, linear dependence is a property of finite character.

The following lemma is inherent in our definitions.

Lemma. Let $V(F)$ be a vector space and $\emptyset \neq T \subseteq S \subseteq V$. If S is a linearly independent set, so also is the set T; conversely, if T is a linearly dependent set, so also is the set S.

There is a minor point to be made here, namely, any set which contains the zero vector is always linearly dependent. This follows from the fact

$$1(0) + 0x_1 + \cdots + 0x_n = 0$$

is a nontrivial linear combination for arbitrary vectors $x_1, x_2, \ldots, x_n$. Accordingly, all vectors in a linearly independent set must be different from zero The set consisting of a single vector x is, in particular, linearly independent if and only if $x \neq 0$.

The next theorem in some sense justifies the use of the word "dependent," for it asserts that in a linearly dependent set one of the vectors belongs to the subspace spanned by the remaining ones; putting the matter informally, one of the vectors "depends" on the others.

Theorem 4–17. A set of nonzero vectors $\{x_1, x_2, \ldots, x_n\}$ is linearly dependent if and only if some vector x_k $(k > 1)$ is a linear combination of the preceding ones, $x_1, x_2, \ldots, x_{k-1}$.

Proof. Suppose the vectors $x_1, x_2, \ldots, x_n$ are linearly dependent, so there is a nontrivial linear relation

$$c_1x_1 + c_2x_2 + \cdots + c_nx_n = 0,$$

where not all the c's are zero. Let k be the largest integer for which $c_k \neq 0$. If $k = 1$, we would have $c_1x_1 = 0$, hence $x_1 = 0$, contrary to assumption. Thus $k > 1$ and

$$c_1x_1 + c_2x_2 + \cdots + c_kx_k = 0.$$

Since c_k^{-1} exists in F, it follows that

$$x_k = c_k^{-1}(-1)(c_1x_1 + c_2x_2 + \cdots + c_{k-1}x_{k-1})$$
$$= (-c_k^{-1} \cdot c_1)x_1 + (-c_k^{-1} \cdot c_2)x_2 + \cdots + (-c_k^{-1} \cdot c_{k-1})x_{k-1}.$$

The vector x_k is therefore expressible as a linear combination of its predecessors, as claimed.

The converse is almost obvious: If the vector x_k depends linearly on $x_1, x_2, \ldots, x_{k-1}$, so that

$$x_k = b_1x_1 + b_2x_2 + \cdots + b_{k-1}x_{k-1}$$

for suitable scalars $b_k \in F$, then

$$b_1 x_1 + \cdots + b_{k-1} x_{k-1} + (-1)x_k + 0x_{k-1} + \cdots + 0x_n = 0.$$

Because the coefficient of x_k is nonzero, $\{x_1, x_2, \ldots, x_n\}$ constitutes a dependent set of vectors.

Theorem 4–18. If $V(F)$ is a finitely generated vector space, say

$$V = [x_1, x_2, \ldots, x_n],$$

then V is spanned by a linearly independent subset of these vectors.

Proof. If the set $\{x_1, x_2, \ldots, x_n\}$ is already independent, nothing needs to be proved. Otherwise, Theorem 4–17 implies that some vector x_k is a linear combination of $x_1, x_2, \ldots, x_{k-1}$. By hypothesis, any vector x in V can be written as a linear combination of the n vectors $x_1, x_2, \ldots, x_n$; in this combination, x_k may be replaced by a linear combination of $x_1, x_2, \ldots, x_{k-1}$, thereby showing $x \in [x_1, \ldots, x_{k-1}, x_{k+1}, \ldots, x_n]$. The net result is that the $n - 1$ vectors $x_1, \ldots, x_{k-1}, x_{k+1}, \ldots, x_n$ generate the space $V(F)$.

Next, examine the set $\{x_1, \ldots, x_{k-1}, x_{k+1}, \ldots, x_n\}$ and repeat the process of removing a vector if it can be written as a linear combination of its predecessors. Continuing in this way, we eventually reach a subset

$$\{x_{i_1}, x_{i_2}, \ldots, x_{i_m}\},$$

where $1 \leq i_1 < i_2 < \cdots < i_m \leq n$, of the original set of n vectors, still having linear span V and such that no x_{i_k} is a linear combination of the preceding vectors. That the set $\{x_{i_1}, x_{i_2}, \ldots, x_{i_m}\}$ is linearly independent follows immediately from Theorem 4–17.

Example 4–18. As a simple illustration of some of these ideas, let us observe that

$$V_3 = [(1, 1, 0), (1, 0, 1), (0, 1, 0), (1, 1, 1)].$$

The reasoning here is justified by the fact that each of the unit vectors e_1, e_2, e_3 is a linear combination of these vectors:

$$e_1 = (1, 1, 0) - (0, 1, 0), \qquad e_2 = (0, 1, 0), \qquad e_3 = (1, 1, 1) - (1, 1, 0).$$

Since $V_3(F)$ is spanned by the unit vectors, we infer that every element of V_3 must be a linear combination of $(1, 1, 0), (1, 0, 1), (0, 1, 0), (1, 1, 1)$.

The linear dependence or independence of this set of vectors is equivalent to the existence or nonexistence of scalars c_1, c_2, c_3, c_4 (not all zero) such that

$$c_1(1, 1, 0) + c_2(1, 0, 1) + c_3(0, 1, 0) + c_4(1, 1, 1) = O.$$

Checking components, we note that the c_k's must satisfy the three equations

$$c_1 + c_2 + c_4 = 0, \qquad c_1 + c_3 + c_4 = 0, \qquad c_2 + c_4 = 0.$$

In terms of an arbitrary choice of c_4, a solution is $c_1 = 0$, $c_2 = -c_4$, $c_3 = -c_4$; for instance, $c_4 = 1$ leads to

$$0(1, 1, 0) + (-1)(1, 0, 1) + (-1)(0, 1, 0) + 1(1, 1, 1) = (0, 0, 0),$$

which, of course, implies that the given set of generators is linearly dependent.

To obtain a linearly independent subset of the aforementioned vectors, we need only remove the element $(1, 1, 1)$. In fact, $(1, 1, 1)$ is the only vector that can be written as a linear combination of those preceding it:

$$(1, 1, 1) = (1, 0, 1) + (0, 1, 0).$$

Any member (a_1, a_2, a_3) of V_3 can obviously be expressed as

$$(a_1, a_2, a_3) = (a_1 - a_3)(1, 1, 0) + a_3(1, 0, 1) + (a_2 - a_1 + a_3)(0, 1, 0),$$

whence

$$V_3 = [(1, 1, 0), (1, 0, 1), (0, 1, 0)].$$

The next, somewhat technical, result is the key to all that follows.

Theorem 4–19. (*Steinitz Replacement Theorem*). Let $W(F)$ be a finitely generated subspace of the vector space $V(F)$, $W = [x_1, x_2, \ldots, x_n]$, and let $\{y_1, y_2, \ldots, y_m\}$ be any linearly independent subset of W. Then m of the x_k's, say $x_1, x_2, \ldots, x_m$, may be replaced by $y_1, y_2, \ldots, y_m$, so that $W = [y_1, \ldots, y_m, x_{m+1}, \ldots, x_n]$, in particular, $m \leq n$.

Proof. Since $\{x_1, x_2, \ldots, x_n\}$ spans $W(F)$, the vector $y_1 \in W$ can be expressed as a linear combination of the x_k's:

$$y_1 = a_1x_1 + a_2x_2 + \cdots + a_nx_n.$$

Not all the coefficients $a_k = 0$, for otherwise $y_1 = 0$, contradicting the linear independence of the set $\{y_1, y_2, \ldots, y_m\}$. Reindexing, if necessary, we may assume that $a_1 \neq 0$. Now solve for the vector x_1 in terms of $y_1, x_2, \ldots, x_n$:

$$x_1 = a_1^{-1}y_1 + (-a_1^{-1} \cdot a_2)x_2 + \cdots + (-a_1^{-1} \cdot a_n)y_n.$$

This relation permits us to replace a linear combination of $x_1, x_2, \ldots, x_n$ by a linear combination of the vectors $y_1, x_2, \ldots, x_n$, and leads to the conclusion that $W = [y_1, x_2, \ldots, x_n]$.

Repeat the replacement process with the vector y_2 and the set $\{y_1, x_2, \ldots, x_n\}$. Because y_2 belongs to the subspace spanned by $y_1, x_2, \ldots, x_n$, we must have

$$y_2 = b_1y_1 + b_2x_2 + \cdots + b_nx_n$$

for suitable scalars $b_1, b_2, \ldots, b_n \in F$. The coefficients $b_2, \ldots, b_n$ cannot all be zero, for this would imply that $b_1 \neq 0$ and, in turn, that

$$b_1 y_1 + (-1) y_2 + 0 y_3 + \cdots + 0 y_m = 0,$$

contrary to the independence hypothesis. Hence, one of the coefficients $b_2, \ldots, b_n$ is nonzero; let us, for simplicity, take this to be b_2. As before, we can solve for x_2 in terms of the vectors $y_1, y_2, x_3, \ldots, x_n$ to obtain

$$W = [y_1, y_2, x_3, \ldots, x_n].$$

Continue in this manner: At each stage a y-vector can be introduced and an x-vector deleted so that the new set still spans $W(F)$. If m were larger than n, after n steps all the x_k's could be removed and the set $\{y_1, y_2, \ldots, y_n\}$ would span $W(F)$. Accordingly, the vector $y_{n+1} \in W$ could be written as a linear combination

$$y_{n+1} = c_1 y_1 + c_2 y_2 + \cdots + c_n y_n$$

with not all the c_k being zero, since $y_{n+1} \neq 0$. Once again a contradiction to the independence of $y_1, y_2, \ldots, y_n$ would arise. It follows that the y's must be exhausted before the x's (that is, $n \geq m$) and $W = [y_1, \ldots, y_m, x_{m+1}, \ldots, x_n]$. Of course, the possibility that $n = m$ is not excluded; in this situation, the set $\{x_{m+1}, \ldots, x_n\}$ is empty and the vectors $y_1, y_2, \ldots, y_n$ themselves span $W(F)$.

Corollary. If a vector space $V(F)$ is spanned by n vectors, then any set of $n + 1$ vectors from V is linearly dependent; in particular, any $n + 1$ vectors of the n-tuple space $V_n(F)$ are dependent.

Proof. A set of $n + 1$ linearly independent vectors from V would be impossible, since the theorem would imply $n \geq n + 1$, an obvious contradiction.

The Replacement Theorem has several notable consequences, but these will have to await further developments.

Definition 4–17. A *basis* for a vector space $V(F)$ is a linearly independent subset of V that spans the entire space $V(F)$.

Example 4–19. The familiar unit vectors $e_1, e_2, \ldots, e_n$ of $V_n(F)$, the space of n-tuples of scalars, form a basis (see Examples 4–14 and 4–17). Hereafter, we shall refer to this particular basis as the *natural* or *standard basis* for $V_n(F)$.

Example 4–20. For a more general example, consider the vector space $V_\infty(F)$ of infinite sequences of elements from F. If

$$e_k = (\delta_{1k}, \delta_{2k}, \delta_{3k}, \ldots), \qquad k = 1, 2, \ldots,$$

then the set $S = \{e_1, e_2, \ldots\}$ is linearly independent. These vectors do not constitute a basis for $V_\infty(F)$, however, since it was shown earlier that the linear span $[S]$ is a proper subset of V_∞.

Example 4–21. Let $M_n(F)$ be the vector space of $n \times n$ matrices over a field F. This space has a basis consisting of the n^2 matrices E_{ij}, where E_{ij} is the square matrix of order n having 1 as its ijth entry and zeros elsewhere. Any matrix $(a_{ij}) \in M_n(F)$ can obviously be written as

$$(a_{ij}) = a_{11}E_{11} + a_{12}E_{12} + \cdots + a_{nn}E_{nn}.$$

Moreover, $(a_{ij}) = O$ if and only if $a_{11} = a_{12} = \cdots = a_{nn} = 0$, hence, $E_{11}, E_{12}, \ldots, E_{nn}$ are linearly independent over F.

Example 4–22. One final example: Consider $F[x]$, the vector space of polynomials in x with coefficients from F. A basis for $F[x]$ is formed by the set

$$S = \{1, x, x^2, \ldots, x^n, \ldots\}.$$

By definition, each polynomial $p(x) = a_0 1 + a_1 x + \cdots + a_n x^n$ of $F[x]$ is a linear combination of elements from S. The independence of S follows from the fact that, for any finite subset

$$\{x^{n_1}, x^{n_2}, \ldots, x^{n_k}\}, \qquad (0 \le n_1 < n_2 < \cdots < n_k),$$

the relation

$$c_1 x^{n_1} + c_2 x^{n_2} + \cdots + c_k x^{n_k} = 0$$

holds if and only if $c_1 = c_2 = \cdots = c_k = 0$.

These are but a few examples of the more frequently encountered bases and should amply illustrate the concept; as we continue our discussion, additional examples will appear.

We ought to point out several things. First, Theorem 4–18 may be rephrased so as to assert that any vector space which is spanned by a finite subset, linearly independent or not, possesses a finite basis. Since a basis S for a vector space $V(F)$ is by necessity a linearly independent subset of V, it is possible to express each vector $x \in V$ as a linear combination of elements from S in exactly one way. The unique scalar coefficients which occur in this representation are called the *coordinates* of x with respect to the given basis. Thus the notion of a basis enables us to *coordinatize* the space.

Finally, let us observe that a given vector space may have more than one basis. Example 4–18, for instance, shows that the vectors

$$x_1 = (1, 1, 0), \qquad x_2 = (1, 0, 1), \qquad x_3 = (0, 1, 0)$$

constitute a second basis for $V_3(F)$. In this case, an arbitrary vector (a_1, a_2, a_3) of V_3 can be written as

$$(a_1, a_2, a_3) = (a_1 - a_3)x_1 + a_3 x_2 + (a_2 - a_1 + a_3)x_3.$$

While the coefficients in the above linear combination are uniquely determined, they obviously differ from those which represent the same vector relative to the standard basis e_1, e_2, e_3; roughly speaking, a vector has different coordinates with respect to different bases.

We next dispose of a natural question that arises here: is it possible to obtain a basis for a given vector space? A closely related question is this: presuming one can select two different bases for a space, must each contain the same number of elements? When our vector space is the zero space $\{0\}(F)$, no subset is linearly independent and certainly no basis exists. On the other hand, the coming theorem guarantees that a nonzero space will always have a basis. The proof is a straightforward application of Zorn's Lemma.

Theorem 4–20. (*Basis Theorem*). Every nonzero vector space $V(F)$ possesses a basis.

Proof. Let $\mathcal{C}$ be the family of all linearly independent subsets of V. If $x \neq 0$, then $\{x\} \in \mathcal{C}$, so that $\mathcal{C}$ is plainly nonempty. Our immediate aim is to show that for any chain of sets $\{A_i\}$ in $\mathcal{C}$, their union $\cup A_i$ also belongs to $\mathcal{C}$. To do so, we assume the vectors $x_1, x_2, \ldots, x_n \in \cup A_i$ and that the linear combination $c_1 x_1 + c_2 x_2 + \cdots + c_n x_n = 0$. Now, each vector x_k lies in some member A_{i_k} of $\{A_i\}$. As $\{A_i\}$ forms a chain, one of the sets $A_{i_1}, A_{i_2}, \ldots, A_{i_n}$ contains all the others, call it $A_{i'}$. This means that the given vectors $x_1, x_2, \ldots, x_n$ are all in $A_{i'}$. But the linear independence of $A_{i'}$ then implies that the scalar coefficients $c_k = 0$ for all $k = 1, 2, \ldots, n$. Thus the union $\cup A_i$ is itself a linearly independent subset of V, whence a member of the family $\mathcal{C}$.

The hypotheses of Zorn's Lemma being satisfied, there exists a maximal element S in $\mathcal{C}$. As a member of $\mathcal{C}$, S is a linearly independent subset of V, so to complete the proof it remains simply to establish $[S] = V$. To see this, let x be any vector of V not in S. Because the set $S' = S \cup \{x\}$ properly contains S, it must be linearly dependent (the maximality of S enters here). Therefore, for some finite subset $\{y_1, y_2, \ldots, y_m\}$ of S, a dependence relation

$$ax + a_1 y_1 + a_2 y + \cdots + a_m y_m = 0$$

exists in which not all the coefficients are zero. Were $a = 0$, we would contradict the linear independence of S; hence $a \neq 0$, which leads to

$$x = (-a^{-1} \cdot a_1) y_1 + (-a^{-1} \cdot a_2) y_2 + \cdots + (-a^{-1} \cdot a_m) y_m$$

or $x \in [S]$. We conclude from this that the linear span of S is the whole space $V(F)$, finishing the proof.

The argument used in Theorem 4–20 suggests the following characterization of a basis: S is a basis for the vector space $V(F)$ if and only if S is a maximal linearly independent subset of V (maximal, in the sense that any subset of V which properly contains S is itself linearly dependent). One direction having already been established, let us observe that if S is a basis for $V(F)$, then any set $S \cup \{x\}$, where $x \in V - S$, is linearly dependent. In fact, since $V = [S]$,

$$x = c_1 x_1 + c_2 x_2 + \cdots + c_n x_n$$

for some finite set $\{x_1, x_2, \ldots, x_n\}$ of vectors from S and suitable scalars $c_k \in F$. But then

$$(-1)x + c_1x_1 + c_2x_2 + \cdots + c_nx_n = 0$$

is a nontrivial dependence relation among vectors of $S \cup \{x\}$ and leads to the conclusion that $S \cup \{x\}$ is linearly dependent.

A set S of generators for a vector space $V(F)$ is termed *minimal* if every subset formed from S by removing one or more vectors fails to span V. This idea gives rise to another characterization of a basis:

Theorem 4–21. A set S is a basis for a vector space $V(F)$ if and only if S is a minimal generating set of V.

The proof of the theorem is routine, and we leave the details to the reader.

We are now prepared to establish the main theorem of this section: all bases for a given vector space have the same number of elements (for the astute reader, the same cardinality). As the proof in full generality is somewhat sophisticated, we shall deal with the finite case only.

Theorem 4–22. If $V(F)$ is a finitely generated nonzero vector space, then any two bases for $V(F)$ have precisely the same number of elements.

Proof. Let $\{x_1, x_2, \ldots, x_n\}$ be one basis for the space $V(F)$ and $\{y_1, y_2, \ldots, y_m\}$ be another. Because the vectors $y_1, y_2, \ldots, y_m$ are linearly independent and $V(F)$ is spanned by $x_1, x_2, \ldots, x_n$, it follows from the Replacement Theorem that the integer m is no larger than n, that is, $m \leq n$. Simply reversing the roles of $\{x_1, x_2, \ldots, x_n\}$ and $\{y_1, y_2, \ldots, y_m\}$ in the argument, we also conclude $n \leq m$, whence $n = m$.

Theorem 4–22 can be used to define dimension. For if a vector space $V(F)$ has a finite basis, then every basis for the space will have the same finite number of elements. This unique integer is called the *dimension* of $V(F)$ and designated by dim V. Although the notion of basis is not applicable to the zero space, it is customary to treat $\{0\}(F)$ as finite-dimensional, with zero dimension. A (nonzero) vector space is said to be *infinite-dimensional* if it is not spanned by any finite subset, that is, if it is not finite-dimensional. Not every space is of finite dimension, as evidenced by $F[x]$, the vector space of polynomials in x.

In most of what follows, we shall for the sake of conceptual simplicity confine our attention to finite-dimensional vector spaces.

The next theorem indicates that at least for finite-dimensional spaces, one can form bases without too much difficulty.

Theorem 4–23. Let $V(F)$ be a finite-dimensional vector space, say dim $V = n$. Then

1) every set of n vectors which span V is a basis,
2) every set of n linearly independent vectors from V is a basis.

Proof. Suppose $V = [x_1, x_2, \ldots, x_n]$. According to Theorem 4–18, some subset of $\{x_1, x_2, \ldots, x_n\}$ is a basis for $V(F)$. But the previous result implies that this subset must contain n elements and accordingly is the entire set $\{x_1, x_2, \ldots, x_n\}$.

For a proof of the second assertion, let $x_1, x_2, \ldots, x_n$ be n linearly independent vectors of V. If $x \in V$ is arbitrary, the set $\{x, x_1, \ldots, x_n\}$ is dependent, since the maximal number of linearly independent vectors in V is n. Thus some nontrivial dependence relation exists among these vectors:

$$cx + c_1 x_1 + \cdots + c_n x_n = 0.$$

Were the coefficient $c = 0$, a contradiction to the linear independence of $x_1, x_2, \ldots, x_n$ would arise. Hence $c \neq 0$, and we may solve for the vector x in terms of $x_1, x_2, \ldots, x_n$ to obtain

$$x = (-c^{-1} \cdot c_1)x_1 + (-c^{-1} \cdot c_2)x_2 + \cdots + (-c^{-1} \cdot c_n)x_n.$$

This argument shows that

$$V = [x_1, x_2, \ldots, x_n],$$

making the set $\{x_1, x_2, \ldots, x_n\}$ a basis for $V(F)$.

Theorem 4–18 told us that it is possible to choose a basis for a vector space $V(F)$ from any set of generators of V. In the opposite direction, the coming theorem asserts that any linearly independent subset of V is either a basis or else can be extended to a basis for $V(F)$, in the sense that vectors may be added to it to form a basis.

Theorem 4–24. If $V(F)$ is a finite-dimensional vector space and $\{x_1, x_2, \ldots, x_n\}$ is a linearly independent subset of V, then there exist vectors $y_{n+1}, \ldots, y_m$ such that $\{x_1, \ldots, x_n, y_{n+1}, \ldots, y_m\}$ forms a basis for $V(F)$.

Proof. The proof is short: Since $V(F)$ is finite-dimensional, it has a finite basis $y_1, y_2, \ldots, y_m$. As $V = [y_1, y_2, \ldots, y_m]$, we may apply the Steinitz Theorem to replace n of the y's by x's and obtain a set $\{x_1, \ldots, x_n, y_{n+1}, \ldots, y_m\}$ whose linear span is still V. But any generating set with m elements in an m-dimensional space is a basis.

Corollary. Every basis for a subspace of a finite-dimensional vector space can be extended to a basis for the entire space.

Example 4–23. As a particular case of this last point, consider the vector space $M_2(F)$ and the three matrices

$$\begin{pmatrix} 1 & 0 \\ 0 & 0 \end{pmatrix}, \quad \begin{pmatrix} 1 & 1 \\ 0 & 0 \end{pmatrix}, \quad \begin{pmatrix} 1 & 1 \\ 1 & 0 \end{pmatrix}.$$

To check the linear independence of these matrices, let

$$c_1\begin{pmatrix} 1 & 0 \\ 0 & 0 \end{pmatrix} + c_2\begin{pmatrix} 1 & 1 \\ 0 & 0 \end{pmatrix} + c_3\begin{pmatrix} 1 & 1 \\ 1 & 0 \end{pmatrix} = \begin{pmatrix} 0 & 0 \\ 0 & 0 \end{pmatrix}.$$

On equating corresponding entries, we see that

$$c_1 + c_2 + c_3 = 0, \qquad c_2 + c_3 = 0, \qquad c_3 = 0,$$

which implies $c_1 = c_2 = c_3 = 0$.

Theorem 4–24 now tells us that the given matrices will form at least part of a basis for $M_2(F)$. We shall leave the details to the reader and content ourselves with this one comment: the addition of any fourth matrix having a nonzero element in the $(2, 2)$-position will yield a linearly independent set. For instance, among the many possibilities, the matrices

$$\begin{pmatrix} 1 & 0 \\ 0 & 0 \end{pmatrix}, \quad \begin{pmatrix} 1 & 1 \\ 0 & 0 \end{pmatrix}, \quad \begin{pmatrix} 1 & 1 \\ 1 & 0 \end{pmatrix}, \quad \begin{pmatrix} 0 & 0 \\ 0 & 1 \end{pmatrix}$$

are linearly independent and, being four in number, must therefore be a basis for the 4-dimensional space $M_2(F)$. This illustrates the wide latitude of choice for bases of $M_2(F)$.

We terminate the present section by giving some useful results concerning the dimensions of subspaces of a given vector space. The reader should first prove the following theorem.

Theorem 4–25. If $W(F)$ is a subspace of a finite-dimensional vector space $V(F)$, then

1) $W(F)$ is also finite-dimensional with dim $W \leq$ dim V.
2) dim $W =$ dim V if and only if $W = V$.

The next theorem relates the dimensions of the sum and intersection of two subspaces.

Theorem 4–26. If $U(F)$ and $W(F)$ are subspaces of a finite-dimensional vector space $V(F)$, then

$$\dim (U + W) = \dim U + \dim W - \dim (U \cap W).$$

In particular,

$$\dim (U \oplus W) = \dim U + \dim W.$$

Proof. Before entering into the details of the proof, we observe that by Theorem 4–25 the four subspaces involved in the statement of our theorem all have finite dimension. Now, let $\{x_1, x_2, \ldots, x_n\}$ be a basis for $(U \cap W)(F)$. According to Theorem 4–24, there will exist vectors $u_1, u_2, \ldots, u_m$ such that $\{x_1, \ldots, x_n, u_1, \ldots, u_m\}$ is a basis for the subspace $U(F)$ and vectors $w_1, w_2, \ldots, w_r$ such that $\{x_1, \ldots, x_n, w_1, \ldots, w_r\}$ is a basis for the subspace $W(F)$. Combine these two bases into a single set

$$\{u_1, \ldots, u_m, x_1, \ldots, x_n, w_1, \ldots, w_r\}.$$

Because the first $m + n$ vectors of the foregoing set are a basis for $U(F)$ and the last $n + r$ vectors are a basis for $W(F)$, any element of the sum $U + W$ may be expressed as a linear combination of the vectors of this set, that is

$$U + W = [u_1, \ldots, u_m, x_1, \ldots, x_n, w_1, \ldots, w_r].$$

We wish to show that the vectors on the right are also linearly independent and consequently a basis for the subspace $(U + W)(F)$; once this is established, it would follow that

$$\dim (U + W) = m + n + r = (m + n) + (n + r) - n$$
$$= \dim U + \dim W - \dim (U \cap W).$$

Therefore, let us suppose

$$a_1 u_1 + \cdots + a_m u_m + b_1 x_1 + \cdots + b_n x_n + c_1 w_1 + \cdots + c_r w_r = 0.$$

Setting $z = c_1 w_1 + \cdots + c_r w_r$, we would then have

$$z = -(a_1 u_1 + \cdots + a_m u_m + b_1 x_1 + \cdots + b_n x_n)$$

or $z \in [x_1, \ldots, x_n, u_1, \ldots, u_m] = U$. Since the vector z also belongs to W, it must be a linear combination of the basis elements $x_1, x_2, \ldots, x_n$ of the subspace $(U \cap W)(F)$, say,

$$z = c_1 w_1 + \cdots + c_r w_r = d_1 x_1 + \cdots + d_n x_n,$$

so that

$$d_1 x_1 + \cdots + d_n x_n - c_1 w_1 - \cdots - c_r w_r = 0.$$

But the set $\{x_1, \ldots, x_n, w_1, \ldots, w_r\}$ is linearly independent, being a basis for the subspace $W(F)$, hence $d_1 = \cdots = d_n = c_1 = \cdots = c_r = 0$. In conjunction with the linear independence of $\{x_1, \ldots, x_n, u_1, \ldots, u_m\}$, this forces $a_1 = \cdots = a_m = b_1 = \cdots = b_n = 0$. We have thus succeeded in proving that the vectors $u_1, \ldots, u_m, x_1, \ldots, x_n, w_1, \ldots, w_r$ are linearly independent, as required.

Theorem 4–27. If $W(F)$ is a subspace of a finite-dimensional vector space $V(F)$, then the quotient space $(V/W)(F)$ is also finite-dimensional and

$$\dim V = \dim W + \dim V/W.$$

Proof. Let $\{x_1, x_2, \ldots, x_n\}$ be a basis for $W(F)$. By adding vectors $y_1, y_2, \ldots, y_m$, we may extend this set to a basis $\{x_1, \ldots, x_n, y_1, \ldots, y_m\}$ for the whole space $V(F)$. Any vector $x \in V$ can then be written in the form $x = a_1 x_1 + \cdots + a_n x_n + b_1 y_1 + \cdots + b_m y_m$ for appropriate choice of coefficients. Since $x - (b_1 y_1 + \cdots + b_m y_m) \in W$, the coset $x + W$ is expressible as

$$x + W = (b_1 y_1 + \cdots + b_m y_m) + W = b_1(y_1 + W) + \cdots + b_m(y_m + W).$$

In other words, the elements $y_1 + W, y_2 + W, \ldots, y_m + W$ span the quotient space $(V/W)(F)$.

The remainder of the proof amounts to showing these cosets to be linearly independent and hence a basis for $(V/W)(F)$. To see this, we suppose

$$c_1(y_1 + W) + c_2(y_2 + W) + \cdots + c_m(y_n + W) = 0 + W,$$

where, of course, $0 + W = W$ is the zero element of V/W. Thus

$$c_1 y_1 + c_2 y_2 + \cdots + c_n y_m \in W$$

and must be a linear combination of the basis vectors $x_1, x_2, \ldots, x_n$ of W, say

$$c_1 y_1 + c_2 y_2 + \cdots + c_m y_m = d_1 x_1 + d_2 x_2 + \cdots + d_n x_n.$$

But the linear independence of the set $\{x_1, \ldots, x_n, y_1, \ldots, y_m\}$ then implies $c_1 = \cdots = c_m = d_1 = \cdots = d_n = 0$.

The foregoing argument indicates that the quotient space $(V/W)(F)$ has a basis consisting of the m cosets $y_1 + W, y_2 + W, \ldots, y_m + W$. The conclusion of the theorem follows immediately from this, since

$$\dim V/W = m = (m + n) - n = \dim V - \dim W.$$

Example 4–24. We illustrate the above by looking again at $V_3(F)$ and the one-dimensional subspace $W(F)$, where

$$W = \{(a, 0, 0) \mid a \in F\}.$$

In this case, the quotient space $(V_3/W)(F)$ has dimension 2, for the equation of Theorem 4–27 reads

$$\dim V_3/W = \dim V_3 - \dim W = 3 - 1 = 2.$$

To actually obtain a basis for the quotient space, one need only employ the procedure of the theorem. First, extend the basis of $W(F)$—that is, the vector $(1, 0, 0)$—to a basis for the entire space $V(F)$, say by adjoining vectors $(0, 1, 0)$ and $(0, 0, 1)$. The corresponding cosets

$$(0, 1, 0) + W \qquad \text{and} \qquad (0, 0, 1) + W$$

then serve as a basis for $(V_3/W)(F)$. Indeed, it is easy to show that any element $(a_1, a_2, a_3) + W$ of V_3/W may be written in the form

$$(a_1, a_2, a_3) + W = a_2[(0, 1, 0) + W] + a_3[(0, 0, 1) + W].$$

PROBLEMS

In the problems below, F will denote an arbitrary field.

1. For each of the following vector spaces, determine whether the sets listed are linearly dependent or independent.
   a) $V_4(F)$: $\{(1, 0, 0, 0), (1, 1, 0, 0), (1, 1, 1, 0), (1, 1, 1, 1)\}$
   b) $F[x]$: $\{x^2 + x - 1, x^2 - x - 2, x^2 + x + 1\}$
   c) $V_3(Z_5)$: $\{(4, 1, 3), (2, 3, 1), (4, 1, 0)\}$
   d) $V_3(C)$: $\{(1, 2 + i, 3), (2 - i, i, 1), (i, 2 + 3i, 2)\}$

2. Prove that if each vector $x \in [x_1, x_2, \ldots, x_n]$ is uniquely representable in the form $x = a_1x_1 + a_2x_2 + \cdots + a_nx_n$ $(a_k \in F)$, then the vectors $x_1, x_2, \ldots, x_n$ are linearly independent.

3. Given vectors $x_1, x_2, \ldots, x_n \in V$, establish the assertions below:
   a) If $x_i = x_j$ for some $i \neq j$, the set $\{x_1, x_2, \ldots, x_n\}$ is linearly dependent.
   b) If $\{x_1, x_2, \ldots, x_n\}$ forms a linearly independent set and $a_1, a_2, \ldots, a_{n-1} \in F$, then
   $$\{x_1 - a_1x_n, x_2 - a_2x_n, \ldots, x_{n-1} - a_{n-1}x_n\}$$
   is also an independent set of vectors.
   c) If $\{x_1, x_2, \ldots, x_n\}$ is linearly independent while $\{x_1, \ldots, x_n, x_{n+1}\}$ is linearly dependent, then the vector $x_{n+1} \in [x_1, x_2, \ldots, x_n]$.

4. Show that the vectors $(3 - i, 2 + 2i, 4)$, $(2, 2 + 4i, 3)$, and $(1 - i, -2i, 1)$ form a basis for the space $V_3(C)$ and determine the coordinates of each of the standard basis vectors $(1, 0, 0)$, $(0, 1, 0)$, and $(0, 0, 1)$ with respect to this basis.

5. a) Find a basis for the vector space $C(R^\#)$ and all bases for the space $V_3(Z_2)$.
   b) For what values of a do the vectors $(1 + a, 1, 1)$, $(1, 1 + a, 1)$, and $(1, 1, 1 + a)$ form a basis of $V_3(R^\#)$?

6. Assume $\{x_1, x_2, x_3\}$ is a basis for the vector space $V_3(R^\#)$. Verify that the sets $\{x_1 + x_2, x_2 + x_3, x_3 + x_1\}$ and $\{x_1, x_1 + x_2, x_1 + x_2 + x_3\}$ also serve as bases of $V_3(R^\#)$. Is this situation true in the space $V_3(Z_3)$?

7. Prove that the subspace of $F[x]$ consisting of all polynomials of degree at most n is finite-dimensional.

8. If diag M_n denotes the set of all diagonal matrices of order n (over the field F), show that (diag M_n)(F) is a subspace of the vector space $M_n(F)$ and determine its dimension.

9. Prove that if $W(F)$ is a proper subspace of the finite-dimensional vector space $V(F)$, then dim $W <$ dim V.

10. Assume the space $V(F)$ is finite-dimensional with basis $\{x_1, x_2, \ldots, x_n\}$. If $W_k(F)$ is the subspace generated by the vector x_k $(k = 1, 2, \ldots, n)$, verify that $V = W_1 \oplus W_2 \oplus \cdots \oplus W_n$.

11. Let $U(F)$ and $W(F)$ be subspaces of $V_n(F)$ such that dim $U > n/2$, dim $W > n/2$. Show $U \cap W \neq \{0\}$.

12. Suppose $\{x_1, x_2, \ldots, x_n\}$ is a basis for the subspace $U(F)$ of $V(F)$ and $\{y_1, y_2, \ldots, y_m\}$ is a basis of the subspace $W(F)$. Given that the set $\{x_1, \ldots, x_n, y_1, \ldots, y_m\}$ forms a basis for the entire space $V(F)$, prove that $V = U \oplus W$.

13. Let $(F[x], +, \cdot)$ be the ring of polynomials in x over F and $p(x) \in F[x]$ be a polynomial of degree n. If $((p(x)), +, \cdot)$ is the principal ideal generated by $p(x)$, establish that $(F[x]/(p(x)))(F)$ is a vector space of dimension n. [*Hint:* Consider the cosets $1 + (p(x))$, $x + (p(x))$, $\ldots$, $x^{n-1} + (p(x))$.]

14. Determine the dimension of the quotient space $(V_3/W)(F)$, where the set W is defined by $W = \{(a, b, a + b) \mid a, b \in F\}$.

15. In the vector space $M_n(F)$, let $T_n(F)$ be the subspace of upper triangular matrices [matrices (a_{ij}) such that $a_{ij} = 0$ for $i > j$] and $T'_n(F)$ be the subspace of lower triangular matrices [matrices (a_{ij}) such that $a_{ij} = 0$ for $i < j$]. Find dim T_n, dim T'_n, dim $(T_n \cap T'_n)$, dim $(T_n + T'_n)$, and verify the truth of Theorem 4–26 in this particular case.

4-4 LINEAR MAPPINGS

In this section, which is our last, we examine the vector space analog of the familiar homomorphism concept. Since a vector space $V(F)$ is comprised of two algebraic systems, a group $(V, +)$ and a field $(F, +, \cdot)$, there may be some initial confusion as to what operations are to be preserved by such functions; the answer is only those operations which explicitly involve vectors: vector addition and scalar multiplication. Traditionally, vector space homomorphisms are called linear mappings or linear transformations, and we adhere to this terminology.

Definition 4–18. Let $V(F)$ and $W(F)$ be vector spaces over a field F. A function $f: V \to W$ is said to be a *linear mapping* from $V(F)$ into $W(F)$ if

$$f(x + y) = f(x) + f(y) \qquad \text{and} \qquad f(cx) = cf(x)$$

for all vectors $x, y \in V$ and all scalars $c \in F$. The set of linear mappings from $V(F)$ into $W(F)$ will subsequently be designated by $L(V, W)$.

Simply put, a linear mapping from the space $V(F)$ into $W(F)$ is a homomorphism from the additive group $(V, +)$ into the additive group $(W, +)$ which, at the same time, preserves scalar multiplication. This is plainly equivalent to the single requirement that

$$f(ax + by) = af(x) + bf(y)$$

for all $x, y \in V$ and $a, b \in F$. Suffice it to say, the above definition makes sense only when both vector spaces are taken over the same field.

Before proceeding to the theory of linear mappings, let us illustrate to some extent the great variety of possible examples.

Example 4–25. Let $M_{mn}(F)$ be the vector space of all $m \times n$ matrices over a field F, and let (a_{ij}) be a fixed $m \times m$ matrix (again, over F). Define a function $f\colon M_{mn} \to M_{mn}$ by

$$f((b_{ij})) = (a_{ij}) \cdot (b_{ij}).$$

Then f is seen to be a linear mapping, because

$$\begin{aligned}
f(r(b_{ij}) + s(c_{ij})) &= (a_{ij}) \cdot [r(b_{ij}) + s(c_{ij})] \\
&= r(a_{ij}) \cdot (b_{ij}) + s(a_{ij}) \cdot (c_{ij}) \\
&= rf((a_{ij})) + sf((c_{ij})).
\end{aligned}$$

Example 4–26. In the space $V_\infty(F)$ of infinite sequences of elements from a field F, we define the *shift function* f as follows: for each sequence $x = (a_1, a_2, a_3, \ldots)$, take

$$f(x) = (a_2, a_3, a_4, \ldots).$$

The reader may easily verify that f is a linear mapping from $V_\infty(F)$ to $V_\infty(F)$. In fact, any power of f is again linear, since

$$f^n(x) = (a_{n+1}, a_{n+2} \, a_{n+3}, \ldots), \qquad n \in Z_+.$$

Example 4–27. Next consider $F[x]$, the space of polynomials in the indeterminant x with coefficients from F. A linear mapping on $F[x]$ is given by means of the so-called *differentiation function*. That is, for an arbitrary polynomial $p(x) = a_0 + a_1 x + a_2 x^2 + \cdots + a_n x^n$ in $F[x]$, let

$$f(p) = a_1 + 2a_2 x + \cdots + na_n x^{n-1}.$$

Example 4–28. One more example: Suppose $W(F)$ is a subspace of the vector space $V(F)$. Then the familiar natural mapping $\mathrm{nat}_W \colon V \to V/W$ defined by taking

$$\mathrm{nat}_W(x) = x + W$$

is a linear transformation. By virtue of the definition of the operations in $(V/W)(F)$, we easily check that

$$\begin{aligned}
\mathrm{nat}_W(ax + by) &= ax + by + W \\
&= a(x + W) + b(y + W) = a \, \mathrm{nat}_W(x) + b \, \mathrm{nat}_W(y).
\end{aligned}$$

One fact which follows almost immediately from Definition 4–18 is that if $\dim V$ is finite, then any linear transformation f from $V(F)$ into $W(F)$ is completely described by specifying its values on a basis for $V(F)$. For suppose $\{x_1, x_2, \ldots, x_n\}$ is a basis of the space $V(F)$; then each vector x in V has the form

$$x = a_1 x + a_2 x_2 + \cdots + a_n x_n$$

for suitable scalars $a_k \in F$. By the linearity condition, extended to n vectors,

$$f(x) = a_1 f(x_1) + a_2 f(x_2) + \cdots + a_n f(x_n).$$

Thus, f is completely determined once its effect on the basis vectors $x_1, x_2, \ldots, x_n$ is known. The next theorem indicates that this effect may be prescribed arbitrarily.

Theorem 4–28. Let $\{x_1, x_2, \ldots, x_n\}$ be a basis for the finite-dimensional vector space $V(F)$ and $\{y_1, y_2, \ldots, y_n\}$ an arbitrary set of n vectors from $W(F)$. Then there is exactly one linear mapping $f \in L(V, W)$ such that

$$f(x_k) = y_k, \qquad (k = 1, 2, \ldots, n).$$

Proof. To prove that there does exist such a mapping f, we proceed as follows: Since $\{x_1, x_2, \ldots, x_n\}$ is a basis for $V(F)$, each vector $x \in V$ is uniquely expressible in the form

$$x = a_1 x + a_2 x_2 + \cdots + a_n x_n.$$

Let us simply define a function $f \colon V \to W$ at the vector x by taking

$$f(x) = a_1 y_1 + a_2 y_2 + \cdots + a_n y_n.$$

To see that this function is actually linear, let $x, y \in V$, where

$$x = a_1 x_1 + \cdots + a_n x_n, \qquad y = b_1 x_1 + \cdots + b_n x_n.$$

Then

$$x + y = (a_1 + b_1) x_1 + \cdots + (a_n + b_n) x_n,$$

and so, by definition,

$$\begin{aligned} f(x + y) &= (a_1 + b_1) y_1 + \cdots + (a_n + b_n) y_n \\ &= (a_1 y_1 + \cdots + a_n y_n) + (b_1 y_1 + \cdots + b_n y_n) = f(x) + f(y). \end{aligned}$$

One establishes similarly that $f(cx) = cf(x)$ for each scalar c in F.

Now, suppose g is any other linear transformation from $V(F)$ to $W(F)$ with the property that $g(x_k) = y_k$. Then, for any vector $x = a_1 x_1 + a_2 x_2 + \cdots + a_n x_n$, the linearity of g implies

$$\begin{aligned} g(x) &= a_1 g(x_1) + a_2 g(x_2) + \cdots + a_n g(x_n) \\ &= a_1 y_1 + a_2 y_2 + \cdots + a_n y_n = f(x). \end{aligned}$$

We therefore conclude that the linear mapping f for which $f(x_k) = y_k$ is the only one possible.

To see how closely linear mappings are associated with matrices, let us now suppose the space $W(F)$ is also finite-dimensional, say, with basis $\{y_1, y_2, \ldots, y_m\}$. Then each vector $f(x_j)$, being in W, is a unique linear combination of these basis vectors:

$$f(x_j) = \sum_{i=1}^{m} a_{ij}y_i, \qquad (j = 1, 2, \ldots, n).$$

(Observe that, in contrast with many texts, the summation is on the first index of a_{ij}.) In this fashion, we produce an $m \times n$ matrix (a_{ij}) called the *matrix representation* of f relative to the bases $\{x_1, x_2, \ldots, x_n\}$ and $\{y_1, y_2, \ldots, y_m\}$. Notice particularly that the matrix (a_{ij}) depends on the pair of bases used for $V(F)$ and $W(F)$ as well as on f; any change in the basis elements, even in their order, would lead to a different matrix. Accordingly, the same linear mapping (whose definition, after all, does not depend on any basis) might be represented by several matrices.

Now, any vector $x \in V$ can be expressed as a linear combination of the basis $\{x_1, x_2, \ldots, x_n\}$:

$$x = c_1x_1 + c_2x_2 + \cdots + c_nx_n.$$

Hence,

$$f(x) = \sum_{j=1}^{n} c_j f(x_j) = \sum_{j=1}^{n} c_j \left(\sum_{i=1}^{m} a_{ij}y_i \right) = \sum_{i=1}^{m} \left(\sum_{j=1}^{n} c_j a_{ij} \right) y_i.$$

Once the bases are picked, the effect of f on each vector of V is therefore completely determined by the scalars c_i and the representing matrix (a_{ij}).

On the other hand, two bases $\{x_1, x_2, \ldots, x_n\}$ and $\{y_1, y_2, \ldots, y_m\}$ for $V(F)$ and $W(F)$, respectively, along with an $m \times n$ matrix (a_{ij}) of elements from F, give rise to a unique linear transformation $f \in L(V, W)$. All we need do is define the proposed mapping on the basis of $V(F)$ by specifying

$$f(x_j) = \sum_{i=1}^{m} a_{ij}y_i,$$

then extend f to all of V by the condition that it be linear.

The reader may well feel, in view of these remarks, that it is unnecessary to distinguish any longer between a linear mapping and its representing matrix, and that all subsequent results could be phrased in the language of matrices. The utility of this approach is diminished by the fact there is no unique correspondence between linear mappings and matrices; before we can introduce the matrix representation, we must first pick bases for the underlying vector spaces, and the matrix depends strongly on the bases chosen. Since most aspects of the theory are best treated as independent of any basis, we shall study linear mappings in the abstract, without reference to matrices.

As a linear mapping $f \in L(V, W)$ is, in particular, a homomorphism of the additive group $(V, +)$ into the additive group $(W, +)$, the results of Chapter 2 may be utilized. For instance, by Theorem 2–40, we already know that f will be a one-to-one function if and only if ker $(f) = \{0\}$; as usual, ker (f) consists of all vectors mapped onto the zero element of W:

$$\ker (f) = \{x \in V \,|\, f(x) = 0\}.$$

Recall also that $f(0) = 0$, whence ker $(f) \neq \emptyset$, and $f(-x) = -f(x)$.

By this stage, the first two parts of the following theorem should come as no surprise; their demonstration is not difficult and we ask the reader to fill in the details.

Theorem 4–29. Let $V(F)$ and $W(F)$ be vector spaces over the field F and the mapping $f \in L(V, W)$. Then

1) $(\ker (f))(F)$ is a subspace of $V(F)$;
2) $(f(V))(F)$ is a subspace of $W(F)$;
3) dim $V = $ dim ker $(f) + $ dim $f(V)$ [Sylvester's Law].

Proof. We establish assertion (3) only in the case where dim V is finite. Suppose first that ker $(f) \neq \{0\}$, so that a basis $\{x_1, x_2, \ldots, x_n\}$ may be selected for the subspace $(\ker (f))(F)$. Using Theorem 4–24, this set can now be extended to a basis $\{x_1, \ldots, x_n, y_1, \ldots, y_m\}$ for the entire space by adding new vectors $y_1, y_2, \ldots, y_m$. Given any element $y \in f(V)$, there will exist some x in V such that $y = f(x)$. In terms of the basis for $V(F)$, the vector x is representable as

$$x = a_1 x_1 + \cdots + a_n x_n + b_1 y_1 + \cdots + b_m y_m.$$

But, $f(x_k) = 0$ for $k = 1, 2, \ldots, n$, which implies

$$y = f(x) = a_1 f(x_1) + \cdots + a_n f(x_n) + b_1 f(y_1) + \cdots + b_m f(y_m)$$
$$= b_1 f(y_1) + \cdots + b_m f(y_m).$$

From this, we deduce that

$$f(V) = [f(y_1), f(y_2), \ldots, f(y_m)].$$

We maintain further that the vectors $f(y_1), f(y_2), \ldots, f(y_m)$ are linearly independent and consequently a basis for $(f(V))(F)$. Assume some linear combination of them is the zero vector, say

$$c_1 f(y_1) + c_2 f(y_2) + \cdots + c_m f(y_m) = 0.$$

Then, $f(c_1 y_1 + c_2 y_2 + \cdots + c_m y_m) = 0$, or expressed otherwise,

$$c_1 y_1 + c_2 y_2 + \cdots + c_m y_m \in \ker (f).$$

Since $x_1, x_2, \ldots, x_n$ are a basis for $(\ker (f))(F)$, there must exist scalars $d_1, \ldots, d_n$ such that

$$c_1 y_1 + \cdots + c_m y_m = d_1 x_1 + \cdots + d_n x_n.$$

Were any of these coefficients nonzero, a contradiction to the linear independence of the set $\{x_1, \ldots, x_n, y_1, \ldots, y_m\}$ would result. Hence $c_1 = \cdots = c_m = 0$ and we have succeeded in proving that the m vectors $f(y_1), f(y_2), \ldots, f(y_m)$ form a basis for the image space $(f(V))(F)$. This means

$$\dim V = n + m = \dim \ker (f) + \dim f(V).$$

If $\ker (f) = \{0\}$, then essentially the same argument shows that f maps any basis for $V(F)$ onto a basis for $(f(V))(F)$; thus $\dim V = \dim f(V)$, establishing Sylvester's Law for this case also.

Corollary. Let $V(F)$ and $W(F)$ be finite-dimensional vector spaces with $\dim V = \dim W$, and let $f \in L(V, W)$. Then f is a one-to-one function if and only if f maps onto V.

Proof. To begin with, suppose f is one-to-one, so that $\ker (f) = \{0\}$. Then $\dim \ker (f) = 0$, and Sylvester's Law reduces to $\dim W = \dim f(V)$. It now follows from Theorem 4–25 that $W = f(V)$, whence f is an onto mapping. Conversely, if the range of f is all of W, the same equation yields $\dim \ker (f) = 0$, or equivalently $\ker (f) = \{0\}$, so f is one-to-one.

Remark. Neither one-to-one nor onto implies the other for linear mappings between spaces of infinite dimension.

Example 4–29. We illustrate Sylvester's Law with the linear mapping $f \colon V_4 \to V_3$ given by

$$f(a_1, a_2, a_3, a_4) = (a_2 - a_3,\ a_3 - a_4,\ a_4 - a_1).$$

The kernel of f is easily seen to be the set of vectors of the type (a, a, a, a), while its range is all of V_3. Hence,

$$\dim V_4 = 4 = 1 + 3 = \dim \ker (f) + \dim V_3.$$

The terms isomorphic and isomorphism have the obvious meanings for vector spaces. Two vector spaces $V(F)$ and $W(F)$ are *isomorphic*, written $V(F) \simeq W(F)$, if and only if there exists a one-to-one mapping $f \colon V \to W$ of V onto W which preserves the basic vector space operations; that is to say, we require $f \in L(V, W)$. As with our earlier systems, such a function f is called an *isomorphism*.

The coming theorem is of considerable interest in that it reveals the n-tuple space $V_n(F)$ to be the prototype of all n-dimensional vector spaces.

Theorem 4–30. If $V(F)$ is a finite-dimensional vector space of dimension n, then $V(F)$ is isomorphic to $V_n(F)$.

Proof. For sake of argument, let $\{x_1, x_2, \ldots, x_n\}$ be a basis for the space $V(F)$. Then each vector $x \in V$ has a unique representation of the form

$$x = a_1 x_1 + a_2 x_2 + \cdots + a_n x_n, \qquad a_k \in F.$$

Since the n-tuple of scalars $(a_1, a_2, \ldots, a_n)$ is uniquely determined by x (relative to the given basis), we may define a function $f \colon V \to V_n$ by taking

$$f(x) = (a_1, a_2, \ldots, a_n).$$

A routine calculation establishes that this mapping effects the required isomorphism.

Corollary. Two finite-dimensional vector spaces $V(F)$ and $W(F)$ are isomorphic if and only if $\dim V = \dim W$.

Proof. If $\dim V = \dim W = n$, then each space is isomorphic to $V_n(F)$, hence isomorphic to one another. Conversely, if $V(F) \simeq W(F)$ under the linear mapping f, Sylvester's Law yields

$$\dim V = \dim \ker (f) + \dim f(V) = \dim \{0\} + \dim W = \dim W.$$

A remark in passing: The isomorphism between $V(F)$ and $V_n(F)$ was obtained by arbitrarily choosing one particular basis for $V(F)$ in preference to all others. If we were to confine further study of finite-dimensional vector spaces exclusively to the n-tuple spaces $V_n(F)$, as the above theorem suggests, we would always be restricted to a prescribed basis. Since this would be contrary to our policy of giving, so far as possible, a basis-free treatment of vector spaces, we shall for the most part ignore Theorem 4–30.

The corollary to Theorem 4–30 enables us to establish a relationship between quotient spaces and complementary subspaces.

Theorem 4–31. Let $U(F)$ and $W(F)$ be complementary subspaces relative to the finite-dimensional vector space $V(F)$; that is, $V = U \oplus W$. Then

$$(V/W)(F) \simeq U(F).$$

Proof. We already know from Theorem 4–26 that $\dim V = \dim U + \dim W$. Appealing to Theorem 4–27,

$$\dim V/W = \dim V - \dim W = \dim U.$$

Hence, the last corollary implies that $(V/W)(F) \simeq U(F)$, as alleged.

Corollary. All subspaces complementary to a given subspace are isomorphic.

So far we have gathered certain information concerning individual linear mappings, but have imposed no structure on the set $L(V, W)$ itself. This will now be remedied by showing that $L(V, W)$ inherits a natural vector space structure from the underlying spaces $V(F)$ and $W(F)$.

The sum $f + g$ of two linear mappings f, $g \in L(V, W)$ is defined, as one might expect, by the rule $(f + g)(x) = f(x) + g(x)$ for all x in V; similarly, when $c \in F$, the scalar product cf is given by means of $(cf)(x) = cf(x)$. (We shall not bother to distinguish between the various uses of the $+$ sign, since the context will ordinarily suffice to make clear which spaces are involved.)

With these operations, one can verify that $L(V, W)(F)$ does indeed satisfy all the axioms for a vector space. What little difficulty there is arises in showing that $L(V, W)$ is closed under the operations. But this poses no real problem, for if x, $y \in V$ and a, $b \in F$, the fact that f and g are themselves linear implies that

$$
\begin{aligned}
(f + g)(ax + by) &= f(ax + by) + g(ax + by) \\
&= af(x) + bf(y) + ag(x) + bg(y) \\
&= a\big(f(x) + g(x)\big) + b\big(f(y) + g(y)\big) \\
&= a(f + g)(x) + b(f + g)(y),
\end{aligned}
$$

whence $f + g \in L(V, W)$. An equally easy computation, which we omit, establishes that cf lies in $L(V, W)$ for each scalar c. The point of all this is summarized by the following theorem.

Theorem 4–32. Let $V(F)$ and $W(F)$ be vector spaces over the field F. With addition and scalar multiplication defined in the usual way for mappings, $L(V, W)(F)$ is itself a vector space.

We can prove considerably more by taking the underlying spaces to be finite-dimensional.

Theorem 4–33. If $V(F)$ and $W(F)$ are finite-dimensional vector spaces over F, then the space $L(V, W)(F)$ is also of finite dimension with

$$
\dim L(V, W) = \dim V \cdot \dim W.
$$

Proof. Assume $\{x_1, x_2, \ldots, x_n\}$ and $\{y_1, y_2, \ldots, y_m\}$ are bases for $V(F)$ and $W(F)$, respectively, so that $\dim V = n$, $\dim W = m$. Our strategy is to construct a specific basis of nm elements for $L(V, W)(F)$. According to Theorem 4–28, for each pair of integers (i, j), where $1 \le i \le n$, $1 \le j \le m$, there is a unique linear mapping $f_{ij}: V \to W$ satisfying the conditions

$$
f_{ij}(x_k) = \delta_{ik} y_j = \begin{cases} 0 & \text{if } i \ne k, \\ y_j & \text{if } i = k. \end{cases}
$$

The contention is that these nm functions serve as a basis for the space $L(V, W)$.

First, let f be an arbitrary linear transformation from $V(F)$ into $W(F)$. For each index i $(1 \leq i \leq n)$, $f(x_i)$ lies in W, hence is a linear combination of the basis vectors $y_1, y_2, \ldots, y_m$, say

$$f(x_i) = a_{i1}y_1 + a_{i2}y_2 + \cdots + a_{im}y_m, \qquad a_{ij} \in F.$$

In this fashion, we produce a set of nm scalars a_{ij}; the problem is now to show that f can be represented as

$$f = \sum_{j=1}^{m} \left(\sum_{i=1}^{n} a_{ij}f_{ij} \right).$$

Evaluating the right-hand side of this equation at the basis elements x_k leads to

$$\left(\sum_{j=1}^{m} \left(\sum_{i=1}^{n} a_{ij}f_{ij} \right) \right)(x_k) = \sum_{j=1}^{m} \left(\sum_{i=1}^{n} a_{ij}f_{ij}(x_k) \right)$$

$$= \sum_{j=1}^{m} \left(\sum_{i=1}^{n} a_{ij}\delta_{ik}y_j \right)$$

$$= \sum_{j=1}^{m} a_{kj}y_j = f(x_k).$$

Since the linear mappings f and $\sum_{j=1}^{m} \left(\sum_{i=1}^{n} a_{ij}f_{ij} \right)$ both have the same effect on the basis of $V(F)$, they must be identical. From this, we conclude that the functions f_{ij} span the space $L(V, W)(F)$.

To establish the linear independence of the f_{ij}, suppose some linear combination of them is the zero mapping:

$$\sum_{j=1}^{m} \left(\sum_{i=1}^{n} c_{ij}f_{ij} \right) = 0, \qquad (c_{ij} \in F).$$

If this expression is evaluated at the vector x_k, it follows, as above, that

$$\sum_{j=1}^{m} c_{kj}y_j = \sum_{j=1}^{m} \left(\sum_{i=1}^{n} c_{ij}f_{ij}(x_k) \right) = 0.$$

However, $\{y_1, y_2, \ldots, y_m\}$ is a basis of $W(F)$, hence a linearly independent set, which forces $c_{k1} = \cdots = c_{km} = 0$. By varying k, we conclude that all the coefficients c_{ij} must be zero, and the theorem is proved in its entirety.

Let us take a closer look at two special classes of linear mappings which occur frequently, namely $L(V, V)$ and $L(V, F)$. In view of our latest results, we already know that $L(V, V)(F)$ is a vector space over F, and if $V(F)$ is of finite dimension n, then dim $L(V, V) = n^2$. There is, however, more algebraic structure on $L(V, V)$ than the vector space structure just described. By restricting the image space, we are able to introduce still another binary operation: composition of mappings. Indeed, if f, $g \in L(V, V)$, it is easy to see that

$$(f \circ g)(ax + by) = f(g(ax + by))$$
$$= f(ag(x) + bg(y))$$
$$= af(g(x)) + bf(g(y))$$
$$= a(f \circ g)(x) + b(f \circ g)(y)$$

for all x, y in V and all a, b in F. This establishes the linearity condition, thereby showing $f \circ g$ to be a member of $L(V, V)$.

The basic algebraic properties of the sum and composition operations are contained in the following theorem; we omit the proof, which consists of little more than copying the results of Example 3–6.

Theorem 3–34. For each vector space $V(F)$, the triple $(L(V, V), +, \circ)$ is a ring with identity.

There is another important fact which is suggested by this discussion.

Corollary. If $GL(V)$ denotes the set of invertible mappings in $L(V, V)$, then $(GL(V), \circ)$ forms a group, called the *general linear group*.

Theorem 4–34 can be sharpened considerably by limiting our attention to finite-dimensional spaces.

Theorem 4–35. If $\dim V = n$, then $(L(V, V), +, \circ)$ is isomorphic to $(M_n(F), +, \cdot)$, the ring of $n \times n$ matrices over F.

Proof. Fix a basis $\{x_1, x_2, \ldots, x_n\}$ for $V(F)$. We claim that the function $\Phi \colon L(V, V) \to M_n(F)$ which assigns to each linear mapping its matrix representation relative to this particular basis is a (ring) isomorphism of $(L(V, V), +, \circ)$ onto $(M_n(F), +, \cdot)$. From our previous discussions, it is already known that the correspondence Φ is one-to-one and onto $M_n(F)$; what remains to be checked here is whether Φ preserves the ring operations.

To begin with, suppose the maps f, $g \in L(V, V)$ possess representing matrices (a_{ij}) and (b_{ij}), respectively, so that

$$f(x_j) = \sum_{i=1}^{n} a_{ij}x_i, \qquad g(x_j) = \sum_{i=1}^{n} b_{ij}x_i, \qquad (j = 1, 2, \ldots, n).$$

Then, for the sum $f + g$, we have

$$(f + g)(x_j) = f(x_j) + g(x_j)$$
$$= \sum_{i=1}^{n} a_{ij}x_i + \sum_{i=1}^{n} b_{ij}x_i = \sum_{i=1}^{n} (a_{ij} + b_{ij})x_i.$$

It follows from what is meant by the matrix of a linear transformation relative to a given basis that $(a_{ij} + b_{ij})$ must be the matrix corresponding to $f + g$; in consequence,

$$\Phi(f + g) = (a_{ij} + b_{ij}) = (a_{ij}) + (b_{ij}) = \Phi(f) + \Phi(g).$$

The problem of representing the composition $f \circ g$ is a little more complicated. First, we compute $(f \circ g)(x_j)$:

$$(f \circ g)(x_j) = f(g(x_j)) = f\left(\sum_{k=1}^{n} b_{kj}x_k\right) = \sum_{k=1}^{n} b_{kj}f(x_k) = \sum_{k=1}^{n} b_{kj}\left(\sum_{i=1}^{n} a_{ik}x_i\right).$$

By reversing the order of summation, this can be expressed in the form

$$(f \circ g)(x_j) = \sum_{i=1}^{n} \left(\sum_{k=1}^{n} a_{ik}b_{kj}\right)x_i, \qquad (j = 1, 2, \ldots, n).$$

Thus, the ijth entry of the matrix associated with $f \circ g$ is seen to be $\sum_{k=1}^{n} a_{ik}b_{kj}$, which is also the ijth entry of the product $(a_{ij}) \cdot (b_{ij})$. Accordingly, we conclude that

$$\Phi(f \circ g) = \left(\sum_{k=1}^{n} a_{ik}b_{kj}\right) = (a_{ij}) \cdot (b_{ij}) = \Phi(f) \cdot \Phi(g),$$

implying that Φ is a ring homomorphism from $(L(V, V), +, \circ)$ onto $(M_n(f), +, \cdot)$; this substantiates our contention and proves the theorem.

A useful consequence of this last theorem is that, if dim $V = n$, the general linear group—now denoted by $(GL_n(V), \circ)$—is isomorphic to the group of all nonsingular $n \times n$ matrices over F.

The proof of Theorem 4–35 brings out a point worth mentioning: The operations for matrices were purposely defined to agree with our operations for linear mappings. To be precise, Definition 4–8 was formulated in such a manner that the matrix of a product of two linear transformations would be the product of their representing matrices.

When $V(F)$ is of finite dimension n, there is another natural way of relating the algebraic structure of $L(V, V)$ to that of $M_n(F)$. Namely, since

$$\dim L(V, V) = n^2 = \dim M_n(F),$$

$L(V, V)(F)$ and $M_n(F)$ must also be isomorphic as vector spaces; in fact, a straightforward calculation shows the function Φ obtained in Theorem 4–35 to be a vector space isomorphism, not only a ring isomorphism.

The structure of $L(V, V)$ can be approached from one more direction. For this, let us define what is meant by an (associative) algebra over a field.

Definition 4–19. A vector space $V(F)$ is said to be an *algebra over the field F* if its elements can be multiplied in such a way that $V(F)$ becomes a ring in which scalar multiplication is related to ring multiplication (denoted by ·) by the following *mixed associative law:*

$$c(x \cdot y) = (cx) \cdot y = x \cdot (cy) \qquad (x, y \in V; c \in F).$$

Our immediate goal is to establish that, for any vector space $V(F)$, the ring $(L(V, V), +, \circ)$ has the structure of an algebra over F. In light of earlier results, all that really need be demonstrated here is the mixed associative law. To obtain this, we let $c \in F, f \in L(V, V)$, and $x \in V$; a straightforward calculation then yields

$$(f \circ (cg))(x) = f((cg)(x)) = f(cg(x)) = cf(g(x)) = c(f \circ g)(x).$$

Since this equality holds for every $x \in V$, we conclude that

$$f \circ (cg) = c(f \circ g).$$

Verification of the property $(cf) \circ g = c(f \circ g)$ follows in a similar vein and is left as an exercise.

Further examples of rings which are also algebras are the ring $(M_n(F), +, \cdot)$ of matrices of order n, the ring of real-valued functions on $R^\#$, as well as the real and complex number fields.

As the reader is so well aware, since an algebra is basically a ring and vector space combined, any homomorphism between algebras must preserve both the ring and vector space operations; more specifically, if f is a homomorphism between two algebras over the same field, then

$$f(x + y) = f(x) + f(y), \qquad f(x \cdot y) = f(x) \cdot f(y), \qquad f(cx) = cf(x).$$

The following example affords a good illustration of this idea.

Example 4–30. Let $T_2(R^\#)$ denote the set of all 2×2 upper triangular matrices with elements from $R^\#$:

$$T_2(R^\#) = \left\{ \begin{pmatrix} a & b \\ 0 & c \end{pmatrix} \middle| a, b, c \in R^\# \right\}.$$

It is already known that $T_2(R^\#)$ is the set of elements of a noncommutative ring with identity [Problem 13(b), Section 4–1] as well as of a vector space over the real numbers [Problem 7(f), Section 4–2]; in other words, $(T_2(R^\#), +, \cdot)$ may be regarded as an algebra over $R^\#$. Our purpose here is to obtain a complete description of the homomorphisms from this algebra into the real numbers.

As a simplifying device, note that upon setting

$$I = \begin{pmatrix} 1 & 0 \\ 0 & 1 \end{pmatrix}, \qquad X = \begin{pmatrix} 0 & 1 \\ 0 & 0 \end{pmatrix}, \qquad Y = \begin{pmatrix} 0 & 0 \\ 0 & 1 \end{pmatrix},$$

each element of $T_2(R^\#)$ may be expressed in the form

$$\begin{pmatrix} a & b \\ 0 & c \end{pmatrix} = aI + bX + (c - a)Y.$$

Now, if f is any nontrivial homomorphism from the algebra $(T_2(R^\#), +, \cdot)$ into the algebra $(R^\#, +, \cdot)$, then

$$f\begin{pmatrix} a & b \\ 0 & c \end{pmatrix} = af(I) + bf(X) + (c - a)f(Y).$$

Since $f(T) = f(T) \cdot f(I)$ for all $T \in T_2(R^\#)$, and f is not identically zero, we must have $f(I) = 1$. What can be said about the functional value $f(Y)$? Observe first that the matrix Y is idempotent with respect to multiplication; this means

$$f(Y) = f(Y^2) = f(Y)^2,$$

which in turn implies $f(Y)$ can only assume the values 0 or 1 (Problem 2, Section 3–3). Finally, the fact that the matrix X is nilpotent (specifically, $X^2 = 0$) leads us to conclude $f(X) = 0$. The effect of these remarks is that

$$f\begin{pmatrix} a & b \\ 0 & c \end{pmatrix} = a \text{ or } c.$$

This suggests consideration of mappings $f_i \colon T_2(R^\#) \to R^\#$ $(i = 1, 2)$ defined by

$$f_1\begin{pmatrix} a & b \\ 0 & c \end{pmatrix} = a, \qquad f_2\begin{pmatrix} a & b \\ 0 & c \end{pmatrix} = c.$$

A routine check establishes that f_1 and f_2 actually are algebra homomorphisms from $(T_2(R^\#), +, \cdot)$ into $(R^\#, +, \cdot)$; barring the trivial homomorphism, our argument shows them to be the only such functions.

Now is perhaps an appropriate point at which to say a brief word about *idempotent linear mappings*, that is, functions $f \in L(V, V)$ such that $f^2 = f$ (here f^2 stands for $f \circ f$). Our object is to show the intimate connection between transformations of this type and direct sum decompositions of the vector space. The precise statement follows.

Theorem 4–36. If $V = U \oplus W$, then the function $f_W \colon V \to W$ which assigns to each vector $x \in V$ its uniquely determined component x_2 in the representation $x = x_1 + x_2$ $(x_1 \in U, x_2 \in W)$ is an idempotent linear mapping with

$$\ker(f_W) = U, \qquad f_W(V) = W.$$

Conversely, every idempotent linear mapping $f \in L(V, V)$ defines a direct

sum decomposition
$$V = \ker(f) \oplus f(V).$$

Proof. We start by showing that the function f_W, as defined in the statement of the theorem, is actually in $L(V, V)$. Suppose $x, y \in V$, so that $x = u_1 + w_1$, $y = u_2 + w_2$, with $u_k \in U$, $w_k \in W$ ($k = 1, 2$). Then for scalars a, b,

$$ax + by = (au_1 + bu_2) + (aw_1 + bw_2),$$

where $au_1 + bu_2 \in U$, $aw_1 + bw_2 \in W$. This means that

$$f_W(ax + by) = aw_1 + bw_2 = af_W(x) + bf_W(y),$$

hence $f_W \in L(V, V)$. In fact, more is true: Since $u = u + 0$ and $w = 0 + w$ serve as the unique decompositions for elements $u \in U$ and $w \in W$, we must have

1) $f_W(u) = 0$ if and only if $u \in U$,
2) $f_W(w) = w$ if and only if $w \in W$.

This leads to the most significant property of the function f_W, its idempotency; given $x = u + w$, with $u \in U$ and $w \in W$,

$$f_W^2(x) = f_W(f_W(x)) = f_W(w) = w = f_W(x),$$

resulting in $f_W^2 = f_W$.

For the converse, suppose that $f \in L(V, V)$ with $f^2 = f$. Taking $u = x - f(x)$ and $w = f(x)$, we may write each vector $x \in V$ as a sum $x = u + w$. By hypothesis f is an idempotent map, so

$$f(u) = f(x) - f^2(x) = 0,$$

while

$$f(w) = f^2(x) = f(x) = w.$$

This shows that $V = \ker(f) + W$, where the set W is given by

$$W = \{x \in V \mid f(x) = x\}.$$

Our contention is that the foregoing sum is direct; in other words,

$$\ker(f) \cap W = \{0\}.$$

This is easy: If a vector x lies in $\ker(f)$, $f(x) = 0$, whereas if x is in W, $f(x) = x$. Thus, whenever x belongs to both $\ker(f)$ and W, we must have $x = 0$. To conclude the proof, it remains to be seen that $W = f(V)$. The inclusion $W \subseteq f(V)$ is an immediate consequence of the definition of the set W; the reverse inclusion is equally obvious, since the equation $f^2 = f$ means $f(x) \in W$ for every $x \in V$.

It is natural to think of the function f_W as *projecting* $V(F)$ onto the subspace $W(F)$. For this reason, the term *projection* is customarily used to refer to any idempotent linear mapping on $V(F)$. Since every subspace of a vector space possesses a complementary subspace, Theorem 4–36 asserts the existence of a projection of the space onto any of its subspaces; needless to say, complements are not unique, so there may exist several projections onto the same subspace.

For a simple case of the above idea, consider the projection $f: V_4 \to V_4$ defined by

$$f(a_1, a_2, a_3, a_4) = (a_1, a_2, 0, 0).$$

It is fairly evident that

$$\ker (f) = \{(0, 0, a_3, a_4) \mid a_3, a_4 \in F\}$$

and

$$f(V_4) = \{(a_1, a_2, 0, 0) \mid a_1, a_2 \in F\}.$$

The reader may verify that the corresponding subspaces are actually complementary.

Throughout the remainder of this section, we restrict our attention to linear mappings on $V(F)$ which assume values in the associated scalar field F [if scalar multiplication is defined to be the multiplication in F, then F may be viewed as a one-dimensional vector space over itself]. It is customary to use a special terminology for such scalar-valued functions and to refer to them as *linear functionals*, or merely *functionals*, on $V(F)$.

Definition 4–20. The vector space $L(V, F)(F)$ consisting of all linear functionals on $V(F)$ is called the *dual space* (often called the *conjugate space*) of $V(F)$ and is denoted by $V^*(F)$.

Example 4–31. Let (a_{ij}) be an $n \times n$ matrix. The sum of all elements on the main diagonal is known as the *trace* of the matrix and is represented by tr (a_{ij}):

$$\text{tr} \ (a_{ij}) = \sum_{k=1}^{n} a_{kk}.$$

It is not difficult to verify that the function tr: $M_n \to F$, defined in this way, is a linear functional on the space $M_n(F)$; for, if (a_{ij}), (b_{ij}) are two matrices of order n and $r, s \in F$, then

$$\text{tr} \ [r(a_{ij}) + s(b_{ij})] = \text{tr} \ (ra_{ij} + sb_{ij}) = \sum_{k=1}^{n} (ra_{kk} + sb_{kk})$$

$$= r \sum_{k=1}^{n} a_{kk} + s \sum_{k=1}^{n} b_{kk} = r \ \text{tr} \ (a_{ij}) + s \ \text{tr} \ (b_{ij}).$$

From Theorem 4–33 we already know something about the space $V^*(F)$; namely, that if $V(F)$ is finite-dimensional, then dim $V^* = $ dim V. Moreover, the proof of this theorem provides an explicit way of constructing a basis of $V^*(F)$: Given a particular basis $\{x_1, x_2, \ldots, x_n\}$ for $V(F)$, a unique linear functional f_i is defined on V by prescribing

$$f_i(x_j) = \delta_{ij}, \qquad (j = 1, 2, \ldots, n).$$

Theorem 4–33 then tells us that the n functions $f_1, f_2, \ldots, f_n$ form a basis for $V^*(F)$, the so-called *dual basis* to $x_1, x_2, \ldots, x_n$ or dual basis of $V^*(F)$.

The definition of f_i is somewhat opaque, but it may be interpreted in a way that is more illuminating. Since any vector $x \in V$ is of the form $x = a_1x_1 + a_2x_2 + \cdots + a_nx_n$, it is clear that

$$f_i(x) = \sum_{j=1}^{n} a_j f_j(x_j) = \sum_{j=1}^{n} a_j \delta_{ij} = a_i.$$

From this, we see that the functional f_i has the effect of assigning to each vector x the coefficient of x_i in the representation of x as a linear combination of the basis vectors. A suggestive name for the mappings f_i might be to call them *coordinate functionals* (with respect to a fixed basis, of course).

An interesting observation which we shall use almost immediately is the following.

Lemma. If $V(F)$ is a finite-dimensional vector space and x is any nonzero vector of V, then there is some linear functional $f \in V^*$ for which $f(x) \neq 0$.

Proof. Since $x \neq 0$, there exists a basis $\{x_1, x_2, \ldots, x_n\}$ of $V(F)$ with $x_1 = x$ (Theorem 4–24). If $\{f_1, f_2, \ldots, f_n\}$ is the corresponding dual basis for $V^*(F)$, we then have

$$f_1(x) = f_1(x_1) = \delta_{11} = 1.$$

Since the dual space $V^*(F)$ is a vector space, $V^*(F)$ has a dual of its own; we shall denote this latter space by $V^{**}(F)$ and refer to it as the *second dual* of $V(F)$. If $V(F)$ is of finite dimension n, we know that $V^*(F)$ has the same dimension, hence in turn dim $V^{**} = n$. By the corollary to Theorem 4–30, this equality of dimensions implies that $V(F)$ and $V^{**}(F)$ are isomorphic. There is one perfectly natural and useful isomorphism between these spaces, the so-called *canonical imbedding*; the full story is told below.

Given a vector $x \in V$ and functional $f \in V^*$, $f(x)$ is a scalar. Although we have grown accustomed to thinking of this as a function of x for fixed f, let us now invert this usual practice and allow f to range over V^*, while holding x fixed [many authors would emphasize this by writing $x(f)$ in place of $f(x)$]. Specifically, define the function $T_x : V^* \to F$ by

$$T_x(f) = f(x), \qquad f \in V^*.$$

It is easy to see that T_x is actually a linear functional on V^*, for

$$T_x(af + bg) = (af + bg)(x)$$
$$= af(x) + bg(x) = aT_x(f) + bT_x(g).$$

T_x, defined in this way, is called the *evaluation functional induced by the vector x*.

The choice of imbedding should now be clear, for what is more natural than to associate x with F_x. Precisely:

Theorem 4–37. If $V(F)$ is a finite-dimensional vector space, then $V(F) \simeq V^{**}(F)$ via the mapping $\phi(x) = T_x$.

Proof. At the outset, note that for any $f \in V^*$, we have

$$T_{ax+by}(f) = f(ax + by)$$
$$= af(x) + bf(y)$$
$$= aT_x(f) + bT_y(f) = (aT_x + bT_y)(f),$$

whence the relation $T_{ax+by} = aT_x + bT_y$. This leads directly to the conclusion that the function ϕ is linear:

$$\phi(ax + by) = T_{ax+by} = aT_x + bT_y = a\phi(x) + b\phi(y).$$

The one-to-one nature of ϕ is established by showing $\ker(f) = \{0\}$ or, in the present context, if $f(x) = 0$ for every f in V^*, then $x = 0$; but this is precisely the content of the previous lemma. Finally, the equality of the dimensions of $V(F)$ and $V^{**}(F)$, together with the fact that ϕ is a one-to-one function, necessitates that ϕ map onto V^{**} (see the corollary to Theorem 4–29). The theorem is now fully proved.

The import of Theorem 4–37 lies in the following rather remarkable corollary which asserts that all functionals on V^* can be obtained by evaluation at elements of V.

Corollary. If $V(F)$ is finite-dimensional, then each linear functional in V^{**} is of the form T_x for some unique vector $x \in V$.

In practice, one usually identifies the vector x with the functional T_x defined by it. When $\dim V$ is finite, we thereby abolish $V^{**}(F)$ and regard $V(F)$ as the space of linear functions on V^*. From this point of view, $V(F)$ and $V^*(F)$ have a natural symmetry and we may justifiably speak of them as being dual spaces (to each other). In the infinite-dimensional case, however, it is not true that the set V^{**} is exhausted by the functionals T_x; our mapping ϕ is into, not onto, so that $V(F)$ can only be regarded as a vector subspace of $V^{**}(F)$.

As a parting shot, we give further evidence of the symmetric relationship between $V(F)$ and $V^*(F)$ by showing that every basis for $V^*(F)$ is the dual of a basis for $V(F)$.

Theorem 4–38. If $V(F)$ is a finite-dimensional vector space, then any basis for $V^*(F)$ is the dual of some basis for $V(F)$.

Proof. Let $\{f_1, f_2, \ldots, f_n\}$ be a basis for $V^*(F)$. We can then find a basis $\{T_1, T_2, \ldots, T_n\}$ in $V^{**}(F)$ which is dual to this given basis; in other words, $T_i(f_j) = \delta_{ij}$. But, according to the preceding corollary, there exist vectors $x_1, x_2, \ldots, x_n$ in V with $T_i(f) = T_{x_i}(f) = f(x_i)$ for all $f \in V^*$; in particular, taking $f = f_j$, we obtain

$$f_j(x_i) = \delta_{ij}, \qquad (i, j = 1, 2, \ldots, n),$$

whence $\{x_1, x_2, \ldots, x_n\}$ is a basis for $V(F)$ having $\{f_1, f_2, \ldots, f_n\}$ as its dual.

PROBLEMS

Unless indicated otherwise, $V(F)$ and $W(F)$ denote vector spaces over an arbitrary field F.

1. Using nothing other than Definition 4–18 and Theorem 4–7, show that if the mapping $f \in L(V, W)$, then $f(0) = 0$ and $f(-x) = -f(x)$ for each $x \in V$.

2. Determine which of the following functions are linear mappings of $V_3(R^{\#})$ into itself:

 a) $f(a_1, a_2, a_3) = (a_2, -a_1, a_3)$,
 b) $f(a_1, a_2, a_3) = (a_1, 0, a_3)$,
 c) $f(a_1, a_2, a_3) = (a_1, a_1 + a_2, a_1 + a_2 + a_3)$,
 d) $f(a_1, a_2, a_3) = (a_1 + 2a_2 - a_3, -a_1 + a_2, 2a_1 + a_2)$.

3. Assume that $f \in L(V, W)$ and $U(F)$ is a vector subspace of $W(F)$. Prove that $f^{-1}(U)(F)$ is a subspace of $V(F)$, where, as usual,

$$f^{-1}(U) = \{x \in V \mid f(x) \in U\}.$$

4. Let f be a linear transformation from $V(F)$ into $W(F)$. If $\{f(x_1), f(x_2), \ldots, f(x_n)\}$ is a linearly independent subset of $W(F)$, prove that the set $\{x_1, x_2, \ldots, x_n\}$ is also independent. From this, deduce that $\dim f(V) \leq \dim V$.

5. Let $p(x) = a_0 + a_1 x + a_2 x^2 + \cdots + a_n x^n \in R^{\#}[x]$, the vector space of polynomials in x over $R^{\#}$. Determine which of the functions below are linear mappings of $R^{\#}[x]$ into itself:

 a) $f(p) = a_0 x + a_1 x^2 + a_2 x^3 + \cdots + a_n x^{n+1}$,
 b) $f(p) = a_0 + a_1 x^2 + a_2 x^4 + \cdots + a_n x^{2n}$,

 c) $f(p) = a_0 x + \dfrac{a_1}{2} x^2 + \dfrac{a_2}{3} x^3 + \cdots + \dfrac{a_n}{n+1} x^{n+1}$.

6. Let the mapping $f \in L(V, V)$ and S denote the set of vectors of V which are left fixed by f:

$$S = \{x \in V \mid f(x) = x\}.$$

Verify that $S(F)$ forms a subspace of the vector space $V(F)$.

7. Prove that if $f \in L(V, W)$, then f is a one-to-one function if and only if the vectors $f(x_1), f(x_2), \ldots, f(x_n)$ are linearly independent whenever $x_1, x_2, \ldots, x_n$ are linearly independent.

8. Show by example that the conclusion of the corollary to Theorem 4–29 is false if $V(F)$ is infinite-dimensional.

9. Suppose the mapping $f \in L(V, W)$, with dim $V >$ dim W. Show that there exists a nonzero vector $x_0 \in V$ for which $f(x_0) = 0$.

10. Obtain the Fundamental Homomorphism Theorem for Vector Spaces: If f is a linear mapping from the vector space $V(F)$ onto the vector space $W(F)$, then $(V/\ker (f))(F) \simeq W(F)$.

11. Let $V(F)$ be finite-dimensional with basis $\{x_1, x_2, \ldots, x_n\}$, and let $y_1, y_2, \ldots, y_n$ be any n elements of V. If the function $f: V \to V$ is defined by taking

$$f(a_1 x_1 + \cdots + a_n x_n) = a_1 y_1 + \cdots + a_n y_n, \qquad (a_k \in F),$$

prove that f is a linear mapping; determine when f will be an isomorphism.

12. Prove that if the mapping $f \in L(V, V)$ is such that ker $(f) =$ ker (f^2), then $V = \ker (f) \oplus f(V)$.

13. For a fixed element $a \in F$, define the *scalar transformation* $f_a: V \to V$ by

$$f_a(x) = ax, \qquad x \in V.$$

Given that $R = \{f_a \mid a \in F\}$ and $R' = R - \{0\}$, show that

a) the triple $(R, +, \circ)$ forms a subring of $(L(V, V), +, \circ)$ isomorphic to $(F, +, \cdot)$;

b) the pair $(R', \circ)$ is a normal subgroup of the linear group $(GL(V), \circ)$; in fact, $R' =$ cent $GL(V)$.

14. A linear mapping $f \in L(V, V)$ is said to be *nilpotent* if $f^n = 0$ for some $n \in Z_+$. If f is nilpotent and if $f^{n-1}(x_0) \neq 0$, prove that

$$\{x_0, f(x_0), f^2(x_0), \ldots, f^{n-1}(x_0)\}$$

is a linearly independent set of vectors.

15. Prove that the result of Theorem 4–31 holds in general; in other words, if $V = U \oplus W$, establish that $(V/W)(F) \simeq U(F)$ regardless of the dimension (finite or infinite) of $V(F)$. [*Hint:* Consider the restriction $\mathrm{nat}_W \mid U$.]

16. Consider the trace functional tr as defined in Example 4–20 of the text. In the vector space $M_n(R^\#)$, prove that

a) tr $((a_{ij}) \cdot (b_{ij})) =$ tr $((b_{ij}) \cdot (a_{ij}))$,

b) tr $((a_{ij}) \cdot (b_{ij}) \cdot (a_{ij})^{-1}) =$ tr (b_{ij}), whenever (a_{ij}) is nonsingular,

c) tr $((a_{ij}) \cdot (a_{ij})^t) = 0$ if and only if $(a_{ij}) = O$.

17. Suppose $\{x_1, x_2, \ldots, x_n\}$ is a basis of the finite-dimensional space $V(F)$ and $\{f_1, f_2, \ldots, f_n\}$ is the corresponding dual basis of $V^*(F)$. Show that for each vector $x \in V$,

$$x = \sum_{k=1}^{n} f_k(x) x_k,$$

while for each functional $f \in V^*$,

$$f = \sum_{k=1}^{n} f(x_k) f_k.$$

18. Let $V(F)$ be a finite-dimensional vector space over F. Prove that

a) if $x_1, x_2 \in V$ with $x_1 \neq x_2$, then there exists a linear functional $f \in V^*$ for which $f(x_1) \neq f(x_2)$;

b) if $W(F)$ is a proper nonzero subspace of $V(F)$ and the vector $x_0 \notin W$, then there is some $f \in V^*$ such that $f(x_0) = 1, f(x) = 0$ for all $x \in W$. [*Hint:* Given any basis $\{x_1, \ldots, x_n\}$ of $W(F)$, the set $x_0, x_1, \ldots, x_n$ is linearly independent, hence contained in a basis for $V(F)$; now, utilize the corresponding dual basis for $V^*(F)$.]

19. If $W(F)$ is a subspace of the vector space $V(F)$, the *annihilator* of W is the set $W^{\perp}$ defined by

$$W^{\perp} = \{f \in V^* \mid f(x) = 0 \text{ for all } x \in W\}.$$

Assuming $V(F)$ is finite-dimensional, prove that

a) $W^{\perp}(F)$ is a subspace of the dual space $V^*(F)$;

b) $\dim W + \dim W^{\perp} = \dim V$; [*Hint:* First, extend any basis $\{x_1, \ldots, x_m\}$ of $W(F)$ to a basis $\{x_1, \ldots, x_n\}$ for $V(F)$. If $\{f_1, \ldots, f_n\}$ is the corresponding dual basis for $V^*(F)$, then $\{f_{m+1}, \ldots, f_n\}$ serves as a basis of $W^{\perp}(F)$.]

c) $(V/W)^*(F) \simeq W^{\perp}(F), (V/W^{\perp})(F) \simeq W^*(F)$;

d) $W^{\perp\perp} = W$. [*Hint:* Use part (b).]

20. Let $U(F)$ and $W(F)$ be two subspaces of the finite-dimensional space $V(F)$. Establish the following facts concerning the annihilators of U and W:

a) $U^{\perp} = W^{\perp}$ if and only if $U = W$.

b) $(U + W)^{\perp} = U^{\perp} \cap W^{\perp}; (U \cap W)^{\perp} = U^{\perp} + W^{\perp}$.

c) If $V = U \oplus W$, then $V^* = U^{\perp} \oplus W^{\perp}$.

21. For each linear mapping $f \in L(V, W)$, the *transpose* (adjoint, dual) of f is the function $f^{\top} : W^* \to V^*$ defined by

$$f^{\top}(g) = g \circ f, \qquad g \in W^*.$$

Given that $V(F)$ and $W(F)$ are finite-dimensional, show that

a) $f^{\top}$ is a linear mapping from $W^*(F)$ into $V^*(F)$,

b) $\ker(f^{\top}) = f(V)^{\perp}; \ker(f)^{\perp} = f^{\top}(W^*)$,

c) $L(V, W) \simeq L(W^*, V^*)$ under the mapping that sends each functional $f \in L(V, W)$ to its transpose $f^{\top}$.

22. Let $\{x_1, x_2, \ldots, x_n\}$ be a basis for the finite-dimensional vector space $V(F)$, and let $\{f_1, f_2, \ldots, f_n\}$ be the corresponding dual basis for $V^*(F)$. Suppose that (a_{ij}) is the representing matrix, relative to $\{x_1, x_2, \ldots, x_n\}$, of the linear mapping $f \in L(V, V)$. Prove that the transpose $f^{\top}$ of f is represented by the matrix $(a_{ij})^t$ relative to $\{f_1, f_2, \ldots, f_n\}$.

23. If the functionals $f, g \in V^*$ are such that $\ker(f) \subseteq \ker(g)$, prove that there exists a scalar a for which $f = ag$.

Selected References

Our purpose here is to present a list of suggestions for collateral reading and further study. Those works classified under General References roughly parallel the content of this book; the specialized sources more fully develop topics mentioned in the text and will carry the reader considerably beyond his present knowledge.

General References

1. A. A. ALBERT, *Fundamental Concepts of Higher Algebra*. Chicago: The University of Chicago Press, 1956.

2. W. BARNES, *Introduction to Abstract Algebra*. Boston: Heath, 1963.

3. R. BEAUMONT and R. BALL, *Introduction to Modern Algebra and Matrix Theory*. New York: Holt, Rinehart and Winston, 1961.

4. G. BIRKHOFF and S. MACLANE, *A Survey of Modern Algebra*, 3rd ed. New York: Macmillan, 1965.

5. R. DEAN, *Elements of Abstract Algebra*. New York: Wiley, 1965.

6. R. DUBISCH, *Introduction to Abstract Algebra*. New York: Wiley, 1965.

7. I. N. HERSTEIN, *Topics in Algebra*. New York: Blaisdell, 1964.

8. N. JACOBSON, *Lectures in Abstract Algebra*, Vol. I, *Basic Concepts*. Princeton: Van Nostrand, 1951.

9. S. LANG, *Algebra*. Reading, Mass.: Addison-Wesley, 1965.

10. D. J. LEWIS, *Introduction to Abstract Algebra*. New York: Harper and Row, 1965.

11. N. MCCOY, *Introduction to Modern Algebra*. Boston: Allyn and Bacon, 1962.

12. G. MOSTOW, J. SAMPSON, and J. P. MEYER, *Fundamental Structures of Algebra*. New York: McGraw-Hill, 1963.

13. H. PALEY and P. WEICHSEL, *A First Course in Abstract Algebra*. New York: Holt, Rinehart and Winston, 1966.

14. R. E. JOHNSON, *University Algebra*. Englewood Cliffs, N. J.: Prentice-Hall, 1966.

15. S. WARNER, *Modern Algebra*, 2 vols. Englewood Cliffs, N. J.: Prentice-Hall, 1965.

16. J. E. WHITESITT, *Principles of Modern Algebra*. Reading, Mass.: Addison-Wesley, 1964.

17. O. ZARISKI and P. SAMUEL, *Commutative Algebra*, Vol. I. Princeton: Van Nostrand, 1958.

Group Theory

18. C. Curtis and I. Reiner, *Representation Theory of Finite Groups and Associative Algebras*. New York: Interscience, 1962.

19. M. Hall, *The Theory of Groups*. New York: Macmillan, 1959.

20. A. Kurosh, *The Theory of Groups*, 2nd ed. New York: Chelsea, 1960.

21. W. Ledermann, *Introduction to the Theory of Finite Groups*, 5th ed. New York: Interscience, 1964.

22. J. Rotman, *The Theory of Groups: An Introduction*. Boston: Allyn and Bacon, 1965.

23. E. Schenkman, *Group Theory*. Princeton: Van Nostrand, 1966.

24. W. Scott, *Group Theory*. Englewood Cliffs, N. J.: Prentice-Hall, 1964.

25. H. Zassenhaus, *The Theory of Groups*, 2nd ed. New York: Chelsea, 1958.

Rings and Fields

26. I. Adamson, *Introduction to Field Theory*. New York: Interscience, 1964.

27. E. Artin, *Galois Theory*, 2nd ed. Notre Dame, Ind.: University of Notre Dame Press, 1955.

28. N. McCoy, *Rings and Ideals*. Buffalo: Mathematical Association of America, 1948.

29. N. McCoy, *The Theory of Rings*. New York: Macmillan, 1964.

30. D. Northcott, *Ideal Theory*. Cambridge, England: Cambridge University Press, 1953.

31. A. Robinson, *Numbers and Ideals*. San Francisco: Holden-Day, 1965.

Linear Algebra

32. C. Curtis, *Linear Algebra: An Introductory Approach*. Boston: Allyn and Bacon, 1963.

33. P. Halmos, *Finite Dimensional Vector Spaces*, 2nd ed. Princeton: Van Nostrand, 1958.

34. K. Hoffman and R. Kunze, *Linear Algebra*. Englewood Cliffs, N. J.: Prentice-Hall, 1961.

35. S. Lang, *Linear Algebra*. Reading, Mass.: Addison-Wesley, 1966.

36. D. Raikov, *Vector Spaces*. Groningen: P. Noordhoff, Ltd., 1965.

37. F. Stewart, *Introduction to Linear Algebra*. Princeton: Van Nostrand, 1963.

Set Theory and Functions

38. P. Halmos, *Naive Set Theory*. Princeton: Van Nostrand, 1960.

39. N. Hamilton and J. Landin, *Set Theory: The Structure of Arithmetic*. Boston: Allyn and Bacon, 1961.

40. R. Stoll, *Set Theory and Logic*. San Francisco: Freeman, 1963.

41. P. Suppes, *Axiomatic Set Theory*. Princeton: Van Nostrand, 1960.

Index of Special Symbols and Notations

In the list below, numbers refer to the page on which the symbol is first defined or used.

$((a), *)$	cyclic subgroup generated by the element a, 69
$A(G)$	set of automorphisms of the group $(G, *)$, 91
$(A_n, \circ)$	alternating group on n symbols, 126
$C(a)$	centralizer of the element a in G, 74
cent G	center of the group $(G, *)$, 66
e	identity element of the group, 32
f_a	multiplication or translation function induced by a, 50
F_G	set of multiplication functions on G, 50
$(G/H, \otimes)$	quotient group of $(G, *)$ by the subgroup $(H, *)$, 84
$(G \times G', \cdot)$	direct product group, 52
$([G, G], *)$	commutator subgroup of the group $(G, *)$, 86
$[G:H]$	index of a subgroup $(H, *)$ in $(G, *)$, 129
$H * K$	product of sets H and K, 71
hom G	set of homomorphisms of $(G, *)$ into itself, 90
$I(G)$	set of inner automorphisms of the group $(G, *)$, 108
ker (f)	kernel of a homomorphism f, 94
nat$_H$	natural mapping of G onto G/H, 96
$N_K(H)$	normalizer of H in K, 129
$N(H)$	normalizer of H in the group $(G, *)$, 88
$o(G)$	order of the group $(G, *)$, 129
σ_a	inner automorphism induced by a, 108
(sym $G, \circ$)	symmetric group of the set G, 62
$(S_n, \circ)$	symmetric group on n symbols, 59
$(Z_n, +_n)$	group of integers modulo n, 56
$\simeq$	is isomorphic to, 97

Notations from Ring Theory

$((a), +, \cdot)$	principal ideal generated by the element a, 158
ann I	annihilator of the set I, 169
$(C, +, \cdot)$	complex number field, 173
deg $f(x)$	degree of the polynomial $f(x)$, 199
δ	derivative function, 218
$I_1 \oplus I_2$	direct sum of ideals, 171
$I_1 \cdot I_2$	product of ideals, 171
$R[x]$	set of polynomials over R in the indeterminant x, 198
$(R^*, \cdot)$	group of invertible elements of the ring $(R, +, \cdot)$, 143
$(R/I, +, \cdot)$	quotient ring of R by the ideal I, 160
rad R	radical of the ring $(R, +, \cdot)$, 191
$Z1$	set of integral multiples of the identity element, 153
$(Z_n, +_n, \cdot_n)$	ring of integers modulo n, 146

Notations from Vector Space Theory

(a_k)	n-dimensional vector, 235
(a_{ij})	$m \times n$ matrix, 238
$(a_{ij})^t$	transpose of the matrix (a_{ij}), 248
diag $M_n(F)$	set of diagonal matrices of order n over F, 248
dim V	dimension of the vector space $V(F)$, 271
δ_{ij}	the Kronecker delta, 241

The following chart should help the reader to visualize the interrelations among the various algebraic systems considered in the text.

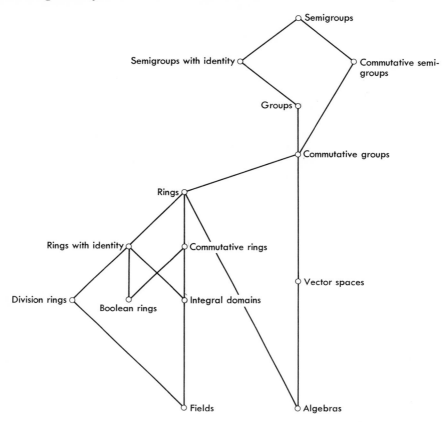

INDEX

INDEX

ABCDE6987